PROGRESS IN

Nucleic Acid Research and Molecular Biology

Volume 39

PROGRESS IN

Nucleic Acid Research and Molecular Biology

edited by

WALDO E. COHN

Biology Division
Oak Ridge National Laboratory
Oak Ridge, Tennessee

KIVIE MOLDAVE

Department of Biology
University of California
Santa Cruz, California

Volume 39

ACADEMIC PRESS, INC.

Harcourt Brace Jovanovich, Publishers

San Diego   New York   Boston
London   Sydney   Tokyo   Toronto

ACADEMIC PRESS, INC.
San Diego, California 92101

United Kingdom Edition published by
ACADEMIC PRESS LIMITED
24-28 Oval Road, London NW1 7DX

LIBRARY OF CONGRESS CATALOG CARD NUMBER: 63-15847

ISBN   0-12-540039-X   (alk. paper)

PRINTED IN THE UNITED STATES OF AMERICA
90 91 92 93   9 8 7 6 5 4 3 2 1

Contents

DNA—Protein Interactions: The Use of Synthetic Oligo- and Polynucleotides for Studying Single-stranded-DNA-binding Proteins and Restriction Endonucleases

Elizavetta S. Gromova and Zoe A. Shabarova

A Tale of Two Enzymes, Deoxycytidylate Deaminase and Thymidylate Synthase

Frank Maley and Gladys F. Maley

Stable DNA Loops *in Vivo* and *in Vitro*: Roles in Gene Regulation at a Distance and in Biophysical Characterization of DNA

Gregory R. Bellomy and M. Thomas Record, Jr.

Mitochondrial Aminoacyl-tRNA Synthetases

Alexander Tzagoloff, Domenico Gatti and Alexandra Gampel

Ribosomal Frameshifting from −2 to +50 Nucleotides

Robert B. Weiss, Diane M. Dunn, John F. Atkins and Raymond F. Gesteland

Inaccuracy and the Recognition of tRNA

M. John Rogers and Dieter Söll

Ribonucleases, tRNA Nucleotidyltransferase, and the 3′ Processing of tRNA

Murray P. Deutscher

The Numerous Modified Nucleotides in Eukaryotic Ribosomal RNA

B. E. H. Maden

Damage to DNA and Chromatin Structure from Ionizing Radiations, and the Radiation Sensitivities of Mammalian Cells

J. T. Lett

Abbreviations and Symbols

All contributors to this Series are asked to use the terminology (abbreviations and symbols) recommended by the IUPAC-IUB Commission on Biochemical Nomenclature (CBN) and approved by IUPAC and IUB, and the Editors endeavor to assure conformity. These Recommendations have been published in many journals (1, 2) and compendia (3) and are available in reprint form from the Office of Biochemical Nomenclature (OBN); they are therefore considered to be generally known. Those used in nucleic acid work, originally set out in section 5 of the first Recommendations (1) and subsequently revised and expanded (2, 3), are given in condensed form in the frontmatter of Volumes 9–33 of this series. A recent expansion of the one-letter system (5) follows.

SINGLE-LETTER CODE RECOMMENDATIONS[a] (5)

Symbol	Meaning	Origin of symbol
G	G	Guanosine
A	A	Adenosine
T(U)	T(U)	(ribo)Thymidine (Uridine)
C	C	Cytidine
R	G or A	puRine
Y	T(U) or C	pYrimidine
M	A or C	aMino
K	G or T(U)	Keto
S	G or C	Strong interaction (3 H-bonds)
W[b]	A or T(U)	Weak interaction (2 H-bonds)
H	A or C or T(U)	not G; H follows G in the alphabet
B	G or T(U) or C	not A; B follows A
V	G or C or A	not T (not U); V follows U
D[c]	G or A or T(U)	not C; D follows C
N	G or A or T(U) or C	aNy nucleoside (i.e., unspecified)
Q	Q	Queuosine (nucleoside of queuine)

[a]Modified from *Proc. Natl. Acad. Sci. U.S.A.* **83**, 4 (1986).
[b]W has been used for wyosine, the nucleoside of "base Y" (wye).
[c]D has been used for dihydrouridine (hU or H_2 Urd).

Enzymes

In naming enzymes, the 1984 recommendations of the IUB Commission on Biochemical Nomenclature (4) are followed as far as possible. At first mention, each enzyme is described *either* by its systematic name *or* by the equation for the reaction catalyzed *or* by the recommended trivial name, followed by its EC number in parentheses. Thereafter, a trivial name may be used. Enzyme names are not to be abbreviated except when the substrate has an approved abbreviation (e.g., ATPase, but not LDH, is acceptable).

REFERENCES

1. *JBC* **241**, 527 (1966); *Bchem* **5**, 1445 (1966); *BJ* **101**, 1 (1966); *ABB* **115**, 1 (1966), **129**, 1 (1969); and elsewhere.† General.
2. *EJB* **15**, 203 (1970); *JBC* **245**, 5171 (1970); *JMB* **55**, 299 (1971); and elsewhere.†
3. "Handbook of Biochemistry" (G. Fasman, ed.), 3rd ed. Chemical Rubber Co., Cleveland, Ohio, 1970, 1975, Nucleic Acids, Vols. I and II, pp. 3–59. Nucleic acids.
4. "Enzyme Nomenclature" [Recommendations (1984) of the Nomenclature Committee of the IUB]. Academic Press, New York, 1984.
5. *EJB* **150**, 1 (1985). Nucleic Acids (One-letter system).†

Abbreviations of Journal Titles

Journals	*Abbreviations used*
Annu. Rev. Biochem.	ARB
Annu. Rev. Genet.	ARGen
Arch. Biochem. Biophys.	ABB
Biochem. Biophys. Res. Commun.	BBRC
Biochemistry	Bchem
Biochem. J.	BJ
Biochim. Biophys. Acta	BBA
Cold Spring Harbor	CSH
Cold Spring Harbor Lab	CSHLab
Cold Spring Harbor Symp. Quant. Biol.	CSHSQB
Eur. J. Biochem.	EJB
Fed. Proc.	FP
Hoppe-Seyler's Z. Physiol. Chem.	ZpChem
J. Amer. Chem. Soc.	JACS
J. Bacteriol.	J. Bact.
J. Biol. Chem.	JBC
J. Chem. Soc.	JCS
J. Mol. Biol.	JMB
J. Nat. Cancer Inst.	JNCI
Mol. Cell. Biol.	MCBiol
Mol. Cell. Biochem.	MCBchem
Mol. Gen. Genet.	MGG
Nature, New Biology	Nature NB
Nucleic Acid Research	NARes
Proc. Natl. Acad. Sci. U.S.A.	PNAS
Proc. Soc. Exp. Biol. Med.	PSEBM
Progr. Nucl. Acid. Res. Mol. Biol.	This Series

†Reprints available from the Office of Biochemical Nomenclature (W. E. Cohn, Director).

Some Articles Planned for Future Volumes

DNA–Protein Interactions: The Use of Synthetic Oligo- and Polynucleotides for Studying Single-stranded-DNA-binding Proteins and Restriction Endonucleases

ELIZAVETTA S. GROMOVA
AND ZOE A. SHABAROVA

Department of Chemistry and A. N. Belozersky Laboratory of Molecular Biology and Bioorganic Chemistry
Moscow State University
Moscow, U.S.S.R.

1

The nature of specific and nonspecific interactions of proteins with DNA is a key problem of molecular biology. Such interactions underlie many processes in a living cell: gene expression control, replication, repair, transcription, cleavage and modification of DNA, etc. Certain progress has been made in this field over the past few years, largely by X-ray diffraction analysis, two-dimensional NMR spectroscopy, and site-directed mutagenesis. Yet the range of objects studied with the aid of these methods is still very limited. The most informative method, that of X-ray analysis, has serious limitations, for it permits only the study of static molecules. Besides, crystallization of DNA–protein complexes encounters many difficulties. Therefore, an essential condition for studying DNA–protein complexes consists of devising new practical methods for investigating them in solution, and using these methods in combination with other techniques.

The idea of modelling nucleic acid components of complexes appealed to us, namely, that of designing arrays of oligo(poly)-nucleotides with specific changes in the structure of the heterocyclic bases, of the sugar–phosphate backbone, and with variations in the length, nucleotide composition, and sequence. Selective modification of synthetic DNAs and a corresponding set of nonmodified compounds may enable a comprehensive analysis of various aspects of protein–nucleic acid interactions, including the mechanism of action of DNA-recognizing enzymes. This is combined with a study of the interactions of native proteins with synthesized fragments of DNA by convenient physicochemical and enzymological methods. We define such a comprehensive approach as an organochemical one.

Strict positional directionality of modifications and their multiple use are an essential factor of this approach. In selecting the type of modification, we aspired to the maximal similarity of the structures of double-stranded oligo(poly)nucleotides with respect to native fragments of DNA. The conformation of modified compounds is a special question. The organochemical approach became possible thanks to the two achievements of our laboratory: the synthesis of concatemer DNA duplexes (see Section II,A,1), and the development of chemical ligation enabling directed modifications in DNA duplexes (1).

This review sums up the data obtained in our laboratory in studying, by the organochemical approach, specific and nonspecific DNA–

protein interactions. As a "nonspecific" test protein we selected the gene-5 protein from bacteriophage f1 (P5) belonging to the group of single-stranded-DNA-binding (SSB) proteins (2). These proteins are involved in DNA synthesis in prokaryotes and eukaryotes. They have a higher affinity for single-stranded than for double-stranded DNA and thus destabilize the double-stranded DNA.

An important class of proteins that have specific interactions with DNA is represented by type-II restriction endonucleases, which are widely used in molecular biology (3). These enzymes recognize short nucleotide sequences in DNA and cleave them in both strands. Although over 800 restriction endonucleases have been isolated, only endonuclease *Eco*RI and several other enzymes have been studied sufficiently (3–7). We have investigated some type-II restriction endonucleases not heretofore studied: *Eco*RII, *Mva*I, and *Sso*II which recognize

$$^\downarrow CCWGG, \ CC^\downarrow WGG, \ and \ ^\downarrow CCNGG^1$$

sequences in DNA, respectively (arrows indicate the cleavage sites). Characteristic of these recognition sites is a disturbance of twofold rotational symmetry at the position of the central base-pair, which is partially (*Eco*RII and *Mva*I) or completely (*Sso*II) degenerated. *Eco*RII and *Mva*I enzymes are isoschizomers.

I. Nonspecific DNA—Protein Complexes: Structural Studies in the System: f1 Gene-5 Protein—Oligo(poly)nucleotides

The product of gene 5 from bacteriophage f1[2] (P5) contains 87 amino acids (2). The role of P5 *in vivo* is related to the regulation of phage DNA replication (2). Its complete amino-acid sequence and three-dimensional structure have been determined (2, 8). P5 exists as a dimer in solution and binds to single-stranded DNA in a cooperative fashion, covering four nucleotide residues per monomer of the protein. Proceeding from the data on X-ray analysis of the protein and on chemical modification and multinuclear NMR of the protein and its complexes with oligonucleotides, it was suggested (2) that single-stranded DNA binding involves three Tyr residues located on the surface of the protein, a Phe residue (due to stacking interactions with nucleic bases), and Lys and Arg residues (via electrostatic interactions

---

[1] W = A or T; N = A, T, C, or G.

[2] Identical to the gene-5 proteins of phages fd and M13 (2).

with phosphate groups of DNA). The structure of the complex was a special problem. The focuses of our investigations were: (1) to determine the essential elements of the structure of the complex of gene-5 protein with oligonucleotides (the oligonucleotide conformation and the location of the aromatic amino-acid side-chains of the protein); (2) to obtain the physicochemical characteristics of the interaction of P5 with single-stranded and double-stranded oligo(poly)nucleotides.

A. Interaction of Gene-5 Protein with Families of Synthetic Oligonucleotides

1. DESIGN OF OLIGONUCLEOTIDE SETS

To resolve structural problems, we designed (9, 10) families of pentanucleotides[3] differing in one of the bases in a definite position of the nucleotide chain (**1, 2** and **2–4, 7, 12**) or having a similar composition and one "sliding" natural (**5–9**) or modified fluorescing (**10–14**) base:

(**1**)	ATGTT	(**8**)	TTTAT
(**2**)	TTGTT	(**9**)	TTTTA
(**3**)	TTm^{7}GTT	(**10**)	ϵATTTT[4]
(**4**)	TTTTT	(**11**)	TϵATTT
(**5**)	ATTTT	(**12**)	TTϵATT
(**6**)	TATTT	(**13**)	TTTϵAT
(**7**)	TTATT	(**14**)	TTTTϵA

Occasionally, the length of oligonucleotides was varied: pGGT (**15**), TGCA (**16**), ATTT (**17**), AACTAGTT (**18**), and (pACC)$_4$ (**19**). Also, the nonanucleotide T[p(Me)T]$_8$ (**20**), containing methylated internucleotide phosphate groups, and the pentanucleotide BrCH$_2$-CONH(CH$_2$)$_2$NH-(5'-N)-pTCTAG (**21**) with a bromacetyl group were used (11).

2. SPECTRAL EFFECTS OF COMPLEX FORMATION: A COMPREHENSIVE METHODICAL APPROACH TO THE STUDY OF PROTEIN–NUCLEIC ACID INTERACTIONS

Mixing P5 with single- and double-stranded oligo(poly)nucleotides quenches the tyrosine fluorescence of P5 and amplifies the fluorescence ϵAde and m^{7}Gua (see Figs. 1 and 2, and Tables I and II) (9, 10,

---

[3] Only oligodeoxyribonucleotides were used in the work. The symbol d (deoxy) is omitted here and elsewhere.

[4] ϵ is 1,N^6-ethenoàdenosine.

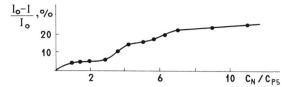

FIG. 1. P5 fluorescence quenching in a mixture with TATTT as a function of the ratio of TATTT to P5. I, I_0: intensity of fluorescence of complexed and uncomplexed P5, respectively. λ excitation = 276 nm, λ fluorescence = 308 nm. In all figures: C_N is oligonucleotide concentration per mole mononucleotide; C_{P5} is protein concentration per mole monomer of P5.

12). Also, changes of the Cotton effect of oligonucleotides at 240–300 nm were observed (Fig. 3). These effects attest to the formation of complexes; they are abolished when these complexes are dissociated by NaCl. [We must stress here that P5 binding to double-stranded polynucleotides and DNA is clearly identifiable by the fluorescence method.]

To obtain as much information as possible on the properties of protein—nucleic acid complexes, we used a dual approach: on the one hand, by studying them "according to the protein," that is, by measuring Tyr fluorescence, and "according to the nucleotide," by registering the CD of the oligonucleotide and the fluorescence of ϵAde and m[7]Gua residues. This possibility was predetermined in the oligonucleotide design. We also studied the effects on the complexes by external quenchers of fluorescence, charged KI and neutral acrylamide. Excitation spectra, excitation energy transfer, and the temperature

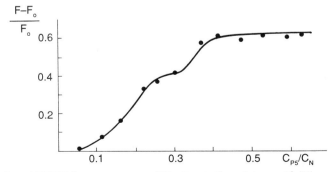

FIG. 2. ϵATTTT fluorescence amplification in the mixture with P5 as a function of the ratio of P5 to ϵATTTT; F, F_0: integral intensity of ϵATTTT fluorescence at a given and at a zero protein concentration, respectively; λ excitation = 320 nm at 20°C.

TABLE I

ETHENOADENINE CHROMOPHORE FLUORESCENCE PARAMETERS IN ETHENOOLIGONUCLEOTIDES (I) AND IN COMPLEXES OF ETHENOOLIGONUCLEOTIDES WITH GENE 5 PROTEIN (II)

| No. | Oligonucleotide or oligonucleotide component of the complex | λ_{flu}^{max} ± 2 nm | | $\dfrac{F - F_0}{F_0}$ [a] (II) | | Relative quantum yields[b] (φ) | | | | | | $\dfrac{I_{LiCl} - I_0}{I_0}$ [c] (I) |
| | | | | | | φ_{320} | | φ_{276} | | $\dfrac{\varphi_{276}}{\varphi_{320}}$ | | (λ_{exc} 320 nm, λ_{flu} 402 nm) |
		I	II	λ_{exc} (320 nm)	λ_{exc} (276 nm)	I	II	I	II	I	II	
(10)	εATTTT	402	401	0.39	0.41	0.18	0.25	0.20	0.28	1.11	1.12	1.7
(11)	TεATTT	401	396	0.27	0.77	0.07	0.09	0.13	0.23	1.86	2.56	1.15
(12)	TTεATT	402	395	0.46	0.60	0.08	0.12	0.14	0.22	1.75	1.86	3.0
(13)	TTTεAT	401	395	0.26	0.29	0.12	0.15	0.19	0.25	1.58	1.67	0.93
(14)	TTTTεA	402	396	0.23	0.24	0.25	0.31	0.26	0.32	1.04	1.03	0.73

[a] F_0, F: integral fluorescence intensities, determined from the spectra of (εA, T$_4$) and (εA, T$_4$) in a complex with P5, respectively. At $\lambda_{excitation}$ 276 nm a correction was made for protein fluorescence.

[b] Determined relative to φ of the products of hydrolysis of a corresponding oligonucleotide by snake venom phosphodiesterase, taken as 1 (I), or as φ of corresponding oligonucleotides at $\lambda_{excitation}$ 276 or 320 nm, multiplied by coefficient F/F_0 (II). The relative error margin is ± 10%.

[c] I_0, I_{LiCl}: fluorescence intensities of (εA, T$_4$) in the absence and in the presence of 6 M LiCl, respectively.

TABLE II

COMPLEXES OF GENE-5 PROTEIN WITH SINGLE- AND DOUBLE-STRANDED POLYNUCLEOTIDES: APPARENT STABILITY CONSTANTS (K_{app}), NaCl CONCENTRATIONS AT WHICH THE COMPLEXES DISSOCIATE (C_{NaCl}), AND VALUES OF RELATIVE GENE 5 PROTEIN FLUORESCENCE QUENCHING $I_o - I/I_o$

No.	Nucleotide component of the complex	$K_{app}{}^a$ (M^{-1}) at 2°C	C_{NaCl} (M) at 20°C	$\dfrac{I_0 - I}{I_0} \times 100$ (%) at 2°C^b
(22)	poly(U)	4×10^8	—	42
(23)	poly(dA)	2×10^8	—	37 ± 6
(24)	Single-stranded DNA	5×10^8	0.5 ± 0.05	46 ± 2
(25)	poly(dA) · poly(dT)	4×10^6	—	28 ± 3
(26)	Double-stranded DNA	5×10^6	0.3 ± 0.05	33 ± 2

^{a} Determined from P5 fluorescence quenching curves.

^{b} I_0, I: fluorescence intensities of uncomplexed and complexed P5.

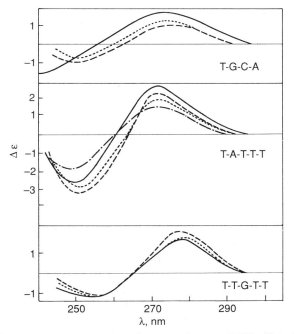

FIG. 3. CD spectra of oligonucleotides in 0.05 M Tris-HCl buffer, pH 7.5, 10^{-3} M EDTA, 10^{-4} M dithioerythritol (—), in 6 M LiCl (---) and in 75% EtOH (— · —) $C_N \sim 10^{-4}$ M. Also shown are the spectra of oligonucleotide–P5 complexes, C_{P5}/C_N 0.3–0.4 in the same buffer (---) at 20°C.

dependence of fluorescence were studied. To interpret spectral properties of the complexes, we drew on information about the effects arising in the interaction of aromatic amino-acids with heterocyclic bases, obtained by studying simple model systems—the amino-acid amidates of mono- and oligonucleotides—with the aid of CD and fluorescence (13–15). The situation in a protein–nucleic acid complex was modelled by selecting a proper solvent.

3. STOICHIOMETRY AND STABILITY OF COMPLEXES.
   IS COOPERATIVE BINDING OF P5 TO
   OLIGONUCLEOTIDES POSSIBLE?

Physicochemical studies (10) have revealed some peculiarities of the interaction of P5 with oligonucleotides. The latter, unlike polymers, may associate with P5 to form complexes of different stoichiometry, depending on the ratio of oligonucleotide to P5 in the mixture. This follows from the multistep titration plots of P5 fluorescence quenching (Fig. 1) or ϵAde fluorescence amplification (Fig. 2). In the case of an equimolecular ratio between P5 and penta(tetra)-nucleotide used in subsequent experiments, two molecules of the oligonucleotide interact with the protein dimer. Such complexes apparently aggregate because of protein–protein interactions. The stoichiometry of the complexes does not depend on the nucleotide composition, sequence, or the presence of modified bases in the oligonucleotide.

Complexes of P5 and oligonucleotide are less stable than those involving polynucleotides. There is a tendency toward a lower stability of the complexes with the transition from pentamers to oligonucleotides containing fewer base-pairs or modified bases. This follows from the apparent stability constants (Table II and N. N. Veiko, unpublished results) and the values of NaCl concentrations at which complete dissociation of the complexes is observed: 0.4, 0.2, 0.1, 0.25, and 0.5 M NaCl for complexes of P5 with pentamers **5–9, 10–14, 15** and **16, 17**, and with single-stranded DNA, respectively.

Cooperative binding of the protein to the template is a distinguishing feature of the interaction of P5 with single-stranded polynucleotides. What length must the template be for this effect to take place? CD and fluorescence measurements show that the interaction of the octamer **18** (under conditions excluding formation of an oligonucleotide duplex) with P5 is not cooperative, while the binding of P5 to the 5'-phosphorylated dodecanucleotide **19** is. In the former case, several types of complex differing in stoichiometry were formed; in the latter case, only one. As in the case of cooperative binding to polynucleotides, one protein monomer is bound to four nucleotide units of dodecanucleotide **19**. Even 12–16-membered oligonucleotides, devoid of 5′-terminal phosphate groups, are bound to P5 in a noncooperative fashion (16, 17). Therefore, the cooperativity threshold depends not only on the length of an oligomer but also on the presence of a 5′-terminal phosphate group.

The interaction of P5 with oligonucleotides (16) is characterized by lower (compared with polynucleotides) values of the cooperativity factor and numbers of nucleotides covered by one protein monomer (about three). Together with our data, these results testify to a peculiar "oligonucleotide" type of P5 binding. Another feature characterizing this type of binding is an arrangement of the protein aromatic side chains different than in the case of a polymer template (Section I,A,6).

4. THE ROLE OF ELECTROSTATIC INTERACTIONS IN COMPLEX FORMATION

The involvement of electrostatic interactions in the stabilization of P5-ssDNA (single-stranded DNA) complexes is based on the following two factors: (1) the chemical modification of Lys residues renders the protein incapable of binding to DNA; (2) the complexes dissociate even at moderate concentrations of metal ions. However, by increasing the ionic strength and thus causing the complexes to dissociate, we not only disturb electrostatic interactions but, possibly, change the structure of the protein (12). An alternative way of proving the importance of ionic contacts for complex formation is to study the binding of P5 to an oligonucleotide that does not carry a negative charge (**20**). The absence of P5 fluorescence quenching in this system shows that the blocking of negative charges of internucleotide phosphate groups, as well as the elimination of the positive charges of Lys residues, prevents P5 from binding to the oligonucleotide.

5. THE OLIGONUCLEOTIDE COMPONENT OF THE COMPLEX: THE CONFORMATION AND THE HYDRATION SHELL

The hypothetic model of a gene-5 protein–DNA complex (18) suggests that the DNA is fully extended in the complex, and that each of the two binding channels of the P5 dimer can accommodate up to five nucleotides. This suggestion is based on the hyperchromic effect concomitant with complex formation (19), and on the dimensions of the DNA-binding channels of the protein, best adapted to the fully extended tetra- or pentanucleotide (8, 18).

However, our results suggest an entirely different conclusion (9, 10). The interaction of P5 with pentanucleosidetetraphosphates alters the mutual orientation of bases in the oligonucleotide component of the complex, but does not distort the stacking conformation; also, the hydration shell of the oligonucleotide is changed, and bases from 2 to 5 find themselves in a hydrophobic environment. The grounds for this inference are as follows. (1) CD of the complexes (Fig. 3) resembles the CD of a free oligonucleotide in 6 M LiCl, but not in 75% EtOH. In the presence of Li$^+$, the hydration shell of the nucleic acids and the geometry of base stacking are changed (20), while in ethanol, base stacking is disturbed. (2) As a result of (ϵA, T$_4$) interaction with P5, the fluorescence of ϵAde is amplified (Table I). But φ_{320} persists <1 (φ_{320} is equal to 1 in the absence of stacking); $\varphi_{276}/\varphi_{320}$ is >1 for all the complexes, i.e., there is the migration of excitation energy from Thy to ϵAde favored by the stacking conformation. The fluorescence of (ϵA, T$_4$) in LiCl is likewise amplified. (3) There is a λ $_{\mathrm{flu}}^{\mathrm{max}}$ of ϵAde blue shift for all the complexes, excluding the complex of P5 with ϵATTTT (Table I), which indicates a decrease in the polarity and an increase in the viscosity of the chromophore environment. (4) The fluorescence of m^{7}Gua in a complex of P5 with oligomer 3 is amplified, i.e., the hydrophobicity of the environment of this chromophore increases. m^{7}Gua in the complex is less exposed to the external quencher KI than in a free oligonucleotide. Two-dimensional NMR spectroscopy demonstrates that the interaction of P5 with (pA)$_4$ results only in a partial base unstacking, while the oligonucleotide path in the protein is much shorter than previously believed (21). This conclusion fully agrees with our viewpoint concerning the conformation of the oligonucleotide partner and with the fact that the entire molecule of the pentanucleotide does not interact with the protein.

6. LOCATION OF THE AROMATIC AMINO-ACID SIDE-CHAINS OF P5 IN THE COMPLEX

The very first work on P5 (2) showed that Tyr and Phe residues of the protein interact with the DNA bases. This generated new questions: where are these amino-acid residues located in the complex? With what bases of the protein-bound DNA fragment do they specifically interact? To answer these questions, we made a comparative study of the Tyr and ϵAde fluorescences of complexes formed by P5 with oligonucleotides 4–14 and model compounds: Tyr derivatives of pT, pA, and pϵA of the general formula TyrOMe-(5' → N)-pN, and the dideoxyribonucleotides pT-ϵA and pϵA-T (Table I) (10, 15). We also studied the accessibility of fluorescent groups to an external quencher and compared the CD of PheOMe-(5′ → N)-pG and CDs of complexes of P5 with pentanucleotides **2** and **3** (Fig. 3) (*9, 10*).

It follows from the sum total of experimental data that no deep insertion of tyrosyls between any two bases of a pentanucleotide occurs; apparently, a part of the phenol residue of Tyr interacts with the bases. This concept is in good agreement with the absence of complete unstacking of the bases in the oligonucleotide. Presumably, a tyrosyl residue interacts with the second base from the 5′ terminus of the pentamer, and a Phe residue interacts with the third base. Most importantly, we did not find that tyrosyls interacted with the other bases. Until 1987, this result ran counter to the widespread view that three tyrosyls were involved in protein-binding (*2, 18*). Two-dimensional NMR spectroscopy (*21*) shows the validity of our conclusion: it is Tyr-26 and Phe-73′ that are involved in the stacking interaction with nucleotide bases.

The values for P5 fluorescence quenching (*10, 12*) and the shift of proton aromatic resonances of the protein (*17*) are different for P5 complexes with oligo- and polynucleotides. Seventy percent of the tyrosyls are accessible to the acrylamide in the P5 complex with ATTTT and none are accessible to this quencher in the complex of P5 with poly(dA). These findings suggest that Tyr residues are located differently in the two types of complexes. It is quite possible that in a complex with a polymer template they intercalate between bases to a greater depth.

7. Affinity Modification of P5

To evaluate the functional significance of amino-acid residues that are difficult to study by spectral methods, we made affinity modifications of P5 (*11*). Pentanucleotide **21**, carrying a chemically active bromacetyl group, alkylates P5. This is an affinity reaction, i.e., it occurs within the complex of P5 with reagent **21**. Consequently, in contact with the oligonucleotide in the P5-reagent complex, there must be some nucleophilic group of the protein, possibly the SH-group of Cys-33. This suggestion is based on the irradiation studies utilizing thymidine-containing oligonucleotides and P5 that have identified a cross-link to Cys-33 (*22*).

An analysis of the efficiency of P5 affinity modification (*11*) produced an entirely different bit of information: the oligonucleotide protects P5 from conformational changes. This effect agrees with an increase in the temperature of denaturation of P5, forming a complex with the polymer template (*12*). Therefore P5 which, in principle, has a low conformational mobility, owing to the high content of β-structure

(8), loses its ability to make conformational transitions when bound in a complex.

B. Interaction of Gene-5 Protein with Polynucleotides

We have made a comparative physicochemical study of P5 binding to single- and double-stranded templates (12), so as to understand the destabilizing effect of this protein *in vitro*. Using the fluorescence method, we demonstrated that P5 interacts with double-stranded polynucleotides, unlike its interaction with single-stranded polymers, in a noncooperative fashion. P5 complexes with double-stranded DNA and poly(dA) · poly(dT) are less stable than those with single-stranded polymers (Table II).

Having studied the salt-dependence of stability constants of complexes (23), we found that the number of electrostatic contacts differs for the complexes of P5 with single- and double-stranded polynucleotides (2.5 and 1.9, respectively), as does the contribution of the energy of nonelectrostatic interactions to the total energy of complex formation (4.3 and 6.6 kcal/mol, respectively). Besides, the location of Tyr residues is different in complexes of P5 with double- and single-stranded polynucleotides: Tyr is not intercalated into a DNA double helix. Indeed, with the double-stranded template, the fluorescence of the protein is quenched less (Table II), while the accessibility of Tyr residues to the external quencher is higher than with the single-stranded template. An increase in temperature causes a cooperative change in the fluorescence of a complex formed by P5 with poly(dA) · poly(dT); this indicates a change of location of Tyr with the transition from the P5-double-stranded polynucleotides complex to the one formed by P5 with single-stranded polymers (12). The perturbation of the 228-nm CD assigned to protein tyrosines is different for P5 complexes with single- and double-stranded templates (24).

The exact location of Tyr residues in the P5-double-stranded DNA complex is yet to be ascertained. There is experimental evidence on their proximity to the DNA double helix; possibly, they make contact with base-pair edges exposed to DNA grooves.

II. Specific Protein–Nucleic Acid Interactions: Restriction Endonucleases *Eco*RII, *Mva*I, and *Sso*II Studied with the Aid of Synthetic Substrates

We have investigated the *Eco*RII restriction endonuclease isolated from the overproducer *Escherichia coli* strain B8 34/pSK 323 (25, 26). We also studied endonucleases *Mva*I (27) and *Sso*II (28), recently isolated from *Micrococcus varians* RFL19 and *Shigella sonnei* 47, respectively. *Eco*RII is a dimer of two subunits, each with a mass of 44kDa (*26*). The mass of *Mva*I is 27 kDa; it is a monomer that dimerizes upon binding to the substrate (*29*). Methylases *Eco*RII, *Mva*I, and *Sso*II modify the second residue (dC) from the 5′ terminus of the recognition site but at different positions of the pyrimidine ring: C-5 (methylases *Eco*RII and *Sso*II) or N-4 (methylase *Mva*I).

A. Design of Substrates: Chemical Synthesis of Double-Stranded DNAs

As mentioned above, the study of DNA–protein interactions, especially the recognition of specific DNA sites by enzymes and regulatory proteins, can be performed with various families of substrates, including compounds with modified bases and unnatural internucleotide bonds. They were assembled into extended DNA duplexes by means of the traditional enzyme, T4 DNA ligase.

This part of our review summarizes our data on covalent reactions within DNA duplexes that are governed by complementary and stacking interactions. The proximity of phosphate and hydroxyl groups in a nick (single-strand break) in the rather rigid structure of a double-stranded DNA creates the "enzyme-like contacts" (Fig. 4). The detailed study of the activation of phosphate groups in nicks in aqueous solution under conditions of duplex stabilization permitted elaboration of a method of chemical assembly of double-stranded DNAs from synthetic oligonucleotides—the "chemical ligase" method (*1, 30*). The potentialities of the method are exemplified by assembly of various DNA duplexes containing natural, as well as modified interoligonucleotide bonds (*1, 31*).

1. DNA-LIKE (CONCATEMERIC) DUPLEXES WITH REPEATS

A new class of synthetic duplexes, the so-called concatemers with palindromic repeats, was described by us (*1, 30*). Their peculiarity is

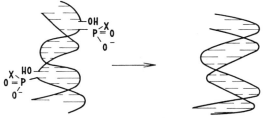

FIG. 4. Diagrammatic representation of the repair of a single-strand break in a double-helix of DNA following activation of the phosphoric residue.

that they can be formed from one, two, or a limited number of single-standed oligonucleotides. The self-association of decanucleotides shown below illustrates the principle of the formation of such duplexes:

5′ T-G-G-C-C-A-A-G-C-T → 5′T-G-G-C-C-A-A-G-C-T
                                 Ṫ-Ċ-Ġ-Ȧ-A-C-C-G-G-T 5′ →

                      ↓

→ 5′ . . . T-G-G-C-C-A-A-G-C-T T-G-G-C-C-A-A-G-C-T . . .
→ 3′ . . . Ȧ-Ċ-Ċ-Ġ-Ġ-Ṫ Ṫ-Ċ-Ġ-Ȧ-Ȧ-Ċ-Ċ-Ġ-Ġ-Ṫ Ṫ-Ċ-Ġ-Ȧ . . .
             ↑   ↑

The "seed" complexes have cohesive ends, thus facilitating subsequent block-association. This results in the formation of the extended DNA duplexes with repeating sequences containing noncoincident interruptions (marked by arrows) in the complementary chains. Some of the concatemeric duplexes synthesized (32, 33) are listed in Table IV (see Section II,A,3). It follows from the formation of these concatemers that the overlapping blocks should be of palindromic structure, which is characteristic of structural elements of sites recognized by restriction and modification enzymes. Therefore, our design of DNA duplexes containing repeats was intended to impart definite genetic sense:

         *Bal*I   *Alu*I   *Bal*I   *Alu*I
5′ . . . T-G-G-C-C-A-A-G-C-T T-G-G-C-C-A-A-G-C-T T . . .
3′ . . . Ȧ-Ċ-Ċ-Ġ-Ġ-Ṫ Ṫ-Ċ-Ġ-Ȧ-Ȧ-Ċ-Ċ-Ġ-Ġ-Ṫ Ṫ-Ċ-Ġ-Ȧ-Ȧ . . .
         *Bsp*RI   *Hind*III   *Bsp*RI   *Hind*III   (A)

         *Eco*RII   *Eco*RII   *Alu*I
5′ . . . C-C-T-G-G-A-A-T-T C-C-A-G-G-A-G-C-T C-C . . .
3′ . . . G-G-A-Ċ-Ċ Ṫ-Ṫ-Ȧ-Ȧ-Ġ-Ġ-Ṫ-Ċ-Ċ Ṫ-Ċ-Ġ-Ȧ-Ġ-Ġ . . .
                *Eco*RI   (B)

         *Eco*RII?   *Eco*RII?
5′ . . . C-C-T-G-G-A-A-T-T C-C-T-G-G-A-A-T-T C-C . . .
3′ . . . Ġ-Ġ-T-Ċ-Ċ Ṫ-Ṫ-Ȧ-Ȧ-Ġ-Ġ-T-Ċ-Ċ Ṫ-Ṫ-Ȧ-Ȧ-Ġ-Ġ . . .
                *Eco*RI   *Eco*RI   (C)

         *Eco*RII?   *Eco*RII?
5′ . . . C-C-A-G-G-A-G-C-T C-C-A-G-G-A-G-C-T C-C . . .
3′ . . . Ġ-Ġ-Ȧ-Ċ-Ċ Ṫ-Ċ-Ġ-Ȧ-Ġ-Ġ-A-Ċ-Ċ Ṫ-Ċ-Ġ-Ȧ -Ġ-Ġ . . .
                *Alu*I   *Alu*I   (D)

The duplex (A) contains sites recognized by four restriction endonucleases. These sites are repeated at 10-base-pair intervals. Two nonanucleotides, CCTGGAATT and CCAGGAGCT, afford three different duplexes. Cross-association gives rise to a duplex (B) containing an *Eco*RII recognition site with an odd number of base pairs, and also *Eco*RI and *Alu*I sites. Self-association of each nonanucleotide may result in the formation of duplexes with mismatched T · T- and A · A-pairs (C and D).

2. "Chemical Ligase," A Method to Prepare Oligonucleotides with Natural and Modified Sugar–Phosphate Backbone

The "chemical ligase" method has been suggested for assembly of double-stranded DNAs containing natural internucleotide bonds, or for site-directed modification of the sugar–phosphate backbone (inter-nucleotide linkage, sugar moiety) (*1, 31*). The method is based on template-directed condensation of synthetic oligonucleotides using chemical reagents to activate the phosphate group in a nick (Fig. 5).

For oligonucleotide coupling reactions (synthesis of the natural phosphodiester bond), we have successfully used water-soluble con-densating agents—carbodiimides (*31, 32*), and cyanogen bromide (BrCN) (*34*)—as well as preactivated derivatives of oligonucleo-tides—phosphorimidazolidates or *N*-hydroxybenzotriazole phos-phodiesters (*31, 35*).

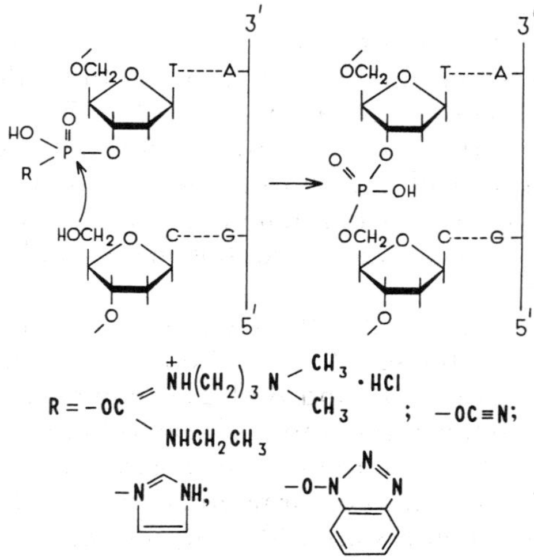

Fig. 5.   Chemical ligation by various reagents subsequent to activation of the phosphoric residue in a single-strand break.

Chemical ligation allows modification of a polynucleotide chain at a particular site when DNA duplexes are being assembled (31, 36). This is not possible enzymatically (using T4 DNA-ligase) because of the substrate specificity of the enzyme. The modifying group is first introduced at the 3'- or 5'-terminus of the oligonucleotides to be ligated, then a DNA-duplex is formed and a condensation directed by a nonenzymatic template is carried out using one of the methods of phosphate activation mentioned above.

Here we demonstrate that chemical ligation is a very promising technique for obtaining DNA duplexes with various sugar-phosphate backbone modifications (36). In the example of synthesis of DNA-duplexes containing single EcoRII sites, initial nick-containing duplexes consist of a 14-membered template and its complementary 6(5)-and 11-membered oligonucleotides, which differ only at the nucleotide residues facing the nick:

```
3'    G-C-C-T-A-G-G-T-C-C-T-C-A-C
5'  A-C̣-G̣-G̣-Ạ-X̣ Ỵ-C̣-Ạ-G̣-G̣-Ạ-G̣-Ṭ-G̣-A-C
```

and

```
3'    G-C-C-T-A-G-G-T-C-C-T-C-A-C
5'  A-C̣-G̣-G̣-Ẓ    Ỵ-C̣-Ạ-G̣-G̣-Ạ-G̣-Ṭ-G̣-A-C
```

The structure of the reactive sites is shown in Table III. As condensing agents N-ethyl-N'-(3-dimethylaminopropyl)carbodiimide (EDC) and BrCN were used.

As a result, a number of DNA duplexes with a single misincorporation were obtained (Table III). There were the following modifications: pyrophosphate; $3'N \rightarrow 5'P$ or $3'P \rightarrow 5'N$ phosphoramide internucleotide bonds; phosphodiester bonds between ribo- and deoxyribonucleotides residues; phosphodiester bonds changed conformationally by adjacent noncomplementary A · A- and A · C-base pairs or by an unpaired base and a pyrophosphate bond across a deleted nucleotide residue.

In Table III there are also the data of enzymatic ligations in the presence of T4 DNA-ligase. [The detailed discussion of the results of chemical ligation are in 31 and 36.] The chemical ligation is most favorable when the hydroxyl group is located in the 5'-position in the nick and the phosphate group in the 3'-position of synthetic oligonucleotides and DNA are in a conformation corresponding to the B-type of DNA. If these structures are different, the reaction is slowed (36). Enzymatic ligation (T4 DNA-ligase) was ineffective for all the duplexes investigated, with the exception of the duplex containing rU in the coupling site.

TABLE III

THE RESULTS OF CHEMICAL AND ENZYMATIC LIGATION OF NICKS IN DNA DUPLEXES

```
3'   G- C- C- T-A- G-G- T- C- C- T- C- A- C
5'   A- C- G- G- A-X Y-C- A- G- A- G- T- G- A- C
```

and

```
3'   G- C- C- T- A- G-G- T- C- C- T- C- A- C
5'   A- C- G- G- G-Z  Y-C- A- G- A- G- T- G- A- C
```

Reactive site structure	EDC[a]		BrCN[b]		T4 DNA ligase[c] yield (%)
	Coupling time (days)	Yield (%)	Coupling time (min)	Yield (%)	
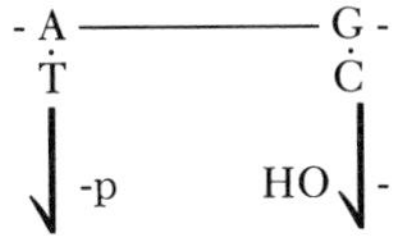 -A / T — G / C — -p HO	4	95	2	95	—
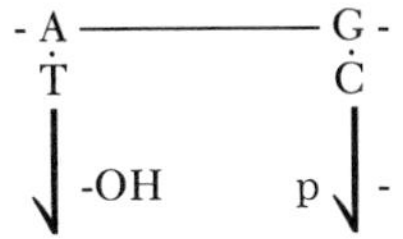 -A / T — G / C — -OH p	6	75	2	35	95
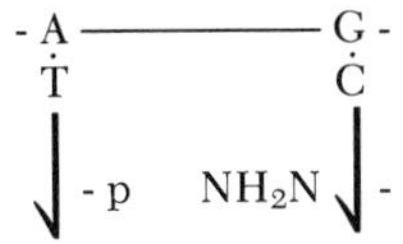 -A / T — G / C — -p NH₂N	0.25	97	—	—	—
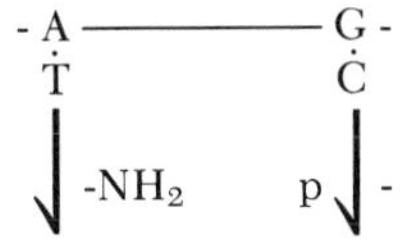 -A / T — G / C — -NH₂ p	0.25	97	2	86	0

(*continued*)

TABLE III *(Continued)*

3′ G-C-C-T-⌈A-G⌉-G-T-C-C-T-C-A-C
5′ A-C-G-G-A-⌊X Y⌋-C-A-G-A-G-T-G-A-C

and

3′ G-C-C-⌈T-A-G⌉-G-T-C-C-T-C-A-C
5′ A-C-G-G-⌊Z   Y⌋-C-A-G-A-G-T-G-A-C

Reactive site structure	EDC[a]		BrCN[b]		T4 DNA ligase[c] yield (%)
	Coupling time (days)	Yield (%)	Coupling time (min)	Yield (%)	
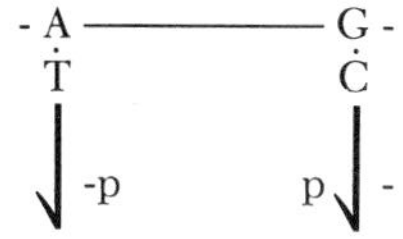 -A / Ṫ, G·/C, -p / p	0.25	92	2	67	0
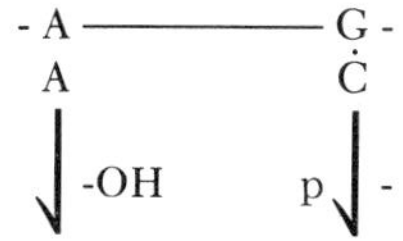 -A / A, G·/C, -OH / p	6	32	2	5	0
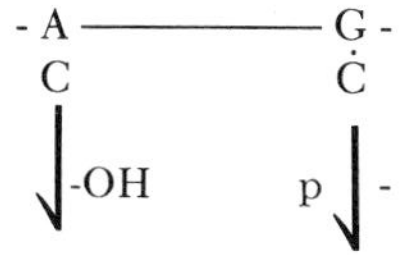 -A / C, G·/C, -OH / p	6	50	2	7	0
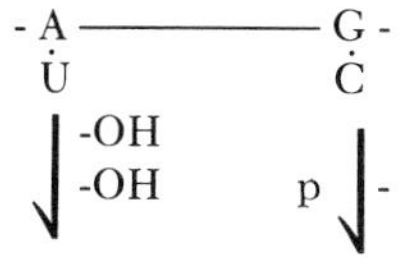 -A / U̇, G·/C, -OH -OH / p	6	28	2	19	80
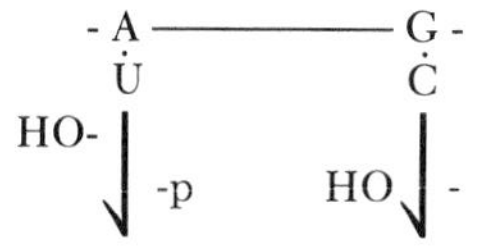 -A / U̇, G·/C, HO- -p / HO-	4	90	2	73	—

18

-A———G- U̇ Ċ- HO- ⌐-OH p⌐	6	17	2	10	0
-A———G- Ṫ Ċ- HO- ⌐ p⌐	6	20	2	26	—
-A———G- Ṫ Ċ- p- HO⌐ ⌐-	6	14	2	4	<5
-T——A———G- Ȧ Ċ- -p HO⌐ ⌐-	6	25	2	9	—
-T——A———G- Ȧ Ċ- -OH p⌐	6	10	—	—	0
-T——A———G- Ȧ Ċ- -p p⌐	4	85	2	70	0

[a] Nucleotide concentration per monomer, $C_N = 10^{-3}$ M, 0.2 M EDC, 0–5°C, 50 mM 2-morpholinoethanesulfonate buffer, pH 6.0, 20 mM MgCl₂.

[b] $C_N = 10^{-3}$ M, 0.2 M BrCN, 0–5°C, 0.25 M Mes-buffer, pH 8.0, 20 mM MgCl₂.

[c] $C_N = 10^{-4}$ M, 50 mM Tris-HCl, pH 7.5, 10 mM MgCl₂, 0.1 mM EDTA, 10 mM 2-mercaptoethanol.

A second group of DNA duplexes containing modified sugar–phosphate backbones was obtained using the carbodiimide as well as the active derivatives of oligonucleotides—phosphorimidazolides or N-hydroxybenzotriazole phosphodiesters (37).

The modifying group is first introduced at the terminal phosphate of one of the oligonucleotide components of the duplex using the activation methods described in 31 and 37). This approach was applied for the preparation of a series of DNA duplexes containing, instead of one or two nucleotide monomers inside one strand of the nonnucleotide duplex "bridges", residues of aliphatic diamines or glycols (31, 38).

The reaction of chemical ligation is more effective when an amino group, a strong nucleophile, participates in the condensation, and is less effective with hydroxy groups. The yields of duplexes that contain aliphatic diamine residues inside the sugar–phosphate backbone are 30–50% (31, 38). Another way to synthesize oligonucleotides containing the "bridges" mentioned above is by automated synthesis in organic solvents (49).

3. DESIGN OF SYNTHETIC SUBSTRATES OF ENDONUCLEASES EcoRII, MvaI, AND SsoII

To ascertain the molecular mechanism of the highly specific recognition of DNA and the mechanisms of its cleavage by EcoRII, MvaI, and SsoII enzymes, we designed DNA duplexes with native and modified recognition sites for these enzymes, and made a comparative study of the binding and splitting of these synthetic duplexes. Two families of substrates were used: extended concatemer DNA duplexes containing repeated recognition sites for EcoRII[5] (Table IV), as well as 30- and 14-membered double-stranded oligonucleotides with one recognition site (Table V).

In our view, these compounds are good prospects for studying specific protein—nucleic acid interactions. To prepare substrates of the first family, both methods of ligation, chemical and enzymatic (T4 DNA-ligase), have been used. Concatemer duplex **27** (Table IV) was obtained by ligation of two nonanucleotides, CCAGGAGCT and CCTGGAATT, capable of chess-pattern organization by hydrogen bonding as Watson–Crick base-pairs (33, 39).

The same principle underlies the synthesis of concatemer DNA duplexes (Table IV) with nucleotide analogues **28–30** (40, 41) and mismatched base-pairs **31** and **32** (33) in the recognition site as well as

---

[5] Also, MvaI and SsoII recognition sites.

TABLE IV

INTERACTION OF *EcoRII*, *MvaI*, AND *SsoII* RESTRICTION ENDONUCLEASES WITH CONCATEMER DNA DUPLEXES

DNA duplex	*EcoRII*			Relative cleavage (%) for one hour[d]		
	K' (M^{-1})[a]	k_d (min^{-1})[b]	$t_{1/2}$ (min)[c]	*EcoRII*	*MvaI*	*SsoII*
5'...T-C-C-T-G-G-A-A-T-T-C-C-A-G-G-A-G-C... 3'...A-G-G-A-C-C-T-T-A-A-G-G-T-C-C-T-C-G... (**27**)	1.6×10^9	3.5×10^{-3}	200	100	100	100
5'...T-C-C-U-G-G-A-A-T-T-C-C-A-G-G-A-G-C...[e] 3'...A-G-G-A-C-C-T-T-A-A-G-G-U-C-C-T-C-G... (**28**)	3.6×10^8	8.7×10^{-3}	80	52	110	110
5'...T-C-C-br^{5}U-G-G-A-A-T-T-C-C - A-G-G-A-G-C...[e] 3'...A-G-G-A-C-T-T-A-A-G-G-br^{5}U-C-C-T-C-G... (**29**)	1.2×10^9	1.9×10^{-3}	360	114	75	90
5'...T-m^{5}C-C-T-G-G-A-A-T-T-C-C-A-G - G-A-G-C...[e] 3'...A - G-G-A-C-C-T-T-A-A-G-G-T-C-m^{5}C-T-C-G... (**30**)	8.3×10^8	1.1×10^{-3}	640	3	92	6
5'...T-C-C-T-G-G-A-A-T-T-C-C-T-G-G-A-A-T... 3'...A-G-G-A-C-C-T-T-A-A-G-G-T-C-C-T-T-A... (**31**)	9.9×10^7	1.2×10^{-2}	57	28	73	140
5'...T-C-C-A-G-G-A-G-C-T-C-C-A-G-G-A-G-C-T... 3'...A-G-G-A-C-C-T-C-G-A-C-C-T-C-C-T-C-G-A... (**32**)	1.8×10^7	8.7×10^{-2}	8	2.8	0	60
5'...T$_{N}$pC-C-T-G-G- A-A-T-T$_{N}$pC-C-A-G-G - A-G-C... 3'...'A - G-G-A-C-C$_{pN}$-T-T-A-A- G-G-T-C-C$_{pN}$-T-C-G... (**33**)	7.4×10^8	1.2×10^{-2}	60	0	—	—
5'...TppC-C-T-G-G - A-A-T-TppC-C-A-G-G - A-G-C... 3'...'A - G-G-A-C-C$_{pp}$T-T-A-A - G-G-T-C-C$_{pp}$T-C-G... (**34**)	1.1×10^9	9.2×10^{-3}	75	0	—	—
5'...T-G-C-A-C-A-T-G... 3'...A-C-G-T-G-T-A-C... (**46**)	1.5×10^7	0.7	1	—	—	—

[a] K' (binding parameter) = $1/(P_0)_{1/2}$, where $(P_0)_{1/2}$ is the overall concentration of the enzyme in a mixture with the substrate when half of the substrate molecules are bound. The substrate concentration is a constant value.

[b] Complex dissociation rate constant.

[c] Half-life period of the complex.

[d] Calculated relative to the cleavage % of duplex **27**. For NN **28–30** (*EcoRII*), determined for 30 minutes.

[e] U, deoxyuridine; br^{5}U, 5-bromodeoxyuridine; m^{5}C, 5-methyldeoxycytidine.

with pyrophosphate (pp) and phosphoramide (Np) bonds, replacing the endonuclease (EcoRII and SsoII)-cleaved phosphodiester (p) bonds in one (**35–38**) or both (**33, 34**) strands of the substrate (*42, 43*):

```
5' . . . TzC-C-T-G-G-A-A-T-TyC-C-A-G-G-A-G-C . . .
3' . . . A-G-G-A-C-CyT-T-A-A-G-G-T-C-CzT-G-G . . .
```

(**35**)   y = pp,   z = p;   (**37**)   y = p,   z = pp;
(**36**)   y = Np,   z = p;   (**38**)   y = p,   z = Np.

Modified nonanucleotides or their dimers, as well as native nonanucleotides separately, were used for polycondensation. A distinctive feature of concatemers consists in their heterogeneity in length: for substrates **33** and **34**, from 90 to 500 base pairs; from 180 to 1000 for the others. Furthermore, the EcoRII recognition sites recur every nine base pairs with the central A · T pair alternating its orientation; and there are also EcoRI and AluI sites. Duplex **27** was fragmented by EcoRI and AluI endonucleases, and this made it possible to expand the number of substrates:

```
5'   pA-A-T-T-C-C-A-G-G-A-G-C-T-C-C-T-G-G
3'            G-G-T-C-C-T-C-G-A-G-G-A-C-C-T-T-A-Ap                    (39)
```

```
5'   pC-T-C-C-T-G-G-A-A-T-T-C-C-A-G-G-A-G
3'   G-A-G-G-A-C-C-T-T-A-A-G-G-T-C-C-T-Cp                              (40)
```

We also succeeded in obtaining individual k-mers of CCTGGAATT and CCAGGAGCT (k = 2,3 . . . ,12) (*39, 44, 45*), for instance, the dimers

```
5'        pC-C-A-G-G-A-G-C-T-C-C-T-G-G-A-A-T-T
3'   T-T-A-A-G-G-T-C-C-T-C-G-A-G-G-A-C-Cp                              (41)
```

```
5'        pC-C-T-G-G-A-A-T-T-C-C-A-G-G-A-G-C-T
3'   T-C-G-A-G-G-A-C-C-T-T-A-A-G-G-T-C-Cp                              (42)
```

the trimer

```
5'        pC-C-T-G-G-A-A-T-T-C-C-A-G-G-A-G-C-T-C-C-T-G-G-A-A-T-T
3'   T-C-G-A-G-G-A-C-C-T-T-A-A-G-G-T-C-C-T-C-G-A-G-G-A-C-Cp          (43)
```

etc. Dimers of nonanucleotides without 5'-terminal phosphate groups were obtained as well:

```
5'        C-C-A-G-G-A-G-C-T-C-C-T-G-G-A-A-T-T
3'   T-T-A-A-G-G-T-C-C-T-C-G-A-G-G-A-C-C                               (41')
```

```
5'        C-C-T-G-G-A-A-T-T-C-C-A-G-G-A-G-C-T
3'   T-C-G-A-G-G-A-C-C-T-T-A-A-G-G-T-C-C                               (42')
```

In trimers, pyrophosphate (44) or phosphoramide (45) bonds were substituted for phosphodiester bonds at the joints of nonanucleotide blocks (45, 46). From pTGCACATG, the concatemer DNA duplex (46), which does not contain EcoRII sites, was synthesized (47).

Selectively modified substrates with a single recognition site (Table V) were assembled from DNA duplexes 47, 55, and 71, differing in length and sequence. We have used chemical ligation to introduce mismatched base pairs (66, 73 and 74), pp and Np-bonds (67, 75, and 76), modified sugar moieties (64, 65 and 72), and nonnucleotide (hydrocarbon) bridges (68–70). DNA-duplexes containing analogs of heterocyclic bases (57–63), cleaved phosphodiester bonds (48–51) as well as eliminated base-pairs (covalent continuity of phosphodiester bonds was occasionally preserved in this case) (52–55) have been prepared in the usual way. Both the recognition site and the flanking sequences were modified. Some modifications were directed at the central A · T pair. Sometimes the "enhancement of modification technique" was used (49, 50 and 53). In addition, we used DNA duplex 77, which is a central fragment of the 30-membered duplex 47 and duplex 78, having a quasipalindromic structure (the symmetry is disturbed only in the center of the EcoRII site):

```
5′  G-C-C-A-A-C̅-C̅-T̅-G̅-G̅-C-T-C-T
3′  C̣-G̣-G̣-Ṭ-Ṭ-G̲-G̲-A̲-C̲-C̲-G̣-Ạ-G̣-Ạ                    (77)

5′  A-A-T-G-C-C-A-G-G-C-A-T-T
3′  Ṭ-Ṭ-Ạ-C̣-G̲-G̲-T̲-C̲-C̲-G̣-Ṭ-Ạ-Ạ                        (78)
```

In the case of "single-site" DNA duplexes, one can correctly discriminate between the cleavage of the substrate A- and T-strands (so designated by the central letter of the EcoRII site) and thus obtain kinetic parameters of the enzymatic reactions.

B. Conformation and Stability of Designed DNA Duplexes

To use modified DNA duplexes as substrates for restriction endonucleases, one must know the changes induced in the conformation and stability of the double helix by each modification. Summing up the results on CD and UV spectroscopy of DNA duplexes listed in Tables IV and V (33, 36, 48–50) and also the data on NMR, X-ray analysis, and CD of double-stranded oligonucleotides (51), we may come to the following conclusions:

(1) Modifications not hindering complementary interactions and not affecting the conformational mobility of individual fragments of a

TABLE V

Cleavage of DNA Duplexes with a Single Recognition Site

DNA duplex[a]	Relative initial rate of hydrolysis[b]		
	EcoRII	MvaI	SsoII
5' GATGCTGCCAACCTGGCTCTAGCTTCATAC 3' CTACGACGGTTGGACCGAGATCGAAGTATG (47)	100 100	100 100	— —
...C-A-A-C-C pT-G-G... ...G-T-T-G-G-A-C-C... (48)	— —	— 18	— —
...C-A-A-C-C-T - G-G... ...G-T-T-G-G-Ap C-C... (49)	3 0	100 —	— —
...C-A-A-C-C-T-G-G... ...G-T-T-G-G-A C-C... (50)	3 0	100 —	— —
...C AA-C-C-T-G-G... ...G-T-T-G-G-A-C-C... (51)	2 6	— —	— —
...C-A-A-C-A G-G... ...G-T-T-G-G-A-C-C... (52)	0 0	0 0	— —
...C-A-A-C-C-T-G-G... ...G-T-T-G-G C-C... (53)	0 0	0 —	— —
...C-A-A-C-A G-G... ...G-T-T-G-G-A-C-C... (54)	0 0	0 0	— —

DNA duplex[a]	Relative initial rate of hydrolysis[b]		
	EcoRII	MvaI	SsoII
...m4C-C-T-G-G...[c] ... G-G-A-C-C... (62)	0 0	0 120	— —
...C-C-T-G- G ...G-G-A-C-m4C... (63)	0 0	180 0	— —
...C-C-rU-G-G...[c] ...G-G- A-C-C... (64)	11 7	100 46	270 280
...C-C-xT-G-G...[c] ...G-G- A-C-C... (65)	— —	77 4	— —
...C-G-T-G-G... ...G-G-A-C-C... (66)	— —	0 1	— —
...C-CppT-G-G... ...G-G- A-C-C... (67)	0 0	0 100	0 0
NH-(CH₂)₃-NH ...C-Cp pG-G... ...G-G - A - C-C... (68)	0 0	0 9	— —
...C-C - T - G-G... ...G-Gp pC-C... O-(CH₂)₃-O (69)	0 0	97 5	— —

NH-(CH₂)₂-NH

Branched structure (70):
```
                    pT-G-G...
...C-Cp            A-C-C...
...G-C                (70)
```

(71):
```
5'  CACTCCTGGATCCC
3'  CAGTGAGGACCTAGGCA
```

Duplex (left strand)				(70)–(76) structures		
...C-A-A-C-C-T-G-G... ...G-T-T-G-G - C-C... **(55)**	0 / 0	0 / 0	— / —	(70) above	0 / 0 0 / 65	— / —
5' ACCTACCTGGTGGT 3' TGGATGGACCACCA **(56)**	100 / 100	100 / 100	100 / 100	(71) above	100 / 100	100 / 100
...C-C-ff⁵U-G-G...ᶜ ...G-G- -A-C-C... **(57)**	5 / 12	97 / 104	59 / 112	...C-C-T-G-G-A... ...G-G-A-C-C-rU... **(72)**	3 / 3	103 / 41
...C-C- T-G-G...ᶜ ...G-G-m⁶A-C-C... **(58)**	1 / 1	100 / 0	— / —	...C-C-T-G-G-A... ...G-G-A-C-C-A... **(73)**	12 / 9	114 / 61
...C-m⁵C-T-G-G... ...G - G-Am⁵C-C... **(59)**	0 / 0	85 / 97	0 / 0	...C-C-T-G-G-A... ...G-G-A-C-C-C... **(74)**	2 / 2	68 / 0
...C-m⁵C-T-G-G... ...G - G-A-C-C... **(60)**	0 / 0	91 / 53	0 / 0	...C-C-T-G-G- A... ...G-G-A-C-C_PN-T... **(75)**	30 / 0	102 / 0
...C-C-T - G-G... ...G-G-A-m⁵C-C... **(61)**	0 / 0	51 / 153	— / —	...C-C-T-G-G- A... ...G-G-A-C-C_N-pT... **(76)**	14 / 0	

ᵃ In duplexes **48–55, 57–70,** and **72–76,** only modified fragments of the molecule are shown; their other parts are identical with the starting compounds **47, 56,** and **71,** respectively, except that the upper chain in **65** and **66** is longer by a dA residue at the 5'-terminus.

ᵇ Ratio of the initial rates of hydrolysis, V_0, of individual strands of modified DNA duplexes to the V_0 of a corresponding strand of the starting duplexes × 100 (for substrates **69** and **70,** the ratio of the cleavage % for 1 hour). The data in the upper and lower lanes relate to T- and A-strands, respectively.

ᶜ ff⁵U, 5-fluorodeoxyuridine; m⁶A, N⁶-methyldeoxyadenosine; m⁴C, N⁴-methyldeoxycytidine; rU, ribouridine; xT, 1-β-2'-deoxy-D-treopentafuranosylthymine.

25

molecule [28–30, 33, 34, 57, 59–61, 64, 65, 67, 72, 75 and 76] do not disturb the thermal stability of duplexes. Other modifications [mismatched base pairs, nucleoside analogues m^4dC and m^6dA, single-strand nicking or nucleotide deletions (31, 32, 48–55, 58, 62, 63, 66, 73 and 74] lower the melting temperature of duplexes. Yet the destabilizing effect is not, as a rule, of decisive significance either for the concatemers and 30-membered substrates, the melting temperature of which is initially above 75°, or for the "single-site" substrates with one modification per 14 base-pairs. Under the conditions of enzymatic hydrolysis (37° or 20°C), all the DNA duplexes obtained are stable.

(2) No significant changes of the double-helix conformation beyond the modification site were detected. However, in mismatched base-pairs there may be distortions of the structure and a different steric disposition of the functional groups essential for contacts with proteins. In rU-containing duplexes, A-form DNA-like domains occur. Conformational perturbations, caused by base analogues, [for example, 28–30, 57, and 59–61] are quite insignificant. It is only in the case of DNA duplexes 68–70 that, owing to the absence of one base as well as to the high conformational mobility and the hydrophobic nature of an inserted hydrocarbon bridge, appreciable destabilization of the double helix and changes of CD spectra are observed (49). We must point to the remarkable feature of substrate 56 and its analogues (48). Judging by the CD, the DNA helix of these compounds has elements of the A form. Under cleavage conditions, substrate 78 persists as a heteroduplex, and not as a hairpin or homoassociate.

C. Substrates with Canonical Recognition Sites:
Binding and Cleavage. Nonspecific Binding

The interaction of a restriction endonuclease with DNA involves two steps: the binding of the enzyme to a specific sequence of the DNA, and the cleavage of the specific complex. Using EcoRII enzyme, we made a comprehensive study of the first step. By a nitrocellulose filter binding assay in the absence of Mg^{2+}, the reaction cofactor, we determined the parameters of EcoRII binding to concatemer duplexes. K' (the exact computation of the equilibrium association constant is impossible in this case), as well as the dissociation rate constants, k_d, and the half-lives of the complexes ($T_{1/2}$) (see Table IV) (45). The dissociation kinetics of the complexes was studied in the presence of a competing DNA. The binding of the enzyme to DNA duplexes 27–34 proceeded in a noncooperative fashion. The difference between the parameters of the specific and the nonspecific complexes was fairly large (27 and 46 in Table IV). In point of fact, EcoRII endonuclease exhibits its specificity on binding to the substrate. The association constant has been determined for a substrate with a single recognition site **43**. It is $3.9 \times 10^8\ M^{-1}$.

To study the kinetics of hydrolysis, we introduced a ^{32}P label at the joints of nonanucleotide blocks in concatemer substrates, or alternately at the 5′-terminus of each strand of single-site substrates. Reaction mixtures were analyzed by electrophoresis in a polyacrylamide gel; kinetic curves were plotted for all the substrates.

*Eco*RII, *Mva*I, and *Sso*II enzymes effectively cleave concatemer **27**; besides the nonanucleotides, products of incomplete hydrolysis, their lengths being multiples of nine base-pairs, are formed (39, 44). Analysis of the composition of the reaction mixtures showed whether the cleavage of the polymer is processive or distributive (see Section II,H).

The cleavage of substrates with one canonical site by *Eco*RII (52, 53), *Sso*II (54), and *Mva* I (55) endonucleases obeys Michaelis-Menten kinetics; K_M and V_{max} were determined. Each of these three enzymes cleaves the identical-length heteroduplexes **56, 71**, and **77** at different rates (52, 54, 56). Also, cleavage rates of both strands in duplexes **47, 56** (only in the case of *Eco*RII and *Sso*II endonucleases) **71** and **77** were different (52–54, 56–58 and Fig. 6).

These effects result mainly from the different nucleotide environment of the recognition site. Hydrolysis by *Mva*I and *Eco*RII endonucleases depends on the geometry of DNA. The reaction proceeds most efficiently for substrate **56** (Fig. 6), which, unlike other substrates with natural recognition sites, exists in the A-form. It is pertinent to ask whether the asymmetric pattern of cleavage might not be related also to the partial asymmetry of the *Eco*RII site. We obtained a positive answer for endonuclease *Mva*I which, in contrast to *Eco*RII, cleaves individual strands of the quasipalinodromic duplex **78** at a different rate (A-strand > T-strand) (Fig. 7). Thus, a restriction endonuclease recognizing the partially degenerate site discriminated between different strands of the substrate. Most importantly, it is the *Mva*I-cleaved sites (. . . CpA . . . and . . . CpT . . .) that are not identical.

We must point to the rather unusual time course of the cleavage for substrate **47** by endonuclease *Mva*I (57, 58). Shortly after the onset of the reaction, the rate of A-strand scission undergoes a dramatic drop, while the hydrolysis of the T-strand proceeds with sufficient efficiency (Fig. 6). As a consequence, after one hour of hydrolysis additional to the products of complete digestion of duplex **47**, a product with a nick in the T-strand accumulates in the reaction mixture. This interesting phenomenon may be explained by the digestion kinetics of substrates

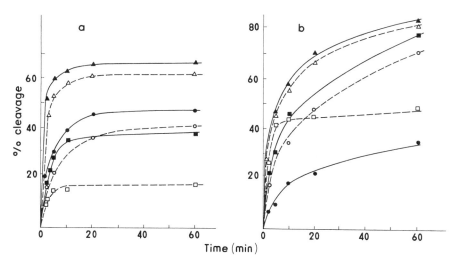

FIG. 6. Cleavage of DNA duplexes **47** (■, □), **56** (▲, △), and **77** (●, ○) by *Eco*RII, 0.4 units (a) and *Mva*I, 2 units (b) restriction endonucleases at 37°C. —, T-strand; ---, A-strand. $C_D = 3.5 \times 10^{-7}$ M (in all figures, C_D is substrate concentration per mole of DNA duplex).

48 and **49,** adequate to the intermediates of substrate **47** hydrolysis. While a nick in the T-strand of **48** leads to a significant decrease of the cleavage rate, a nick in the A-strand (**49**) increases the efficiency of digestion. The nicking of the A- and T-strands of duplex **77**, identical to duplex **47** according to the ambient nucleotide environment of the

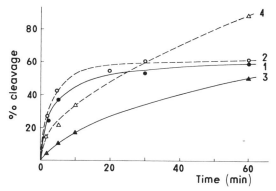

FIG. 7. Cleavage of DNA duplex **78** by *Eco*RII, 0.4 units, $C_D = 6.6 \times 10^{-7}$ M (●, ○), and *Mva*I, 2.4 units, $C_D = 1.63 \times 10^{-7}$ M (▲, △). —, T-strand; ---, A-strand.

recognition site, follows the usual time course (Fig. 6). Consequently, the hydrolysis kinetics depends on the length of the recognition site that flanks the DNA fragments. The single-strand nicking capability is predetermined by the entire nucleotide sequence of 30-membered substrate **47.**. Studying the interaction of duplexes **47** and **77** with *Eco*RII enzyme, we observed no unusual cleavage behavior (*56*) (Fig. 6).

D. The Role of Recognition-Site Flanking by Nucleotides. Assessing the *Eco*RII Binding Site on the DNA

The interaction of restriction endonucleases with DNA extends beyond the recognition site. This is confirmed by the effect of recognition-site flanking sequences on the rates of reactions catalyzed by *Eco*RII, *Mva*I, and *Sso*II (Section II,C). Relative to *Eco*RII, we have other arguments at our disposal (*39, 43*). Substrates in which the recognition site is not flanked by nucleotides in one of the strands from the 5′ (**41** and **42**) or 3′ (**39**) termini are cleaved by endonuclease *Eco*RII very slowly compared with polymer **27**. Besides, cleavage of dimers **41** and **42** is possible, in principle, owing to their capacity for association at "sticky" ends; this gives rise to more extended structures and "noncovalent" flanking of the *Eco*RII site. If we preclude association, e.g., by adding a nucleotide residue to one of the sticky ends, the cleavage of the duplex will be blocked. DNA duplex **40**, in which *Eco*RII sites are flanked on one side by two base-pairs, is resistant to enzymatic action. In contrast, DNA duplex **51** (the "noncovalent" flanking version) is cleaved, albeit at a very slow rate, by endonuclease *Eco*RII (*53*). So the DNA fragments adjoining the recognition site are essential attributes of the *Eco*RII substrate. In the worst case, this may be a "noncovalent" flanking.

Now, how long do these fragments have to be? As shown by the results of *Eco*RII-effected hydrolysis of substrates **56, 71,** and **77** (*52, 53, 56*), it would suffice for effective cleavage if the flanking sequences are four to five base-pairs long on both sides of the recognition site. However, the high value of K_M for duplex **71** ($1.6 \times 10^{-5}\,M$) compared with the K_M for duplex **47** ($4.6 \times 10^{-7}\,M$) shows that 14 base-pairs are apparently not sufficient for the formation of a good enzyme–substrate complex. To assess the dimensions of the *Eco*RII binding site, the binding parameters and the efficiency of cleavage (*43*) by this enzyme of the nonanucleotide CCAGGAGCT and CCTGGAATT k-mers ($k = 2,3, \ldots , 12$), in which the number of *Eco*RII sites and the length of the duplexes increased successively, were compared (Fig. 8). *Eco*RII bound to a fairly long (21–23 base-pair) fragment of DNA.

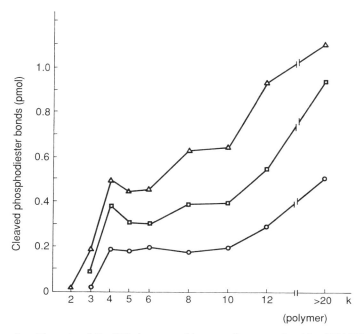

FIG. 8.   The rate of *Eco*RII cleavage of *k*-mers of nonanucleotides CCAGGAGCT and CCTGGAATT versus their length (*k*). The numbers of phosphodiester bonds, cleaved in 3 (○), 10 (□), and 30 (△) minutes of the reaction (C_N = 2.5 μM, 2.5–3 units of *Eco*RII) are given.

E. Interaction of Restriction Endonucleases with Substrates Containing Mismatched Base-Pairs

We have examined the binding and cleavage of DNA duplexes with T · T-, A · A-, G · G- and A · C-mismatches within the recognition site and in the flanking sequences. The T · T-pair in the *Eco*RII site (**31**) does not hinder hydrolysis by *Eco*RII and *Mva*I enzymes, while the A · A-pair (**32**) slows it significantly (in the case of *Eco*RII) or blocks it altogether (in the case of *Mva*I) (39, 59), (Table IV). The G · G-mismatch containing substrate (**66**) is not cleaved by *Mva*I either (Table V). It must be observed here that, in the case of *Mva*I endonuclease, the mismatched pairs adjoin the cleavage site. The AA- and TT-pairs, even in a completely degenerate position of the *Sso*II site, affect the *Sso*II enzymatic reaction (Table IV and 59).

A · A- and A · C-mispairs outside the recognition site next to the scissile bond (**73** and **74**) result in the abrupt deceleration of the hydrolysis of both strands of the substrate by *Eco*RII, especially in the case of the AC-pair (Table V and 52). Endonuclease *Sso*II is not particularly sensitive to the modification of this position (54). The larger inhibiting effect of the AC-pair compared with the AA-pair correlates with the degree of destabilization and distortion of the DNA helix effected by these mismatches (36, 60).

Endonuclease *Eco*RII is less efficient in attacking AA-containing recognition sites (32) than the canonical *Eco*RII site with AA-mismatch adjacent to it in the vicinity of the scissile bond (73). The conformational changes induced by the A · A-pair in each of these positions are similar.

Endonuclease *Eco*RII binds to polymers containing mismatched pairs, with the thermodynamic stabilities and the half-lives of the complexes decreasing in the order: AT (27) > TT(31) ≫ AA (32) (Table IV and 45). On the other hand, substitution of nonhydrolyzable bonds for scissile ones exerts no significant effect on the formation of a specific complex (Section II,I). These facts corroborate the conclusion about the specificity of *Eco*RII for the target sequence in the binding step. A comparison of the data on the interaction of this enzyme with polymers 32 and 46 (Table IV) suggests that the catalytic step of the reaction involves some "additional recognition" of the substrate by the enzyme, and this accounts for the very high specificity of the enzymatic reaction. Analysis of the binding and cleavage of polymers with T · T-and A · A-pairs show that endonuclease *Eco*RII recognizes

$$\cdots\text{CCTGG}\cdots \atop \cdots\text{GGTCC}\cdots \text{ and } \cdots\text{CCAGG}\cdots \atop \cdots\text{GGACC}\cdots$$

sequences. This fact, as well as the correlation between the rate of cleavage of polymers 27, 31 and 32 (39) and the tightness of complexes formed by them (A · T > T · T ≫ A · A) may indicate the specific interaction of the enzyme with the bases of the A · T-pair at the step of enzyme—substrate complex formation. But the alternative interpretation is likewise possible: the effects observed may be due to local distortion in the double helix caused by T · T- and, especially, A · A-mispairs. We must add here that repair enzymes perform better in correcting A · A- rather than T · T-pairs (61).

F. Possible Contacts of Enzymes *Eco*RII, *Mva*I, and *Sso*II with Synthetic Substrates

To identify those groups of atoms in heterocyclic bases that are in direct contact with the proteins investigated and that ensure the recognition of a corresponding template, as well as the phosphate groups stabilizing the protein—nucleic acid complex, we studied the effects of base-analog substitutions, nucleoside or phosphate deletions, nucleotide-substituting hydrocarbon bridges, etc., on binding and cleavage by the restriction endonucleases *Eco*RII, *Mva*I, and *Sso*II.

The change of enzymatic activity in response to the introduction of some chemical group into the recognition site or its elimination is not always amenable to direct and simple interpretation; one cannot simply attribute the observed effect to the close proximity of the enzyme with this group during the reaction. Depending on the character of modification, local perturbations in the structure of the recognition site are possible, as well as the prohibition of conformational changes in the DNA and protein necessary for recognition, indirect effects on the interaction involving other groups of atoms, etc. However, one may redress the drawbacks of every single substrate by expanding the spectrum of substrates and thus obtain a more or less truthful picture. Needless to say, a certain caution about the conclusions will be needed just the same.

We began our investigation into endonuclease–DNA interactions with the central degenerate pair of the recognition site. A number of factors enable us to suggest the interaction of *Eco*RII with each of the bases in the A · T-pair. Removal of dA or dT from the site (the covalent continuity of phsophodiester bonds may be disturbed or remain intact), as well as substitution of a trimethylene bridge or nucleotide analogues (fl^{5}dU and m^{6}dA in particular) for these residues results in a blockage (**52–55, 68** and **69** in Table V), or a dramatic decrease (**57** and **58**) of the rates of cleavage of both strands of the duplex (*50, 52, 53*). Analysis of the cleavage of similar substrates by *Mva*I (*50, 55, 57*) points to the interaction of the enzyme with dA residue of the recognition site.

The next problem concerned the group of atoms in the A · T-pair contacting the proteins. The substituent at the C-5 atom of dT affects the properties of a complex formed by *Eco*RII with the substrates and the rate of hydrolysis (**27–29** in Table IV and Fig. 9) (*41, 45*). Substitution of dU for dT, in contrast to the substitution of br^{5}dU for dT, accelerates dissociation of the complex. Substrate **27** forms a tighter complex with the enzyme and is hydrolyzed faster than duplex **28**. These data suggest a hydrophobic contact of endonuclease *Eco*RII with a CH$_3$-group of thymine (Fig. 10). An analogous contact appears also to be materialized for polymer **29**, which is bound and cleaved almost as well as substrate **27**. This could be anticipated, bearing in mind the similarity of the sizes of Br and CH$_3$. No such contact seems to be formed in the case of endonuclease *Mva*I, as the cleavages of duplexes **27** and **28**, as well as of **56** and **57**, actually occur at similar rates.

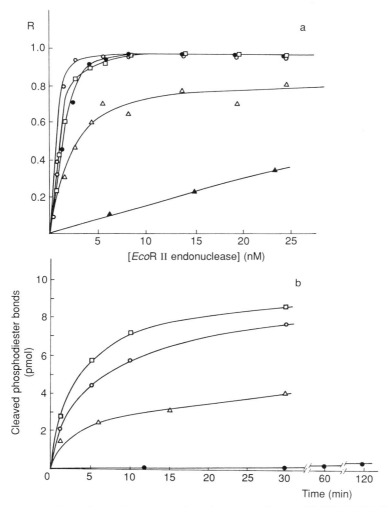

FIG. 9. (a) Binding of *Eco*RII endonuclease to polymers **27** (○), **28** (△), **29** (□), **30** (●), and **46** (▲) in 40 mM Tris-HCl buffer, pH 7.6, 50 mM NaCl, 7 mM β-mercaptoethanol, 50 mg/ml bovine serum albumin at 37°C, C_N = 125 nM. (b) Rates of cleavage of the same polymers by endonuclease *Eco*RII. 40 mM Tris-HCl buffer, pH 7.5, 5 mM MgCl$_2$, 50 mM NaCl, 5 mM dithiothreitol, 4% (v/v) glycerol, C_N = 12.8 μM, 7–8 units of *Eco*RII at 37°C.

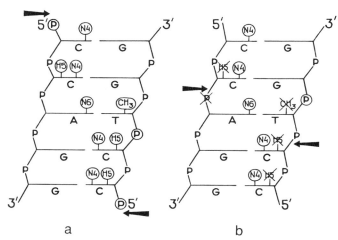

Fig. 10. Groups of atoms of recognition site, presumably involved in interaction with *Eco*RII (a) and *Mva*I (b) restriction endonuclease. O, contact or proximity; x, no contact.

It is noteworthy that in duplex **57** the presence of the electronegative fluorine atom causes a change in the electronic structure and deprotonation of the pyrimidine base (*62*). Enzyme *Sso*II, despite the complete degeneracy of the central position of the recognition site, discriminates against the fl^5dU residue (*54*) (Table V).

The activity of restriction endonuclease *Eco*RII decreases dramatically if the 6-amino group of adenine in the recognition site is methylated (**58**), and enzyme *Mva*I attacks only the nonmodified strand of such substrate (*50*). This indicates the contact or proximity of the functional groups of both proteins with this amino group (Fig. 10).

Methylation of any of the dC residues in one or both strands of the recognition site at the 5-C position or the 4-amino group of cytosine (**30** in Table IV; **59–63** in Table V) blocked[6] the hydrolysis of both strands of the substrate by *Eco*RII (*41, 50, 52, 63*) and *Sso*II (*54, 59*). m^4dC-containing DNA duplexes are not substrates for enzyme *Mva*I either (*50, 63*). But in the hemimethylated duplexes **62** and **63**, the intact strand was cleaved at an ordinary rate. *Mva*I enzyme is tolerant to the substitutions of m^5dC for both dCs **30, 60** and **61**, not counting the small deceleration of hydrolysis of the nonmodified strand in **60** and **61** (*55, 59*).

---

[6] Duplex **30** is cleaved at a very slow rate.

The methyl group at the N-4 of cytosine like that at N-6 of adenine, prevents digestion, either by sterically hindering the necessary contacts with the enzymes in the major groove of DNA, or by hindering hydrogen bond formation between the 4-amino groups of the cytosines and the proteins. Thus, one may suggest contact or proximity of the 4-amino groups of both dC residues with the functional groups of the enzymes (Fig. 10). Besides, enzymes *Eco*RII and *Sso*II interact with hydrogen atoms at the C-5 position of cytosine; such contacts are absent in the case of endonuclease *Mva*I. The pattern of the suggested contacts of *Sso*II with dC residues of the recognition site is about the same as for *Eco*RII endonuclease.

A complex formed by endonuclease *Eco*RII with DNA duplex 30 is distinguished by high stability and a high value of $T_{1/2}$ (Table IV) (*41*). But hydrolysis of this substrate is largely inhibited (Fig. 9); therefore, the complex is unproductive. Thus, the formation of a tight complex is not a sufficient condition for the reaction catalyzed by restriction endonucleases to proceed with much success. Possibly conformational changes of the enzyme are needed as well, but they are hindered by the CH_3-group. Alternatively, the complex of *Eco*RII endonuclease with polymer 30 may have an anomalous structure.

The electrostatic interactions of *Eco*RII with the sugar—phosphate backbone of DNA (Fig. 10) was assessed by the effect exerted on hydrolysis by the removal of phosphate groups (41', 42', 50, and 51) or by their replacement with a pyrophosphate group (67) (39, 53); see Sections II,G,I,J. There appear to be interactions between *Eco*RII and phosphate groups located at both cleavage sites [in the case of *Mva*I endonuclease, one such contact is most probably absent (57)], at a central dT residue, and at a distance of two base-pairs from the recognition site.

DNA—protein contacts, indicated in Fig. 10, are located in the major groove of the DNA helix, and, in the case of *Mva*I, in the center of this groove (*64*). The symmetric pattern of the contacts and their difference for *Eco*RII and *Mva*I are noteworthy.

G. The Effect of DNA Conformation on the Interaction of *Eco*RII, *Mva*I, and *Sso*II with Substrates

Recognition of DNA by proteins depends on the sequence-related structure of the DNA double-helix. Possibly, there is some conformational motif promoting specific DNA—protein interaction. It is likewise significant that according to X-ray analysis data (5), a characteristic departure from the canonical conformation of DNA is observed in

complexes formed by restriction endonuclease *Eco*RI with the substrate.

We have studied the substrate properties of DNA duplexes modelling the structural microheterogeneity of DNA via modification of the
sugar–phosphate backbone (Table V). Introduction of single ribonu-
cleotides (**64** and **72**, Table V) causes the appearance of local A-like
domains in the B-DNA. Such a conformational motif is less well recognized and cleaved by endonuclease *Eco*RII than is the native one,
especially if a base-pair adjoining the recognition site and the scissle
bond is modified (52).

Conversely, it is favorable for enzymatic hydrolysis in the case of
*Sso*II (54). The enzymatic reaction may be accelerated if the substrate
has a form corresponding to the transition state in the enzyme–
substrate complex (65). In complexes of *Sso*II endonuclease with substrate, it is not excluded that the conformation of a degenerate pair at
the recognition site resembles A-DNA.

The local distortion of the *Eco*RII recognition site in a nicked substrate (**49**), owing to the higher mobility of groups located near the nick,
causes a very significant deceleration in the cleavage of both strands by
*Eco*RII (53). It may be suggested that the structural defect in the

$$- \text{T} - \text{G}-$$
$$- \dot{\text{A}}\text{p} \quad \dot{\text{C}}-$$

fragment leads to a disturbance of specific DNA–protein contacts.
Thus, the structural anomalies examined, in particular the hybrid
dA · rU pair, did not favor the formation of a productive complex between *Eco*RII and the substrate. At the same time, the global A-like
geometry of the double-helix of substrate **56** resulted in the higher
efficiency of *Eco*RII endonuclease (Section II,C).

The high sensitivity to defects in the conformation of the substrate
is an essential characteristic of *Eco*RII endonuclease (see also cleavage
of duplexes **70, 73** and **74**, Table V and Section II,E). The response of
*Mva*I endonuclease to ribose and deoxyxylose insertions in the recognition site (**64** and **65**, Table V) is surprising indeed (55). As in the case
of methylated duplexes **60** and **61**, only the cleavage of the intact strand
is inhibited. Such "cross-influence" may be attributed to the following: for one of the subunits of the enzyme to cleave this strand, the
subunit should contact the other strand as well. Since both ribose (**64**)
and deoxyxylose (**65**) substitutions disturb the orientation of a phosphate group in the . . . TpG . . . fragment of the recognition site, an
electrostatic contact of *Mva*I enzyme with this phosphate is possible
(Fig. 10).

H. Processive Cleavage of Concatemer DNA Duplexes

A characteristic feature of concatemer polymers is the proximity of *Eco*RII recognition sites to one another. This factor may lead to their processive cleavage when the bound molecule of the restriction enzyme slides along the DNA duplex and cleaves the substrate at several recognition sites. With the alternative type of cleavage, the distributive one, the transition of the enzyme molecule to another recognition site occurs only after the complete dissociation of the enzyme—substrate complex. We have proposed to determine the nature of cleavage (processive or distributive) of concatemer substrates so as to clarify the capacity of the bound enzyme for linear diffusion along DNA, and to investigate the interaction of the protein with the central A · T base pair of the recognition site. Accordingly, the concatemer structure **27** was designed in such a way that the canonical recognition sites recurred with the alternation of this pair.

If it is presumed that the cleavage occurs distributively and the probability of cleavage is the same for each recognition site irrespective of its position, the composition of the cleavage products for polymer duplex **27** can be calculated *a priori* (*44*). The type of cleavage was established by comparing the calculated and experimental compositions of the products of cleavage of polymer **27** by *Eco*RII (*44*).

It should be noted that the rate of *Eco*RII cleavage of individual nonanucleotide oligomers, which one may consider as intermediate products of polymer **27** hydrolysis, falls with decrease in length (Fig. 8). Furthermore, *Eco*RII binds to a rather long DNA fragment (Section II,D) and may protect several neighboring recognition sites in duplex **27** against an attack by other enzyme molecules. In distributive cleavage, these conditions should lead to a higher content of short oligomers ($2 \leq k \leq 6$) at the expense of longer ones and products of complete cleavage—the nonanucleotides. Analysis of the compositions of the products (Fig. 11) showed that the experimental data deviate in the opposite direction from the calculated ones. This points to a processive type of cleavage of polymer **27**. Analogously, the character of cleavage of **27** by *Mva*I and *Sso*I endonucleases has been established (*59*).

The ability of *Eco*RII endonuclease to cleave polymer **27** in a processive mode with nonanucleotides as the main products enables us to draw several conclusions. First, the bound enzyme may slide along the DNA to a distance of at least nine base-pairs. Second, no major alterations of DNA structure occur upon interaction with the

$M_k, \overline{M}_k$

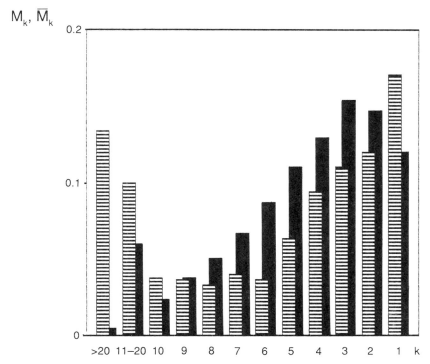

FIG. 11.   Experimental (M_k, hatched columns) and calculated ($\overline{M}_k$, dark columns) compositions of EcoRII cleavage products of polymer **27**. The degree of hydrolysis is 0.345.

enzyme; it is unlikely for unusual forms of DNA to appear and disappear many times within the same enzyme–substrate complex. Third, EcoRII recognizes and cleaves the substrate at both possible orientations of the central A · T base-pair relative to the bound molecule of the enzyme. Considering the conclusion on the interaction of EcoRII with the CH_3 group of thymine and the NH_2 group of adenine (Section II,F), we may suggest that endonuclease EcoRII is capable of conformational adjustment with respect to the orientation of the "asymmetrical" A · T base-pair in the bound substrate.

I. Substrate Properties of DNA Duplexes with Unnatural Internucleotide Bonds

An essential part of the study of restriction enzymes is the synthesis of nonhydrolyzable substrate analogs required for characterizing enzyme–substrate complexes (also in the presence of Mg^{2+}) and for investigating the mechanism of the enzymatic reaction. We have proposed (*42, 43, 46*) a new class of such compounds, the DNA duplexes containing, instead of phosphodiester bonds, pyrophosphate (**34, 35, 37,** and **67**) or phosphoramide (**33, 36, 38, 75,** and **76**) bonds with different ($3'N \rightarrow 5'P$ or $3'P \rightarrow 5'N$) locations of nitrogen atoms (**75** and **76**). Such bonds replace one or both phosphodiester bonds at the cleavage site of enzymes *Eco*RII (*Sso*II) and *Mva*I. Pyrophosphate or phosphoramide-modified internucleotide bonds are not cleaved by *Eco*RII (*42, 43, 46, 66*), *Sso*II (*46*), and *Mva*I (*57, 58*) (Tables IV and V). The fact that modified bonds are not cleaved might be due to the inability of restriction enzymes to bind to such duplexes. But, as shown for *Eco*RII, this is not so: phosphoramide and pyrophosphate-containing concatemers (**33, 34**), and trimers (**44, 45**) form stable complexes with *Eco*RII endonuclease, similar in their properties to the corresponding nonmodified systems (Table IV) (*42, 45*). Furthermore, the observed competition between polymers **27** and **34** for the formation of a complex with *Eco*RII enzyme shows that this endonuclease binds specifically to the modified polymer. Consequently, replacement of *Eco*RII endonuclease—scissile phosphodiester bonds with phosphoramide or pyrophosphate bonds converts the substrate into its nonhydrolyzable analog, which can be sequence-specifically bound to the enzyme, but cannot be cleaved. The blocking of hydrolysis may be explained by the differences in the electronic structure of the phosphodiester and modified internucleotide bonds.

The nonhydrolyzable analogs we designed allowed us to look into enzyme—substrate complexation in the presence of Mg^{2+}, the cofactor required for catalysis (*45, 46*). Under catalytic conditions, K_{ass} of the complex formed by *Eco*RII endonuclease with duplex **45** decreases to a third, while k_d increases by 50%. These findings, together with the data on *Eco*RI endonuclease (*67*), suggest that restriction endonucleases not only require Mg^{2+} for the hydrolytic reaction, but that Mg^{2+} ions may affect substrate binding as well.

It came as a surprise to us that the introduction of a pyrophosphate bond in the recognition, but not in the cleavage site (**67**, Table V) likewise blocked the actions of *Eco*RII and *Sso*II, whereas the other restriction enzymes (*Eco*RI and *Hind*III) were quite indifferent to such modification (*66, 67a*). The pyrophosphate bond in duplex **34** does not prevent the action of methylase *Eco*RII (*42*). Apparently, the phosphate group modified in duplex **67** was important for making contact with *Eco*RII and *Sso*II. Also, the inhibition might be caused by the appearance of an additional negative charge in the *Eco*RII (*Sso*II) recognition site.

J. Enforced Single-strand Breaks

The cleavage of both strands of DNA by restriction enzymes (67–69) may proceed within one enzyme–substrate complex ("one-step" mechanism):

$$E + S \rightleftharpoons ES \longrightarrow EN \longrightarrow EP \longrightarrow E + P \qquad (1)$$
$$\downarrow\uparrow$$
$$E + N$$

or with the dissociation of the enzyme–substrate complex after the break of one of the strands (two-step mechanism):

$$E + S \rightleftharpoons ES \longrightarrow EN \longrightarrow E + N$$
$$\qquad (2)$$
$$E + N \rightleftharpoons EN \longrightarrow EP \longrightarrow E + P$$

where E = enzyme, S = substrate, N = single-strand-cut (nicked) intermediate, P = product (the site is cleaved in both strands).

According to both catalytic pathways, the hydrolysis of DNA proceeds via two single-strand breaks, ES → EN and EN → EP. We investigated the ability of restriction endonucleases to catalyze single-strand cleavages (and also studied the interconnection between the cleavage of one strand and that of the other) by modelling them with synthetic substrates in which one of the scissile bonds is replaced with the nonhydrolyzable bond (**35–38, 67, 75** and **76**) or is absent (**41, 42, 48** and **49. Dimers 41** and **42** were used as models because of their association at sticky ends (*39, 43*).

*Eco*RII endonuclease catalyzes single-strand breaks of both types, which may occur in either of the two strands of the recognition site (*39, 43*). In polymers **35** and **36,** dimer **41,** and in duplexes **75** and **76,** the T-strand is cleaved, and in polymers **37** and **38,** and in dimer **42,** the A-strand. The efficiency of nicking largely depends on the structure of the other strand at the cleavage site, and it decreases according to the order: polymer **27** > pN polymers (**36** and **38**) > pp polymers (**35** and **37**). The stronger inhibiting effect of the pyrophosphate bond correlates with the more significant local conformational alterations of the DNA caused by this bond compared to a phosphoramide bond. The absence of a 5'-terminal phosphate group in dimers **41'** and **42'** prevents cleavage of the other strand of the recognition site. These facts point to the interaction of *Eco*RII with both strands of the recognition site (see also Section III,A).

On the other hand, the cleavage of the nonmodified bond in the pN- and Np-containing substrates proceeds with sufficiently good efficiency. This shows that the hydrolysis of either of the two strands of the recognition site takes place even if the cleavage of the other strand is "switched off." Therefore, it is possible that the EcoRII-effected cleavage of both strands of the substrate is catalyzed by two active sites.

The possibility of single-strand cleavages was also demonstrated for restriction endonucleases MvaI and SsoII (**48, 49, 67, 75** and **76**, Table V) (46, 57, 58). Pyrophosphate modification of one of the scissile bonds (**67**) has no effect on the hydrolysis of the intact strand by MvaI. This argues in favor of the two-step mechanism of hydrolysis. Besides, in contrast to endonuclease EcoRII (39, 43), MvaI effectively cleaves the unmodified strand of the recognition site, in spite of the nick in the T- or A-strand (**48** and **49**), or removal of a phosphate group from the cleavage point (**50**).

The principal conclusion from the results obtained is that the catalytic function of restriction endonucleases is pushed toward nicking, achieved by the introduction of nonhydrolyzable bonds.

III. Mechanism of Cleavage of DNA Duplexes by Endonucleases EcoRII, MvaI, and SsoII

A. The Catalytic Pathway of the Reaction

The crucial point in selecting the catalytic pathway of DNA hydrolysis by EcoRII and MvaI restriction endonucleases was consideration of the effect of modification of one strand of the substrate on the cleavage of the other. Such analysis becomes possible due to positional selectivity of modifications and separate monitoring of individual-strand hydrolysis. That these enzymes can cleave one strand of the substrate was demonstrated above. The effect of all the modifications considered above on the EcoRII enzyme activity was applied to both strands of the substrate; as a rule, the deceleration rate in the cleavage of both strands was the same (43, 46, 52, 53). Consequently, the recognition of DNA bases and the cleavage of both phosphodiester bonds by EcoRII proceeded within a single enzyme—substrate complex, i.e., according to a one-step mechanism [Eq. (1)]. [We might note here that the array of our substrates included DNA duplexes with single nucleotide alterations beyond the recognition site.] Had the reaction proceeded according to a two-step mechanism [Eq. (2)], the consequences of single nucleotide alterations beyond the recognition site would have been abolished after the dissociation of the complex EN, which would be at variance with the experimental data.

A different pattern is obtained in the case of MvaI. Some

modifications in one strand of the substrate (pyrophosphate bond, m^4dC, m^6dA, etc.) in no way affected the cleavage of the other, i.e., hydrolysis of both strands proceeded quite autonomously. These findings suggest a two-step mechanism for the reaction [Eq. (2)]. Such an interpretation is consistent with the unusual kinetics of the hydrolysis of the 30-membered duplex **47**, when the nicked intermediate is accumulated, as well as with the different rates of the cleavage of A- and T-strands of the quasipalindromic duplex **78**. The above scheme does not contradict the fact that the incorporation of A · A- and G · G-pairs, or deletion of nucleotides in the substrate, prevents the catalysis, for it is these modifications that, in all likelihood, inject structural distortions in both strands of the substrate.

B. A Symmetrical Model of an Enzyme–Substrate Complex

The recognition of the target sequence by restriction enzymes may follow a "symmetrical model" even if this sequence is partly asymmetrical. According to this model, suggested for type-II restriction endonucleases with palindromic recognition sites (*70*) and later found to be valid for *Eco*RI by X-ray analysis (*5*), two identical subunits of the protein are symmetrically located in two strands of DNA; there is a common axis of twofold rotational symmetry both for the recognized sequence and for the enzyme subunits. No unusual forms of DNA, e.g., cruciform structures, were discovered.

The *Eco*RII–substrate complex is symmetrical because the cleavage of both strands of DNA duplexes takes place within a single enzyme–substrate complex, the protein molecule has a dimeric structure, the B-form of DNA does not undergo radical changes during complex formation, and the DNA–protein contacts in the major groove obey the symmetrical pattern. We assume that two *Eco*RII subunits in the complex are bound symmetrically to four G · C-pairs; the enzyme interacts also either with the A · T- or T · A-pair located in the center of the recognition site; two catalytic sites are located symmetrically near two scissile bonds.

How does the protein adapt to the partially degenerate base-pair? In our view, two options are possible: (i) through contacts in the minor groove that do not interfere with the symmetry of the complex (*71*) and that allow us to distinguish T · A (A · T) base-pairs from G · C (C · G) base-pairs (T · A is not distinguished from the A · T-pair); (ii) via conformational adaptation of the enzyme molecule to a T · A or an A · T base-pair. In the case of *Eco*RII, there are some arguments in favor of the latter mechanism—due to the contacts with CH_3 and NH_2 groups of dT and dA residues, respectively, in the major groove, and because of possible conformational changes of the protein in the enzyme–substrate complex.

As far as enzyme SsoII is concerned, it seems that preference should be given to the symmetrical model as well, considering the symmetry of some DNA–protein contacts, and also the putative dimeric structure of the protein (I. I. Nikolskaya *et al.*, unpublished). Remarkable in the case of endonuclease MvaI are the "symmetry" of the effect of the modification of one strand on the cleavage of the other, and the symmetrical pattern of DNA–protein contacts. Besides, it was shown quite recently (29) that the dimer of identical subunits may be a functionally active form of this protein. Therefore, the principle of symmetric interaction of restriction endonucleases with DNA is most probably of general character.

C. Comparison of Enzymes

From the standpoint of protein–nucleic acid interactions, it would be of interest to compare the functioning of the isoschizomer–endonucleases EcoRII and MvaI, cleaving the recognition site at different positions, as well as endonucleases EcoRII and SsoII, recognizing sequences of different degrees of degeneracy. These three enzymes have the following common features: the ability to cleave one of the strands of the substrate, and to interact with nucleotide sequences flanking the recognition site.

Endonucleases EcoRII and SsoII show similarity in the nature of contacts with symmetrical G · C base-pairs, with respect to conformational alterations beyond the recognition site (EcoRII is more sensitive to defects in this position) and the occurrence of pyrophosphate bond in it. On the other hand, as we anticipated, the enzymes react differently to the perturbation of a degenerate base-pair in the recognition site. Most surprising is that there are some substitutions in this position (**31, 32** and **57**, Tables IV aı.d V) that alter the rate of cleavage by SsoII, sometimes to the extent of enhancing the hydrolysis.

It follows from our data that endonucleases EcoRII and MvaI operate according to different mechanisms. They form different contacts with the recognition site. In the case of MvaI, the recognition of a substrate and formation of the required configuration in the active site are possible even with large changes in the conformations and electronic properties of the recognition site. However, EcoRII reacts to any defect in the structure of a substrate. Yet another peculiarity of MvaI (and in some cases, of SsoII as well) consists in the selective effect of many modifications on one strand only, something that never happens to EcoRII.

The reason for such differences, in our view, may be that two subunits of EcoRII enzyme, originally associated into a dimer, operate interdependently, forming, as in the case of EcoRI restriction endonuclease (5), a single recognition module. Specific interactions take place with both strands of the substrate. In the case of MvaI endonuclease, there is probably no close contact between subunits in the enzyme–substrate complex. The subunits of the protein, even though they are dimerized on binding to the substrate, operate in a sufficiently autonomous mode. It may be proposed that each subunit of MvaI endonuclease forms specific contacts with one strand of the substrate (for example, with exocyclic amino groups of dC and dA residues in the A-strand of the recognition site) and hydrolyzes a phosphodiester bond located in the selfsame DNA strand. Simultaneously, this subunit is responsible for a number of additional contacts with the opposite strand of a DNA duplex (thus it apparently forms an electrostatic contact with a phosphate group between dT and dG residues in the T-strand of the substrate).

IV. Conclusion

Summing up the use of the organochemical approach in studying relatively simple specific and nonspecific DNA–protein complexes and defining its prospects for future investigations, it would not be amiss to stress several points. The data obtained demonstrate that the range of problems solved this way is fairly wide. These are: determining the structure of DNA–protein complexes, as well as discriminatory and electrostatic contacts; assessing the protein-binding site on the template; elucidating the role of conformation of DNA and nucleotide sequences flanking the recognition site in DNA–protein interactions; obtaining nonhydrolyzable analogs of substrates; nicking of DNA duplexes; determining the catalytic pathway of the reaction, etc. Of positive significance for the development of the organochemical trend in the present work was (1) design of new modifications of DNA and a new view on the possibilities of their use (designing families of oligonucleotides with a "sliding" label; substitution of hydrocarbon chains for single nucleotides; modelling DNA conformational distortions and the protein binding site on the template; selection of modified systems on a compensatory basis with respect to their "structural drawbacks"; evaluating the effect of modifications on the functional activity of enzymes with respect to individual strands of the substrate, etc.); (2) comprehensive study of nonspecific interactions of proteins with oligonucleotides of predetermined structure by physical methods; (3) multivariant use of each modification (e.g., DNA duplexes with pyrophosphate and phosphoramide bonds hold good prospects as non-hydrolyzable analogs of substrates of restriction endonucleases, for effecting single-strand cleavages, for studying the interconnection of the cleavages of DNA single strands, and so on). A standard scheme for studying the mechanism of action of restriction-modification enzymes with the aid of a set of substrates of predetermined structure appears to be a real possibility.

Needless to say, the aspects of nonspecific and specific DNA–protein interactions dealt with in the present review by far do not exhaust the potential of the organochemical approach. It may be recommended for research into more sophisticated DNA–protein complexes.

ACKNOWLEDGMENTS

We are deeply grateful to Dr. V. Butkus for the gift of compounds **62** and **63**. We wish to express our appreciation to Dr. E. A. Kubareva and Dr. S. A. Kuznetsova for assistance in preparing the manuscript.

REFERENCES

1. Z. A. Shabarova, in "Physicochemical Biology Reviews, Soviet Scientific Reviews, Section D" (V. P. Skulachev, ed.), Vol. 5, p. 1. Harwood Acad. Publ. GmbH, Amsterdam, 1984.
2. J. E. Coleman and J. L. Oakley, *CRC Crit. Rev. Biochem.* **7**, 247 (1980).
3. P. Modrich and R. J. Roberts, in "Nucleases" (S. M. Linn and R. J. Roberts, eds.), p. 109. Cold Spring Harbor Laboratory, Cold Spring Harbor, NY, 1982.
4. R. Kaddurah-Daouk, Cho and H. O. Smith, *JBC* **260**, 15345 (1985).
5. J. A. McClarin, C. A. Frederick, B.-C. Wang, P. Greene, H. W. Boyer, J. Grable and J. M. Rosenberg, *Science* **234**, 1526 (1986).
6. C. A. Brennan, M. D. van Cleve and R. I. Gumport, *JBC* **261**, 7270 (1986).
7. S. E. Halford and A. J. Goodall, *Bchem* **27**, 1771 (1988).
8. G. D. Brayer and A. McPherson, *JMB* **169**, 565 (1983).
9. M. N. Blinova, N. N. Veiko and E. S. Gromova, *Vestn. Mosk. Univ.* **21**, 86 (1980).
10. N. N. Veiko, E. S. Gromova, A. B. Sigalov and Z. A. Shabarova, *Mol. Biol. (Russ.)* **15**, 1385 (1981).
11. M. N. Vinogradova, V. L. Drutsa, M. G. Ivanovskaya and Z. A. Shabarova, *Biokhimia (Russ.)* **48**, 286 (1983).
12. N. N. Veiko, E. S. Gromova and Z. A. Shabarova, *Mol. Biol. (Russ.)* **13**, 1136 (1979).
13. E. S. Gromova, B. V. Tyaglov and Z. A. Shabarova, *BBA* **223**, 1 (1971).
14. B. V. Tyaglov, E. S. Gromova, S. V. Zenin, G. B. Sergeev, Z. A. Shabarova and M. A. Prokofiev, *Mol. Biol. (Russ.)* **9**, 652 (1975).

15. H. Netzold, V. V. Smirnov, A. P. Razjivin, E. S. Gromova and Z. A. Shabarova, *J. Obschei. Khim.* (*Russ.*) **53**, 647 (1983).
16. N. C. Alma, B. J. Harmsen, J. H. van Boom, G. van der Marel and C. W. Hilbers, *EJB* **133**, 319 (1982).
17. N. C. Alma, B. J. Harmsen, J. H. van Boom, G. van der Marel and C. W. Hilbers, *Bchem* **22**, 2104 (1983).
18. G. D. Brayer and A. McPherson, *Bchem 23*, 340 (1984).
19. L. A. Day, *Bchem* **12**, 5329 (1973).
20. J. T. Powell and E. G. Richards, *BBA* **281**, 145 (1972).
21. G. C. King and J. E. Coleman, *Bchem* **26**, 2929 (1987).
22. P. R. Paradiso and W. Konigsberg, *JBC* **257**, 1462 (1982).
23. M. T. Record, T. M. Lohman and P. deHaseth, *JMB* **107**, 145 (1976).
24. B.-C. Sang and D. M. Gray, *Bchem* **26**, 7210 (1987).
25. V. G. Kosykh, Ya. I. Buryanov and A. A. Baev, *MGG*, **178**, 717 (1980).
26. V. G. Kosykh, S. A. Pumtejis, Ya. I. Buryanov and A. A. Bayev, *Biokhimia* (*Russ.*) **47**, 619 (1982).
27. A. Janulaitis and D. Vaitkevičius, *Biotekhnologija* (*Russ.*) **1**, 39 (1985).
28. I. I. Nikolskaja, L. S. Karpez, I. M. Kartashova, N. G. Lopatina, E. A. Skripkin, S. V. Suchkov, T. M. Uporova, I. M. Gruber and S. S. Debov, *Mol. Genet. Mikrobiol. Virusol.* (*Russ.*) **12**, 5 (1983).
29. K. G. Ovechkina, S. R. Popova, V. V. Zinoviev, D. Vaitkevičius, A. Janulaitis, J. A. Gorbunov and E. G. Malygin, *Biopolimery Kletka* (*Russ.*) **4**, 239 (1988).
30. Z. A. Shabarova, *NARes Symp. Ser. N* **7**, 259 (1980).
31. Z. A. Shabarova, *Biochimie* **70**, 1323 (1988).
32. Z. A. Shabarova, N. G. Dolinnaya, V. L. Drutsa, N. P. Melnikova and A. A. Purmal, *NARes* **9**, 5747 (1981).
33. E. S. Gromova, M. N. Vinogradova, A. A. Yolov, V. P. Veiko, N. G. Dolinnaya, V. L. Drutsa, V. G. Metelev, T. S. Oretskaya and Z. A. Shabarova, *Mol. Biol.* (*Russ.*) **18**, 370 (1984).
34. N. I. Sokolova, D. T. Ashirbekova, N. G. Dolinnaya and Z. A. Shabarova, *FEBS Lett.* **232**, 153 (1988).
35. M. B. Gottikh, M. G. Ivanovskaya and Z. A. Shabarova, *Bioorg. Khim.* (*Russ.*) **14**, 500 (1988).
36. N. G. Dolinnaya, N. I. Sokolova, O. I. Gryaznova and Z. A. Shabarova, *NARes* **16**, 3721 (1988).
37. M. G. Ivanovskaya, M. B. Gottikh and Z. A. Shabarova, *Nucleosides Nucleotides* **6**, 913 (1987).
38. S. A. Kuznetsova, M. G. Ivanovskaya, M. B. Gottikh, A. A. Yolov and Z. A. Shabarova, *Bioorg. Khim.* (*Russ.*) **14**, 490 (1988).
39. A. A. Yolov, E. S. Gromova, E. A. Romanova, T. S. Oretskaya, A. A. Oganov, Ya. I. Buryanov and Z. A. Shabarova, *FEBS Lett.* **167**, 147 (1984).
40. A. Rosental, D. Cech, V. P. Veiko, T. S. Oretskaya, E. A. Romanova, A. A. Yolov, V. G. Metelev, E. S. Gromova and Z. A. Shabarova, *Tetrahedron Lett.* **25**, 4353 (1984).
41. A. A. Yolov, M. N. Vinogradova, E. S. Gromova, A. Rosental, D. Cech, V. P. Veiko, V. G. Metelev, V. G. Kosykh, Ya. I. Buryanov, A. A. Baev and Z. A. Shabarova, *NARes* **13**, 8983 (1985).
42. A. A. Purmal, M. N. Vinogradova, A. A. Yolov, E. S. Gromova, V. L. Drutsa, V. G. Metelev, O. A. Kholodkov, Ya. I. Buryanov, Z. A. Shabarova and M. A. Prokofiev, *Dokl. Akad. Nauk SSSR* **276**, 992 (1984).
43. A. A. Yolov, E. S. Gromova, E. A. Kubareva, V. K. Potapov and Z. A. Shabarova, *NARes* **13**, 8969 (1985).

44. A. A. Yolov, E. S. Gromova and Z. A. Shabarova, *Mol. Biol. Rep.* **10**,173 (1985).
45. M. N. Vinogradova, E. S. Gromova, A. A. Purmal, V. G. Kosykh and Z. A. Shabarova, *Mol. Biol. (Russ.)* **20**, 1329 (1986).
46. E. S. Gromova, M. N. Vinogradova, T. M. Uporova, O. I. Gryaznova, M. G. Isagulyants, V. G. Kosykh, I. I. Nikolskaya and Z. A. Shabarova, *Bioorg. Khim. (Russ.)* **13**, 269 (1987).
47. Z. A. Shabarova, N. G. Dolinnaya, S. I. Turkin and E. S. Gromova, *NARes* **8**, 2413 (1980).
48. S. A. Kuznetsova, E. A. Kubareva, T. S. Oretskaya, N. G. Dolinnaya, N. F. Krynetskaya, E. S. Gromova, Z. A. Shabarova and D. Cech, *Biopolimery Kletka (Russ.)* **3**, 283 (1987).
49. S. A. Kuznetsova, E. M. Volkov, E. S. Gromova, V. K. Potapov and Z. A. Shabarova, *Bioorg. Khim. (Russ.)***14**, 1656 (1988).
50. E. A. Kubareva, E. S. Gromova, E. A. Romanova, T. S. Oretskaya and Z. A. Shabarova, *Bioorg. Khim. (Russ.)* **16**, 501 (1990).
51. N. G. Dolinnaya and O. I. Gryaznova, *Usp. Khim. (Russ.)* LVIII, N 8 (1989).
52. M. N. Vinogradova, E. S. Gromova, O. I. Gryaznova, M. G. Isagulyants, S. A. Kuznetsova, V. G. Kosykh and Z. A. Shabarova, *Bioorg. Khim. (Russ.)* **13**, 1194 (1987).
53. E. A. Kubareva, E. S. Gromova, T. S. Oretskaya and Z. A. Shabarova, *Bioorg. Khim. (Russ.)* **13**, 1205 (1987).
54. M. N. Vinogradova, E. S. Gromova, T. M. Uporova, I. I. Nikolskaya, Z. A. Shabarova and C. C. Debov, *Dokl. Avad. Nauk SSSR* **295**, 732 (1987).
55. E. A. Kubareva, C.-D. Pein, E. S. Gromova, S. A. Kuznetsova, V. N. Tashlitzki, D. Cech and Z. A. Shabarova, *EJB* **175**, 615 (1988).
56. D. Cech, C.-D. Pein, E. A. Kubareva, E. S. Gromova, T. S. Oretskaya and Z. A. Shabarova, *Nucleosides Nucleotides* **7**, 585 (1988).
57. E. S. Gromova, E. A. Kubareva, C.-D. Pein, T. S. Oretskaya, Z. A. Shabarova, D. Cech and M. A. Prokofiev, *Dokl. Akad. Nauk SSSR* **295**, 1493 (1987).
58. C.-D. Pein, D. Cech, E. S. Gromova, T. S. Oretskaya, Z. A. Shabarova and E. A. Kubareva, *NARes Symp. Ser. N.* **18**, 225 (1987).
59. E. S. Gromova, E. A. Kubareva, A. A. Yolov, E. A. Akatova, I. I. Nikolskaya and Z. A. Shabarova, *Biokhimia (Russ.)*, submitted for publication.
60. N. Tibanyenda, S. H. de Bruin, C. A. G. Haasnoot, G. A. van der Marel, J. H. van Boom and C. W. Hilbers, *EJB* **139**, 19 (1984).
61. H. Werntges, G. Steger, D. Riesner and H.-J. Fritz, *NARes* **14**, 3773 (1986).
62. A. B. Kremer, T. Mikita and G. P. Beardsley, *Bchem* **26**,391 (1987).
63. V. Butkus, S. Klimašauskas, D. Keršulyte, D. Vaitkevičius, A. Lebionka and A. Janulaitis, *NARes* **13**, 5727 (1985).
64. E. S. Gromova, E. A. Kubareva, N. Vinogradova, T. S. Oretskaya and Z. A. Shabarova, *NARes*, submitted for publication.
65. W. P. Jencks, in "Advances in Enzymology and Related Areas in Molecular Biology" (Alton Meister, ed.), vol. 43, p. 219. Wiley-Interscience, New York, 1975.
66. E. S. Gromova, A. A. Yolov, E. A. Kubareva, V. G. Metelev and Z. A. Shabarova, *Mol. Biol. (Russ.)* **20**, 29 (1986).
67. S. E. Halford, *TIBS* **8**, 455 (1983).
67a. A. A. Purmal, V. L. Drutsa and Z. A. Shabaiova, *Biorg. Khim. (Russ.)* **10**, 395 (1984).
68. P. Modrich, *Q. Rev. Biophys.* **12**, 315 (1979).
69. G. Snounou, A. D. B. Malcolm, *EJB* **138**, 275 (1984).
70. H. O. Smith, *Science* **205**, 455 (1979).
71. J. M. Rosenberg, H. W. Boyer and P. Greene, in "Gene Amplification and Analysis" (J. Chirikjian, ed.), vol. 1, p. 131. Elsevier, New York, 1981.

A Tale of Two Enzymes, Deoxycytidylate Deaminase and Thymidylate Synthase

FRANK MALEY AND
GLADYS F. MALEY

*Wadsworth Center for Laboratories
and Research
New York State Department
of Health
Albany, New York 12201*

I. Deoxycytidylate Deaminase: Historical Perspective[1]

Our initial exposure to the enzymes that are the subject of this review, deoxycytidylate (dCMP) deaminase (dCMP aminohydrolase; EC 3.5.4.12) and thymidylate (dTMP) synthase (EC 2.1.1.45) was the

---

[1] Abbreviations: HIV, human immunodeficiency virus; $H_2PteGlu$, dihydrofolate; $5,10\text{-}CH_2H_4PteGlu$ (or $CH_2H_4PteGlu$), 5,10-methylenetetrahydrofolate; FdUMP, 5-fluoro-2′-deoxyuridylate; PDDF, 10-propargyldideazafolate; MTX, methotrexate; CD, circular dichroism; UV, ultraviolet light; IRF, internal open reading frame; $td\triangle I$, T4-

49

result of pure and simple serendipity. Following a post-doctoral period (1956–1958) in Severo Ochoa's laboratory at New York University Medical Center, where we were exposed to the enzymes polynucleotide phosphorylase and dCMP kinase (1) in bacterial systems, we undertook similar studies involving deoxynucleotide metabolism in chick and rat embryos, mostly because these tissue sources were readily available at our present institution. During the course of a study on the metabolism of dCMP by embryonic rat liver extracts, a new UV-absorbing spot, which turned out to be dUMP, was obtained on borate electrophoresis (2). We termed this apparently new enzyme "dCMP deaminase" for obvious reasons. However, unbeknown to us at that time, a similar activity had been found about a year earlier in sea urchin eggs (3).

What was exciting about this finding was that the enzyme provided a substrate, dUMP, for the recently discovered enzyme dTMP synthase (4), with both enzymes being present in strikingly higher amounts in rapidly dividing cells associated with embryos (2), tumors (2, 5), and regenerating liver (6), relative to that found in nondividing cells. In addition, since ribonucleotide reductase (EC 1.17.4.1, .2) (7) had not been discovered, dCMP deaminase appeared to be the only supplier of substrate for dTMP synthase. The potential role of these enzymes in cell division took on added significance when it was found that both increased from practically undetectable levels to those that were easily measurable during a time frame that was just prior to mitosis (6). Since these enzymes appeared to be associated mainly with dividing tissues, it was reasonable to consider them as potential diagnostic tools for various disease states in which the enzymes are elevated. Some attempts at employing dCMP deaminase for this purpose were made (8, 9), and, while an increase in enzyme activity seemed to be consistent with this thesis, the sensitivity of the assay at that time was not good enough to be statistically relevant.

Despite the fact that these early studies possessed the potential of significant import, the most exciting and stimulating finding that came from them was the discovery that dCMP deaminase appears to be regulated specifically by the end products of its metabolic pathway, dCTP and dTTP (10).

A. Allosteric Regulation of dCMP Deaminase

This discovery resulted mainly from attempts to stabilize the apparently labile deaminase during the course of its purification from chick

---

phage thymidylate synthase gene minus its intron; Td, the latter gene, but with the intron; SDS–PAGE, sodium dodecyl sulfate–polyacrylamide gel electrophoresis; bp and kbp, base-pairs and kilobase-pairs.

embryo extracts (*10*). Of the compounds tested, dCTP was found to be most effective in stabilizing dCMP deaminase and was also found to activate the enzyme by markedly reducing the substrate concentration required for activity to be measured. By contrast, the activation by dCTP was negated by dTTP, which implied that the ratios of these deoxynucleoside triphosphates within the cell could in effect regulate the activity of the deaminase. These findings were confirmed subsequently with a dCMP deaminase from donkey spleen (*11*). Inasmuch as the phenomenon of enzyme regulation by its metabolic end products was in its infancy, with only aspartate carbamoyltransferase (EC 21.3.2) (*12*) and a couple of other bacterial enzymes falling within this category, every experiment provided new and exciting data. It soon became apparent that these "allosteric regulators" (*13*) exerted their effects by promoting or impairing enzyme subunit interaction, with dCTP stabilizing a hexameric state, and dTTP destabilizing it (*14*)

A typical response of the enzyme to dCTP is shown in Fig. 1, which clearly reveals the sigmoid shape of the curve of activity versus substrate concentration to revert to the more normal hyperbolic Mi-

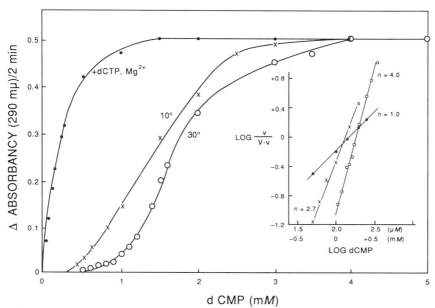

FIG. 1. Kinetics of dCMP deamination in the presence and absence of dCTP. Note the difference in the Hill plots (inset) for the reaction at 10°C and 30°C, in addition to that in the presence of 20 μM dCTP, which clearly delineates the allosteric nature of the reaction. [From Maley and Maley (*14*).]

chaelis–Menten kinetics in the presence of this positive allosteric effector. The inset in Fig. 1 reveals a characteristic change in the Hill constants from 4.0 to 1.0 promoted by the activator. It is of interest to note that the allosteric response is less at 10°C, suggesting that the conformation of the enzyme subunits at their interfaces differs at this temperature relative to that at 30°C. Since the observed allosteric response occurred at nanomolar levels of the nucleotide regulators, its physiologic significance was readily apparent. Thus, if dCMP deaminase is responsible for controlling the levels as well as the ratios of dCTP and dTTP within a cell, it was reasoned that creation of an excess of dTTP by the addition of thymidine should spare the conversion of cell deoxycytidine to dUMP, and enable more dCMP to be incorporated into DNA. This effect was indeed observed in both rat (15) and chick embryo (16) mince systems, thus confirming that the pyrimidine deoxynucleotide pool can be regulated by the flux of substrate through dCMP deaminase.

The marked effect of the allosteric ligands on dCMP deaminase activity can be attributed solely to their ability to regulate the interaction between the enzyme's six identical subunits. This was observed in our very early studies with the chick embryo and T2-phage deaminases, in which dCTP promoted an aggregation of the enzyme subunits to the active state of the deaminase, while dTTP favored the disaggregated or inhibited state (14). A more extensive account of the regulation of the chick embryo (14) and T2-phage (17) dCMP deaminases was described earlier by us, where the conformational transitions elicited by the allosteric ligands were characteristic of the respective R and T states of the allosteric model described by Monod et al. (18). In support of this model, fixing or "freezing" the subunits in a hexameric state with glutaraldehyde in the presence of dCTP desensitizes the enzyme to the action of its allosteric ligands, and is associated with a loss in the cooperative responses promoted by dCMP (19). When the fixation occurred in the presence of dTTP, an inactive state was obtained in that dCMP was no longer a substrate, but paradoxically 5-HgdCMP was. Even more bizarre was the fact that dCTP now acted as an inhibitor and dTTP an activator with this substrate (20).

The degree to which the allosteric nucleotides interact with the deaminase and with each other was shown rather succinctly by exposing the enzyme to UV light (254 nm) in the presence of dTTP (21). As seen in Fig. 2, maximal fixation of dTTP occurred in about 1 minute with greater than 50% of each subunit containing dTTP. Although dCTP was not fixed to the enzyme by this procedure, adding dCTP to the reaction and continuing the irradiation resulted in almost complete release of the photofixed dTTP. The specificity of this reaction was

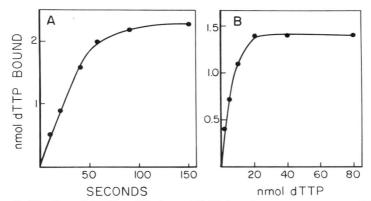

FIG. 2. Fixation of dTTP to T2-phage dCMP deaminase on exposure to 254 nm. (A) [α-^{32}P]dTTP (50 nmol) was irradiated with 4 nmol of the deaminase in a volume of 0.2 ml. The extent of fixation was determined by taking aliquots at the indicated times and precipitating the enzyme with 200 μg of carrier bovine serum albumin, which was then counted after filtration onto a glass fiber filter. (B) Maximal amount of dTTP fixed per nmol of dCMP deaminase subunit (six per mole of enzyme). [From Maley and Maley (21).]

confirmed by the finding that neither dATP nor dGTP could affect a comparable release of dTTP.

B. Universality of dCMP Deaminase

Although the deaminase is not present in all organisms, it occurs in most; when absent, it is substituted for by other reactions that provide the cell with dUMP. Thus, in the case of the enteric bacteria, *Escherichia coli* (22) and *Salmonella typhimurium* (23), neither of which contain dCMP deaminase, a dCTP deaminase provides an alternative pathway for the synthesis of dUMP via a specific dUTP pyrophosphatase (EC 3.6.2.34) (24).

The overall significance of dCMP deaminase is still to be defined in view of its varied degrees of regulation in different environments. Thus, in the case of the induction of T2-, T4-, and T6-phage specific dCMP deaminases in *E. coli*, each enzyme possesses slightly different allosteric responses (25–27). In contrast, the dCMP deaminase induced in *Bacillus subtilis* by certain of its phages in not regulated allosterically (28), as is the deaminase normally present in this organism (29). Aside from the prokaryotic viruses, dCMP deaminase also appears to be induced by some eukaryotic viruses such as herpes (30), SV40 (31), and polyoma (32). While this enzyme has not been described in such parasites as the *Plasmodia*, deoxycytidine is a major precursor of dCMP via the salvage pathway, which is believed to provide dUMP via a dCMP deaminase (33).

C. Physiologic Significance of dCMP Deaminase

The fact that both prokaryotes (34) and eukaryotes (35) can survive without a dCMP deaminase indicates that, while the enzyme may play an important role in supplying dUMP, alternative routes to this compound, either via ribonucleotide reductase or the salvage route can overcome this defect. However, it should be emphasized that the absence of or impairment of dCMP deaminase can affect cells unfavorably by promoting an imbalance in their deoxyribonucleotide pools. The net effect of this imbalance is a large increase in dCTP and a severe depletion in dTTP, making the cells dependent on thymidine for growth (36). This effect can also be caused by an impairment or a depletion of ribonucleotide reductase, which results in a greatly enhanced mutation rate (37) as well as shortening of the G_1 phase of the cell cycle and a corresponding prolongation of the S phase (38).

Another example of the importance of dCMP deaminase in maintaining a balanced pyrimidine deoxynucleotide pool has been seen during the course of 3'-azathymidine treatment, which is toxic to the bone marrow progenitor cells. This toxicity is a consequence of the depletion of dCTP and dTTP, both of which can be restored by the addition of deoxycytidine to the cells. The latter, by being converted to dCMP and then phosphorylated to dCTP, or by being deaminated to dUMP, yields dTTP via dTMP synthase and the appropriate kinases. It is believed that this regimen can reduce cellular cytotoxicity without suppressing the effectiveness of 3'-azathymidine against HIV[1] (39).

Of interest is the difference in specificity of the T2-phage deaminase relative to those from eukaryotic sources where increasing the size of a substituent at position 5 of the pyrimidine ring results in a progressive loss in the phage enzyme's ability to deaminate the dCMP derivative (40) (Table I). The stringency of this reaction appears to provide a selective advantage to the phage since its inability to deaminate 5-hydroxymethyl-dCMP, a constituent of T-even phage DNA in place of dCMP, must obviously be of consequence to the phage's survival. By contrast, neither the chick embryo nor HeLa cell deaminase are constrained by the size of the substituent on carbon 5, and we have used this to advantage in preparing an affinity ligand for the purification of the latter to homogeneity (unpublished).

A logical role that one can ascribe to the deaminase is that of providing an adequate supply of dUMP for the formation of dTMP, via dTMP synthase. However, a similar role can be assigned to ribonucleotide reductase in converting UDP to dUDP, which can then yield dUMP as a result of a phosphatase or the conversion of dUTP to dUMP

TABLE I
SUBSTRATE SPECIFICITY OF dCMP DEAMINASE FROM CHICK
EMBRYO AND T2r$^+$-INFECTED *E. coli* B[a]

	Enzyme source	
Substrate	Chick embryo	T2r$^+$-infected *E. coli* B
dCMP	0.220[b]	0.202
5-Fluoro-dCMP	0.221	0.266
5-Methyl-dCMP	0.247	0.260
5-Bromo-dCMP	0.254	0.187
5-Iodo-dCMP	0.196	0.053
5-Hydroxymethyl-dCMP	0.200	0.00

[a] From Maley and Maley (*21*).
[b] In micromoles of dCMP deaminated in 5 minutes.

by a specific dUTP pyrophosphatase in bacterial (*24*) or animal cells (*41, 42*).

Another function recently ascribed to the deaminase is that of enhancing the stability of a T4-phage multienzyme complex involved in dNTP synthesis, based on the finding that the complex is less stable in *cd* mutants (*43*).

Because of the deaminase's role in providing a crucial intermediate for the synthesis of DNA, the possibility must be considered that this enzyme might be a reasonable target for chemotherapeutic agents directed against parasitic as well as neoplastic diseases, particularly when used in combination with inhibitors of dTMP synthase. This is a subject that warrants further investigation.

D. Location and Sequence Analysis of the *cd* Gene in the Genomic Map of Bacteriophage T4

Our attempts at isolating the *cd* gene as an intact DNA fragment capable of expressing its encoded enzyme were quite frustrating at first, but eventually provided a rewarding experience from which we learned a great deal about the utility of genetic engineering, as well as its pitfalls. The intact gene was originally isolated from the bacteriophage T4-genome as part of an *Eco*RI library, and then inserted into a unique *Eco*RI site in the immunity region of a λ phage (NM607) to yield NM1208 (*44*). While the protein product of the *cd* gene could be detected on infection of *E. coli* with NM1208, removal of the gene from the latter as an *Eco*RI fragment and placement into pUC18 in the correct orientation led surprisingly to the absence of detectable enzyme activity when cells transformed with this plasmid were induced with iPrSGal. On sequence analysis of the gene (45), it became evident that what had been considered an intact gene had in reality been truncated by 14 nucleotides at its 3′ end (Fig. 3). This point was clearly established by comparing the deduced amino-acid sequence of the *Eco*RI fragment with the protein sequence determined previously for the T2-phage dCMP deaminase (46). Why, therefore, was the gene expressed when inserted as a truncated fragment into the λ phage NM607 but not when placed in pUC18?

An explanation was provided by examining the sequence of the CI gene of λ434, which showed that the truncated *Eco*RI *cd* gene when placed into this phage was fused to nucleotide 599 of the CI region, which extended the gene by 35 nucleotides (47). This addition in effect added 12 amino acids to the asparagine at the truncated carboxy terminus of the deaminase (Fig. 3), which, although modified from the original gene, was still active. That the *cd* gene had indeed been truncated as indicated was verified by reisolating the intact gene within an 8.2-kb *Bgl*II fragment from the T4 *alc*7 genome, which was then reduced in size to 1.9 kb by *Hae*II. This fragment was placed in pUC18 and subjected to double-strand sequence analysis using specific primers for each strand. The sequence obtained provided the entire open reading frame of the *cd* gene and verified that the original 1.1-kb *Eco*RI fragment in NM1208 had been truncated by 14 nucleotides or five amino acids. The similarity of three or four amino acids on the carboxyl end of the intact T4-dCMP deaminase to those in comparable positions in the modified enzyme that had been extended by 12 amino acids may be the reason why activity is associated with this protein. By contrast, placement of the truncated *cd* gene into pUC18 adds 28 amino acids to the carboxy terminus, and results in an inactive enzyme. It is of interest to note that a cysteine is not present near the same location as in the T2 or T4 deaminases, perhaps supporting the need for a cysteine in this position.

Based on the known location of various restriction sites in the T4-phage genomic map (48), and those enzymes used to excise the *cd* gene (*Hae*II and *Bgl*II), we were able to locate this gene within the genome precisely (45). As an added bonus, gene 31 was included within the isolated restriction fragment and located downstream of the *cd* gene, as indicated by the underlined section in Fig. 4. Since the T4-genomic map is presented in a counterclockwise manner, the first *Eco*RI site is located at 131.3 kb on the map, with the start codon 538 bp

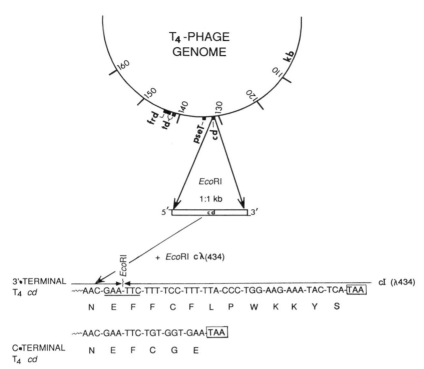

Fig. 3. Scheme depicting the cloning of a 1.1 kb *cd*-containing *Eco*RI fragment from T4-bacteriophage into the *Eco*RI restricted C_1 site of λ434. The G residue on the 3'-end of the *Eco*RI cleavage site in the truncated *cd* gene had been ligated to the 5'-end of the *Eco*RI site in λ434 (*44*) resulting in the extension of the putative amino-acid sequence by 11 residues. The carboxy-terminal sequence of the complete T4-*cd* gene-encoded enzyme is shown beneath it for comparison. [From Maley *et al.* (*45*).]

downstream from the first G of the *Eco*RI site (Fig. 4). The second *Eco*RI site is at 130.3 kb, and is the one that effectively truncates the *cd* gene when restricted. The *Bgl*II site is located at 129.1 kb with the 3'-end of gene 31 being only 62 bp upstream from this site.

From the sequence of the *cd* gene it is clear that *Hae*II cuts prior to the 5' end of the gene, although the restriction map of the T4 genome indicates otherwise (*48*), and should be rectified accordingly. A specific goal of the cloning and sequencing procedures for the *cd* gene was to place the gene in a high expression vector so that sufficient enzyme could be obtained for crystallographic and active-site studies. The intact gene when placed in pUC18 has yielded at best about 0.5% of the cellular protein as dCMP deaminase. This relatively poor yield for

GAATTCCAAGAAAAAGTTAAACTATTTGCGCCAGG
         EcoRI
AATTAGTAAATAACGGTTTCTGAACCATTTCCTGAAACATCGGTTCGTGTTATTACCGAAACTC

CTCCGTTCAGTATTAGTAATTGTGAATCCAGGTGATCGCCATCAAATATCGCATCTTAAACTGG

ATTTTGATGCATTAGTTGAAGCACAAAGGGTGTATGGCGTACTATGATGAATTTAACTGATAT

AATTGATAATTGTCTTGAAAATGATACTGGCCGATCATAGAGCGCTTGATTCTGAAACAGCACA
                                    HaeII
GTTCATTAGAATAACTTTAATGAATCATACTCTGGTGAATAGTATTCATCCTTCTGTGTATGA

TGCTATTATTGTGACGAAGTATCCAGTTGAGCTTCACAAAAAGATGACTGGCCGCAGTTTTTAT

TGATAAGAAAAACCGCTTTAAAGATCGGCAGAATATAATTAGTTCTGTTATTAAAAGTATAAC

TAAACTTCGTCACGAAATTTATCGTGTTGAAACTGCTAAATCTGCTTATCTGGTGATTATGAA

   1 Met Lys Ala Ser Thr Val Leu Gln Ile Ala Tyr Leu Val Ser Gln Glu   16
 539 ATG AAA GCG AGT ACA GTA CTT CAA ATT GCA TAT TTA GTA TCG CAG GAA   586

  17 Ser Lys Cys Cys Ser Trp Lys Val Gly Ala Val Ile Glu Lys Asn Gly   32
 587 TCA AAA TGT TGC TCC TGG AAG GTA GGA GCA GTA ATT GAA AAG AAT GGA   634

  33 Arg Ile Ile Ser Thr Gly Tyr Asn Gly Ser Pro Ala Gly Gly Val Asn   48
 635 CGT ATT ATT TCT ACT GGG TAT AAT GGT TCA CCC GCA GGG GGT GTG AAC   682

  49 Cys Cys Asp Tyr Ala Ala Glu Gln Gly Trp Leu Leu Asn Lys Pro Lys   64
 683 TGT TGT GAT TAT GCT GCT CAG CAA GGA TCG TTG TTG AAT AAG CCT AAA   730

  65 His Ala Ile Ile Gln Gly His Lys Pro Glu Cys Val Ser Phe Gly Ser   80
 731 CAT GCT ATC ATT CAA GGT CAT AAG CCT GAA TGC GTA TCA TTT GGT TCA   778

  81 Thr Asp Arg Phe Val Leu Ala Lys Glu His Arg Ser Ala His Ser Glu   96
 779 ACT GAT CGT TTT GTT TTG GCG AAA GAA CAT CGT AGT GCT CAC TCG GAA   826

  97 Trp Ser Ser Lys Asn Glu Ile His Ala Glu Leu Asn Ala Ile Leu Phe   112
 827 TGG TCA TCT AAA AAT GAA ATT CAT GCT GAA CTA AAT GCA ATT TTG TTT   874

 113 Ala Ala Arg Asn Gly Ser Ser Ile Glu Gly Ala Thr Met Tyr Val Thr   128
 875 GCT GCA CGA AAT GGT TCT TCT ATT GAA GGT GCT ACT ATG TAT GTA ACA   922

 129 Leu Ser Pro Cys Pro Asp Cys Ala Lys Ala Ile Ala Gln Ser Gly Ile   144
 923 CTT TCT CCT TGT CCA GAT TGC GCA AAA GCG ATA GCT CAA TCT GGT ATT   970

 145 Lys Lys Leu Val Tyr Cys Glu Thr Tyr Asp Lys Asn Lys Pro Gly Trp   160
 971 AAA AAG CTG GTT TAT TGT GAA ACA TAC GAC AAA AAT AAA CCC GGT TGG   1018

 161 Asp Asp Ile Leu Arg Asn Ala Gly Ile Glu Val Phe Asn Val Pro Lys   176
1019 GAT GAT ATT CTG CGA AAT GCA GGT ATT GAA GTG TTT AAT GTT CCT AAG   1066

 177 Lys Asn Leu Asn Lys Leu Asn Trp Glu Asn Ile Asn Glu Phe Cys Gly   192
1067 AAA AAC TTG AAT AAG TTA AAC TGG GAA AAT ATC AAC GAA TTC TGT GGT   1114
                                                         EcoRI
 193 Glu ***
1115 GAA TAATGAAATTTCGTTTGGTAAAACTCACAGCAATTAGTTCTTATTCTAACGAGAACATC

TCATTTGCTGTAGAGTATAAGAAATATTTTTTCTCTAAATGGAAACAGTATTATAAGACAAAT

TGGGTTTGTATTGATAGACCATATAGTTGGAAATCTGATTTAGAAAAATGCCAAAAATTACTT

TCCACCCTTAAAGAACGTGGAACAACTCATATTAAAACTGTAATAGGTAAATAAATGAAACTG

ACAACTGAGCAGAAAGTAGCCAATTCGTGAAATTTTTAAAACTAAATTGTCCATGGGCGTTTCA

AACCGTAGTTTTTGAAAAGTCTGATCGTACTATTCGTACTATGAAAGGTACTCGTGATGCAGAC

TTTATGCCAACCATGCAAACTGGCAAATTGACTGAATCTACTCGGAAAGAATCTACTGACATG

ATTCCAGTATTTGATGTTGAGCTTGCTGCGTGGCGGAGGTTTTTGTATTGACAAATTGATTTCC

GTTAATGCTATGAAAGTTGAGCATTTGCTTCAATTTATTGGTAAATAAATGCTTTAAGCAACTA

TTTGTTATTATTAATTCATCTGTTAACAAAAAGGAAAAACGATGTCTGAAGTACAACAGCTAC

CAATTCGTGCTGTCGGTGAATATGTTATTTTAGTTTCTGAACCTGCACAAGCCGGTGATGAAG

AAGTTACAGAATCAGGACTTATTATCGGTAAACGTGTTCAAGGTGAAGTTCCTGAACTGTGTG

TAGTTCACTCTGTCGGTCCTGATGTTCCTGAAGGTTTCTGCGGAAGTTGGTGATTTGACTTCTC

TTCCAGTTGGTCAAATTCGAAATGTTCCGCCATCCTTTTGTAGCTCTGGGTCTTAAGCAGCCAA

AAGAAATTAAACAAAAATTCGTTACCTGTCACTATAAAAGCTATTCCGTGTCTTTATAAGTGAT

ATAAATAATAATATGAATTGGGTGTCGGAATAATAAGTTAACCGAACAATTCTATGTGGTAGT

CTACAACTGAGAGATCT
              BglII

an expression vector may be due in part to the nonconsensus Shine–Dalgarno region that precedes the start codon. However, attempts to improve this sequence by mutagenesis have not enhanced the yields, possibly due to the toxic effects that high levels of the deaminase might impose on the cell as a consequence of disrupting the pools of dCTP and dTTP. Since high levels of dCMP deaminase would tend to raise the latter, known to be toxic by virtue of its ability to inhibit pyrimidine ribonucleotide reduction (49, 50), another route for the high-level expression of dCMP deaminase is being sought. One being considered is that provided by a system in which foreign genes are induced only when the desired level of cell growth is achieved (51).

On comparing the amino-acid sequences of the T4- and T2-dCMP deaminases (45, 46), there is, to no one's surprise, a striking homology, but also some differences. Thus it is apparent that there is a deletion of five amino acids at the carboxy terminus (shown below as dots) of the T2-deaminase, and that nine amino acids differ between the two enzymes (differences are designated by letters below the T4 sequences).

```
T4   MKASTVLQIAYLVSQESKCCSWKVGAVIEKNGRIISTGYNGSPAGGVNCCDYAAEQGWLL      60
T2                                                 DN    IE

T4   NKPKHAIIQGHKPECVSFGSTDRFVLAKEHRSAHSEWSSKNEIHAELNAILFAARNGSSI     120
T2       T              TS

T4   EGATMYVTLSPCPDCAKAIAQSGIKKLVYCETYDKNKPGWDDILRNAGIEVFNVPKKNLN     180
T2                                                    L  ..

T4   KLNWENINEFCGE     193
T2   ...    S          188
```

The only other dCMP deaminase whose sequence has been determined so far, is that from S. cerevisiae, which is less than 30% homologous to the phage enzymes and contains only 162 amino acids (52).

The T2-phage deaminase has been crystallized (Fig. 5), so the T4 deaminase should not pose too difficult a problem. X-ray crystallographic analysis of the latter, in the presence and absence of its effectors, should provide a more realistic appraisal of what happens during allosteric regulation, although CD studies (Fig. 6) suggest that a rather dramatic change in the enzyme's conformation occurs in the presence of dCTP. This finding is consistent with the highly cooperative manner

---

Fig. 4. DNA sequence of the T4-cd gene and flanking regions. The data depicted are numbered from an EcoRI restriction enzyme recognition site 539 bases upstream of the initiation codon and include approximately 1 kb of sequence information in the 3'-flanking region. The deduced amino-acid sequence of the cd gene is indicated as well as the location of gene 31 (underlined). [From Maley et al. (45).]

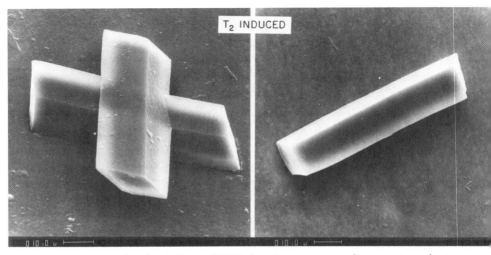

FIG. 5. Crystals of T2-phage dCMP deaminase as seen by scanning electron microscopy. Crystals were obtained by a slight modification of the hanging drop–vapor diffusion method (for details see 46).

in which dCMP and dCTP are bound by the deaminase. In both instances, one mole of nucleotide was bound to each of the enzyme's six subunits (53).

E. Human Deoxycytidylate Deaminase

HeLa cell dCMP deaminase purified to homogeneity by an affinity column procedure (unpublished) is less sensitive to allosteric regulation than either the chick embryo or the T-even phage enzymes. This is based on the fact that the human enzyme is fully active at 0.5 mM dCMP in the absence of dCTP, although 1 to 2 mM dCMP is required for maximal activity in the absence of dCTP with the other deaminases. However, at 0.2 mM dCMP, activation by 20 μM dCTP was clearly evident with the HeLa cell deaminase, which could be reversed by dTTP.

HeLa cell dCMP deaminase is the most active deaminase described to date, with a specific activity of 500 μmol/minute/mg of protein at 30°C, which would make this enzyme's turnover number about 1000 times that reported for the HeLa cell dTMP synthase (54). The deaminase is present also at comparably lower levels within the cell, thus greatly limiting its isolation for structural analyses. The only other report on the isolation of a pure human dCMP deaminase, that

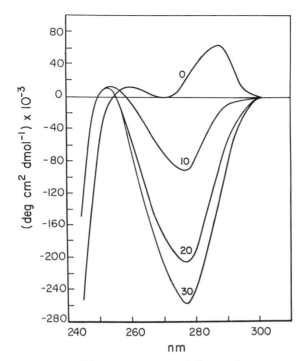

FIG. 6. Modification of the CD pattern of dCMP deaminase with increasing concentration of dCTP. The solution on which the CD analysis was taken contained in a volume of 3 ml 0.2 M potassium phosphate, pH 7.1, 10 mM 2-mercaptoethanol, 1 mM MgCl$_2$, 4.34 μM dCMP deaminase and, where indicated, 0, 10, 20, and 30 M dCTP. [From Maley and Maley (53).]

from spleen (55), yielded a specific activity that was 1/50th that of the HeLa deaminase. Aside from this difference, the spleen deaminase is composed of two 53-kDa subunits relative to the phage, chick embryo, and HeLa dCMP deaminases, with each containing six 20,000 Da subunits per mole of enzyme. It is possible that the spleen enzyme differs both structurally and catalytically from those already described, but this point must be verified.

II. Thymidylate Synthase: Historical Perspective

Enzymes are unique biological catalysts that are unparalleled in nature, except perhaps for the recently described properties ascribed to ribozymes (56). How and why they arose, as well as the mechanism by which they affect their catalytic activities, were often left to those with unbridled imaginations and a flair for theoretical exposition. However, in this era of computers that can rapidly provide the three-dimensional structure of proteins and the location of their substrate ligands, it is now possible to present a more rational explanation for how amino acids within a protein can promote catalysis. This has been made even more plausible through the development of such techniques as site-directed mutagenesis and computer-aided modeling procedures.

If enzymes are unique creatures of nature, thymidylate synthase might be considered one of the more unique among them, as if not only affects the transfer of a methylene group from a rather unusual substrate, $5,10\text{-}CH_2H_4PteGlu^1$, to carbon 5 of dUMP, but promotes the intramolecular reduction of the methylene to a methyl group by a proton coming from position 6 of the pteridine ring of the folate derivative (57). The resultant products are dTMP and $H_2PteGlu$. The enzyme was discovered more than 30 years ago by Friedkin and Kornberg (4), who suggested at that time the involvement of a transition-state intermediate that, with some variation, stands to this day.

As indicated in the previous section, our interest in thymidylate synthase was stimulated soon after its discovery, mainly to complement our dCMP deaminase studies (2), since the latter enzyme provided substrate for the former. The two enzymes were also complementary in that they were barely, if at all, detectable in nondividing cells, but their activities increased rather dramatically in hepatocytes induced to divide by partial hepatectomy (6). To understand the regulatory processes affecting the induction of these enzymes prior to the clarification of transcription factors, promoters and enhancers, was beyond the capacity of those interested in such studies. Indeed, about all one could do at that time was to study the effect of inhibitors on transcription and translation and potential chemotherapeutic agents, such as 5-fluorouracil, on thymidylate synthase and perhaps provide a plausible but speculative explanation for their mechanism of action. 5-Fluorouracil, a compound that has been in use for about 33 years (58), exerts its inhibition on the synthase by first being converted to FdUMP (59). At the time it was believed to be the primary site of inhibition by the compound and the means by which it exerted its toxicity, although more recently it has been shown to elicit a toxic response by being incorporated into RNA (60).

Since the levels of dTMP synthase in mitotically inactive tissues are practically nonexistent, we undertook the isolation of this enzyme from 6-day-old chick embryos, in which the enzyme is readily detectable. Although the enzyme was not plentiful, fertile eggs were, and we would stockpile the embryos from 100 dozen eggs each week. The embryo extracts provided us an added bonus, dCMP deaminase, which we eventually purified to homogeneity (61). Once the dTMP synthase was highly purified we were able to study both the kinetics of the reaction and the mechanism of inhibition by compounds such as FdUMP (57). A spectrophotometric assay (62), revealed that, of the two substrates, dUMP added to the enzyme first and departed last (57). These findings have since been verified by kinetic studies with the *L. casei* dTMP synthase (63), the pig liver synthase (64), and by equilibrium dialysis (65), provided that $CH_2H_4PteGlu_1$ was the second substrate. It was shown that FdUMP and N^4-hydroxy-dCMP also inhibit the enzyme in a competitive manner, if the enzyme was not incubated with these compounds before the addition of dUMP to initiate the reaction. In the former case, the inhibition became noncompetitive, due, as we know now, to a structural perturbation in the conformation of the enzyme. The phenomenon has more recently been shown to occur with inhibitory folate analogs of the synthase such as PDDF[1] (66).

A. Nature of the Active Site in *L. casei* Thymidylate Synthase

The key to opening this field of research, which enabled more in-depth studies to be undertaken in such areas as protein structure, quantitation of substrate binding in addition to localizing their sites of fixation, mechanism of catalytic reaction, and eventually a union of all of this information by means of X-ray crystallographic analyses, came about as a result of the development of methotrexate mutants of *L. casei* containing greatly enhanced levels of dTMP synthase (67, 68). The purified enzyme was shown to contain two identical 35-kDa subunits, and was sensitive to sulfhydryl reagents (67). Improvements in the purification procedure yielded larger amounts of synthase (69), and verified the thesis (70, 71) that the reaction was initiated by the addition of an enzyme-associated nucleophile across the 5,6-double bond of dUMP's pyrimidine ring. The formation of a tight ternary complex of [6-^{3}H]FdUMP and $CH_2H_2PteGlu$ with the *L. casei* synthase, followed by proteolysis or CNBr treatment and peptide isolation, showed that the nucleophile was a cysteinyl-SH group (72, 73). This cysteine was shown subsequently to be residue 198 (74). In similar studies, it was also possible to identify the folate-binding site as that involving either or both of the lysines at residues 50 and 51. Very recent studies employing site-directed mutagenesis, discussed below (Section II,H) appear to favor lysine-50.

B. The Interaction of Folate and Its Analogs with dTMP Synthase

All of the early studies with dTMP synthase, including kinetics and bindings, employed the monoglutamate derivative of folate, until it became evident that the natural substrate was a folylpolyglutamate (75), a much better substrate than the monoglutamate (76). In eukaryotes, the number of glutamates ranges from five to seven, with the major form in rat liver being a pentaglutamate (77). The earliest studies with PteGlu$_6$, H$_2$PteGlu$_6$, and H$_4$PteGlu$_6$ revealed these compounds to be very effective inhibitors of the synthase, much more so than the corresponding monoglutamates (78). Similar results were obtained with methotrexate (79) and the folate analog, PDDF[1] (80). These findings are reflected in the much tighter binding of the folylpolyglutamates relative to the monoglutamate, as determined by equilibrium dialysis (81) and by their protection of the L. casei synthase against proteolysis (82), particularly in combination with dUMP, FdUMP, or N^4-hydroxy-dCMP. In the former case, while (6R)CH$_2$H$_4$PteGlu binding could not be detected at all, its binding was greatly improved by N^4-hydroxy-dCMP to a K_D of 1.9 μM, which can be greatly enhanced by either N^4-hydroxy-dCMP or FdUMP (81). A clear dichotomy in the binding of these substrates was obtained on treatment of the synthase with carboxypeptidase A or iodoacetate. The former inactivates the synthase by removal of the carboxyterminal valine of L. casei dTMP synthase (83), which in effect prevents the binding of CH$_2$H$_4$PteGlu$_4$, but not dUMP (81). By contrast, sulfylhydryl inhibitors of the synthase prevent the binding of dUMP but not CH$_2$H$_4$PteGlu$_4$. Both substrates (dUMP and CH$_2$H$_4$PteGlu$_4$) however, bind to the carboxypeptidase-A-inactivated enzyme when added together (82), indicating that the energy of binding is insufficient to form a transition state intermediate with the modified enzyme.

It was apparent from these binding studies that the buffer used had a marked effect on the nucleotide binding constant, with phosphate being inhibitory relative to Tris-Cl (65). It was also evident from these early studies, particularly when coupled with CD spectra analyses (69), that a conformational change in the synthase occurs on the binding of its substrates or analogs. Thus, in the latter instance, a CD spectrum was not observed when CH$_2$H$_4$PteGlu or FdUMP alone was added to dTMP synthase, but a dramatic change was obtained when both were added together to the enzyme, as shown in Fig. 7. In fact, the spectral shift at 305 nm was good enough to allow the use of Scatchard plots for the (S) and (R) isomers of $CH_2H_4PteGlu$, which indicated that the (R) isomer bound more tightly than the (S) isomer. More concrete evidence for structural perturbations in the dTMP synthase structure are discussed below (Section II,H).

The implications of these binding studies became more apparent in attempting to explain why MTX[1] so markedly elevated dTMP synthase activity in regenerating rat liver (84), an effect also observed in cultured regenerating liver hepatocytes (85). From the latter studies it was clear that MTX and dUMP, as well as $H_2PteGlu$, decrease the rate of loss in synthase activity in extracts of these cells. These observations, coupled with the fact that inhibitors of protein synthesis do not affect the level of synthase activity, suggested that the enzyme can be protected *in vivo* against proteolytic degradation by its substrates or analogs. From what we now know about the accumulation of MTX in cells as polyglutamates, these earlier observations can most likely be explained by the protection of the synthase against proteases due to the binding of MTX polyglutamates to the enzyme, an effect that can be enhanced by dUMP. Although this combination of substrate and substrate analog is quite inhibitory to the synthase, it is analogous to what we found on the protection of dTMP synthase against various proteases by the folylpolyglutamates (82).

C. The Isolation of Homogeneous Thymidylate Synthases from Other Sources

Inserting the dTMP synthase genes from *E. coli* (*ThyA*) and bacteriophage T4 (*td*) into the high expression vector pKC30, induces these

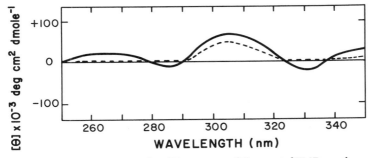

FIG. 7. Effect of FdUMP on the CD spectra of *L. casei* dTMP synthase in the presence of 6(R) and 6(S) 5,10-$CH_2H_4PteGlu$. The solid line represents the former isomer and the broken line the latter isomer (for details see 69).

proteins to at least 5% of the cellular proteins (86, 87). Figure 8 presents the unique bipyramidyl crystal structure of the T2-phage synthase, which has also been obtained for the T4-enzyme. For comparison, crystals of the *L. casei* synthase are presented, revealing that despite their high degree of homology, these proteins have rather different crystal forms. The complete sequence of the *thyA* gene was determined and its encoded amino-acid sequence was shown to be 62% homologous to the *L. casei* synthase, despite a 51 amino-acid deletion in the *E. coli* synthase (88). The active site region was even more homologous (82%). After unraveling the *E. coli* dTMP synthase sequence, it was decided to compare this sequence with that encoded in the *td* gene of T4-phage in an effort to determine why the two enzymes are inhibited so differently by the folylpolyglutamates (89). For this analysis we fortunately employed both protein and DNA sequencing procedures, since (as will be seen) using either technique alone might have missed the important finding described below.

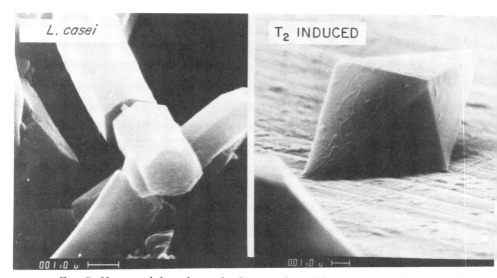

FIG. 8. Hexagonal shaped crystals of *L. casei* thymidylate synthase and bipyramidyl crystal structure of T2-phage dTMP synthase as seen by scanning electron microscopy. The latter crystal was obtained in a manner similar to that described for the T2-phage dCMP deaminase (46).

D. The First Description of an Intron in the Structural Gene of a Prokaryote

This discovery can only be attributed to serendipity and to the unrelenting efforts of Fred Chu. The serendipity part of this problem comes from the fact that we decided to sequence the protein at the same time that he was sequencing the *td* gene. At a point two-thirds through the apparent DNA sequence of the gene, a region was encountered that did not coincide with any of the peptides we had at that time. However, on sequencing through 1016 bases (originally reported as 1017) of apparent gibberish, Chu encountered an encoded sequence that coincided exactly with one of the isolated peptides, but was preceded by an AUG codon (90). The latter turned out to be the initiation codon for the second exon of the *td* gene, with the two exons being separated by an intervening sequence or intron. Although small introns in the tRNAs of archaebacteria had been described, this was the first indication of an intron in a prokaryotic gene analogous to those present in eukaryotic genes. Subsequent reports of similar introns in the *nrdB* (91, 92) and *sunY* genes (93, 94) of the T4 phage, as well as in other prokaryotes, clearly establishes that these anomalous regions are here to stay, at least within this realm.

Another interesting revelation that came from the clarification of the sequence of the *td* gene was that the *frd* and *td* genes, which were believed to be separated slightly on the T4-phage genomic map (48), in reality overlap at their respective carboxyl and amino ends (95). This apparently occurs through an ATGA sequence, with the last three nucleotides specifying the stop codon for the *frd* gene transcript, and the first three, the start codon for the *td* gene transcript.

E. Properties of the *td* Intron

It soon became apparent that the intron, which also contains a very basic 245 amino-acid open reading frame (96), possesses many of the characteristics attributed to the large rRNA intron of *Tetrahymena*, as well as those of the other group I introns from yeast, fungal mitochondria and chloroplasts (97, 98). These include similar consensus regions and structural features (99), in addition to such intron-excision requirements as Mg^{2+} and guanosine or its nucleotide derivatives, and the capacity to undergo autocatalysis or self-splicing reactions *in vitro* by the mechanism described in Fig. 9 (100). Although the products formed (linear and circular introns, as well as mature mRNA for dTMP synthase) are consistent with those described originally for the self-splicing reaction of *Tetrahymena* rRNA (101), only a dinucleotide was

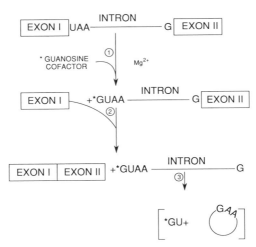

Fɪɢ. 9. RNA splicing scheme for *td* precurrsor RNA. The circled numbers show the sequence of the three proposed transesterification reactions involved in intron excision, exon ligation, and cyclization of the intron (for details see *99, 100*).

released on cyclization of the linear *td* intron. This is in contrast to the 15- and 19-mers obtained from the *Tetrahymena* rRNA.

To determine the potential functional role of the intron in the *td* gene, the intron was precisely deleted by deletion mutagenesis to yield an intronless gene, which was expressed many times better in an *in vitro* transcription–translation system than the intron-containing gene (*102*). By contrast, this effect was not observed in *E. coli* transformed with intron-containing or intron-deleted *td* genes within specific plasmids, indicating that while introns can be excised by autocatalysis *in vitro*, specific proteins most likely assist this process *in vivo*.

It was at first believed that the intron-encoded protein might be involved in aiding the splicing process, such as described for the maturases encoded within certain yeast mitochondrial introns (*103*), but deletions within the *td* intron-encoded protein not only did not impair the splicing reaction; if anything, they enhanced it (*102*).

Even if the intron-encoded protein was involved in some manner in the splicing reaction, attempts to demonstrate the synthesis of this protein *in vivo* were unsuccessful, although the fact that it could be translated as a 30-kDa peptide was demonstrated by means of an *in vitro* wheat-germ translation system (D. West, unpublished).

F. Properties of the Intron Open Reading Frame (IRF) Protein

Attempts to prepare this protein in amounts adequate to study by cloning the gene within a high expression vector met initially with disappointing results, probably because of the toxic nature of the protein, which was suggested in earlier studies. Because most of the vectors used were slightly "leaky," it was reasoned that a vector without this characteristic might be more successful. We therefore employed a system (51) that does not express vector-incorporated genes until the *E. coli* are infected with a λ phage containing the T7 RNA-polymerase gene. Although successful production of the intron-encoded protein was obtained, the product was inactive as a consequence of being incorporated into an insoluble inclusion complex (104). However, the complex could be dissolved in 6-M guanidine-HCl and renatured to a soluble protein on dialysis. More recently, this protein (IRF)[1] was purified to homogeneity and shown to exist as a single subunit with a mass of about 22 kDa. It was immediately apparent that an incongruity exists here since the protein, based on its encoded 245 amino-acid residues, should have migrated slower on SDS–PAGE considering that the gene had been fused to a segment encoding 17 amino acids. Sequence analysis of the amino end of the gel-purified protein verified the correctness of this fusion. However, carboxypeptidase sequencing revealed that the carboxyl terminal end had been truncated precisely at isoleucine-157 of the IRF protein. The fact that the IRF protein migrates on electrophoresis at about 22 kDa and not at 17–18 kDa, which would be the size of the truncated IRF protein plus fusion peptide, may be an artifact due to the highly basic nature of this protein. The solution to this anomaly remains to be unraveled. The most likely explanation at present is that the entire 245-amino-acid protein is synthesized, but is rapidly processed by a specific protease in *E. coli*.

G. Nature of the IRF Protein Activity and Function

Recent studies (105) with a yeast mitochondrial r1 open reading frame protein, similar in size and basicity to the *td* IRF, have shown the former protein to act as an ω-transposase with specific endonuclease activity for a site within the intronless rRNA gene. It was apparent from these studies that a similar function might be attributed to the IRF protein and, as indicated in Fig. 10, it was indeed capable of cleaving the intronless *td* gene when present in a linearized plasmid

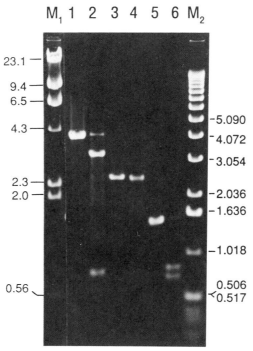

Fɪɢ. 10. Specificity of the IRF endonuclease. The DNA samples (0.10–0.15 pmol) were incubated under the conditions described by West *et al.* (*104*). The reactions that were run in the even-numbered lanes had been treated with 1.5 μg of partially purified endonuclease. Lanes 1 and 2, pUCtd△I restricted with *Bam*HI; lanes 3 and 4, *Eco*RI–HI *Td* fragment; lanes 5 and 6, *Eco*RI–*Bam*HI *Td*△ fragment. Lane M₁ is a γ/*Hin*dIII digest and lane M₂ is a 1-kb ladder. [Taken in part from West *et al.* (*104*).]

(lane 2), but not if the intron or an intron fragment (lane 4) was present in the gene. When removed from the plasmid as 1.6-kbp fragment, the intronless gene was cleaved by the endonuclease to 830 and 770 kbp fragments (land 6) (*104*). That this hydrolysis is not completely specific is indicated by the fact that circular plasmid containing the *thy*A gene is also linearized (unpublished) at a site similar to that in the intronless *td* gene. The fact that the *thy*A gene is susceptible to hydrolysis by the *IRF* protein could explain the apparent toxicity of the *td* gene for *E. coli* when transformed with plasmids containing this gene. In a similar vein, the presence of this intron within the T-even phage genome could contribute to the demise of these cells when expressed in phage-infected cells. Introns within the cytochrome oxidase (*105*) and cytochrome *b* (*106, 107*) genes have also been shown to encode a potent and toxic endonuclease.

The precise function of the IRF protein is still not clear, although, as suggested (*105*) for the ω-transposase, it might aid in mediating recombination events associated with intron mobility. This suggestion appears to be borne out in experiments showing that the *td* intron can be transferred from the *intron*-containing *td* gene to *td* genes missing the intron (*108*). Another function attributed to such introns is that of moving exons to other genes (*109*). Whether the IRF protein is involved in this process remains to be seen.

H. Structure/Function Relationships in Thymidylate Synthase

Since our first disclosures on the sequences for the synthases of *L. casei* (*74*), *E. coli* (*86*), and T4-phage (*90*), 14 more have been added. Some of these are closely related particularly those from the eukaryotes *Leishmania and Herpes,* but extensive differences would not be expected among members of a class. Even so, this enzyme is among the most highly conserved, naturally occurring proteins, with 18% of the residues being identical. This conservation is even greater in those regions shown to be involved in dUMP (Table II) and folate binding (Table III). X-ray crystallographic analysis of the *L. casei* synthesis has enabled some very educated guesses to be made regarding the contribution of various functional groups to substrate binding and the catalytic process itself (*124*). However, until an analysis of the structure of the ligand-bound enzyme is presented, which should be forthcoming soon with the solution of the three-dimensional structure of the ternary complex of *E. coli* dTMP synthase, dUMP, and PDDF (*125a*), the specific groups involved in promoting substrate binding cannot be presented with certainty. The importance of analyzing the liganded enzyme structure is of greater relevance because of the known conformational changes that occur upon the binding of substrates and their analogs. These have been observed in several studies and include hydrodynamic changes (*125*), NMR shifts (*126*), circular dichroic (*69, 127*), UV spectral (*71*), and fluorescence changes (*128, 129*), as well as an alteration in the symmetry of binding (*65, 130*) and protection against proteolysis (*82*).

Functional groups modifying reagents have already implicated the potential involvement of arginine (*131, 132*), tyrosine (*133*), and cysteine residues (*67, 70, 134, 135*) as being directly or indirectly involved in the catalytic process. The involvement of a specific histidine is less

TABLE II

AMINO-ACID SEQUENCE AT THE NUCLEOTIDE ACTIVE SITE REGION
OF VARIOUS THYMIDYLATE SYNTHASES[a]

Human	M-A-L-P -	P-C-H -	T-K-Y-Q	(110)
Mouse	M-A-L-P -	P-C-H -	T-L-Y-Q	(111)
H. saimiri	M-V-L-P -	P-C-H -	V-L-S-Q	(112)
H. ateles	M-A-L-P -	P-C-H -	V-I-S-Q	(113)
Lei. major	M-A-L-P -	P-C-H -	L-L-A-Q	(114)
Lei. tropica	M-A-V-P -	P-C-H -	L-L-A-Q	(115)
E. coli	M-A-L-A -	P-C-H -	A-F-F-Q	(85)
P. carinii	M-A-L-P -	P-C-H -	M-F-C-Q	(116)
V. zoster	M-V-L-P -	P-C-H -	T-L-C-Q	(117)
C. fasiculata	M-A-V-R -	P-C-H -	L-L-G-Q	(118)
T4-phage	M-A-L-P -	P-C-H -	M-F-Y-Q	(89)
Yeast	M-A-L-P -	P-C-H -	I-F-S-Q	(119)
L. casei	M-A-L-P -	P-C-H -	T-L-Y-Q	(73)
Phage 3T	M-A-L-T -	P-C-Ⓥ -	Y-E-T-Q	(120)
P. falciparum	M-A-L-P -	P-C-H -	I-L-C-Q	(121)
Ca. albicans	M-A-L-P -	P-C-H -	V-F-C-Q	(122)
B. subtilis	M-A-L-A -	P-C-H -	C-L-F-Q	(123)

[a] Abbreviations H., Herpesvirus; Lei., Leishmania; E., Escherichia; P., Pneumocystis; V., Varicella virus; C, Crithidia; L., Lactobacillus; P., Plasmodium; Ca., Candida; B., Bacillus.

TABLE III

AMINO-ACID SEQUENCE AT THE FOLIATE BINDING REGION OF
VARIOUS THYMIDYLATE SYNTHASES[a]

Human	P-L-L-T-T -	K-R -	V-F-W-K	(110)
Mouse	P-L-L-T-T -	K-R -	V-F-W-K	(111)
H. saimiri	P-L-L-T-T -	K-R -	V-F-W-K	(112)
H. ateles	P-L-L-T-T -	K-R -	V-F-W-R	(113)
L. major	P-L-L-T-T -	K-R -	V-F-W-R	(114)
L. tropica	P-L-L-T-T -	K-R -	V-F-W-R	(115)
E. coli	P-L-V-T-T -	K-R -	Ⓒ-H-L-R	(85)
P. carinii	P-A-V-T-T -	K-R -	V-F-I-R	(116)
C. fasiculata	P-L-L-T-T -	K-R -	V-F-W-R	(117)
V. zoster	P-L-L-T-T -	K-R -	V-F-W-R	(118)
T4-phage	P-A-V-T-T -	K-K -	L-A-W-K	(89)
Yeast	P-L-L-T-T -	K-K -	V-F-T-R	(119)
L. casei	P-L-L-T-T -	K-K -	V-P-F-G	(73)
Phage-3T	P-I-L-T-T -	K-K -	V-A-W-K	(120)
P. falciparum	P-L-L-T-T -	K-K -	L-F-L-R	(121)
C. albicans	P-L-L-T-T -	K-K -	V-F-S-K	(122)
B. subtilis	P-M-L-T-T -	K-L -	L-H-F-K	(123)

[a] Abbreviations same as in Table II.

clear, as activity was progressively lost as the histidines were modified by diethyl pyrocarbonate (*132, 136*).

A peculiar finding with respect to the enzyme's sensitivity to sulfhydryl reagents is the apparent loss of activity on inactivation of one of the two active-site cysteines (*130, 134, 135*). Since the enzyme consists of two identical subunits, it might be expected that both active-site cysteines would have to be titrated for a complete loss in activity to be obtained, particularly since the enzyme's crystal structure (*124*) reveals that the two active sites do not impact on one another. These sulfhydryl studies are consistent with dUMP binding studies indicating that only 1 mol of dUMP binds per mole of enzyme (*65, 130, 134, 135, 137*). It is possible that the binding of dUMP or a sulfhydryl reagent to one subunit effects a conformational change in the other subunit, resulting in an impairment in its ability to bind substrate. This apparent half-the-sites of reactivity remains to be verified, although it should be indicated that there is not complete agreement on this subject (*138*).

Another approach to defining the potential involvement of amino acids in an enzymic reaction has been that of site-directed mutagenesis. By this means, amino acids contributing directly to the catalytic process may be revealed, as opposed to those that influence the three-dimensional structure of the protein and thus affect the catalytic reaction indirectly. This field should virtually explode in the near future with respect to the introduction of mutations in various regions of dTMP synthase. In particular, there are studies with *L. casei* synthase in which the complete gene has been synthesized and multiple mutations placed within specific regions by cassettes (*138a*).

Our own studies have focused on mutations in those regions of the T4-phage synthase believed to be involved in the active site and the binding of folate (*139*). Thus amino-acid residues 155, 156, and 157, corresponding to the conserved active-site amino acids proline, cysteine, and histidine, were modified individually, and the effect that these changes have on enzyme activity was assayed. Of particular interest is the presence of this sequence (*140*) in O^6-alkylguanine—DNA methyltransferase (EC 2.1.1.63) a "repair" enzyme that transfers the O^6 alkyl group to the cysteinyl residue of the enzyme resulting in its "suicide" inactivation. As expected, the most dramatic effect was obtained by changing cysteine-156 of the T4-phage synthase to serine. These results are similar to those described by Dev *et al.* (*141*) in that, while a minimal amount of activity was detected (about 0.05% of the wild type), it was insufficient to support the growth of *E. coli* (thyA⁻)

transformed with a plasmid containing the modified gene. Paradoxically, the P155A mutation retained almost wild-type activity, but was very unstable to incubation at 40°C, in contrast to C156S or H157V. This is not entirely surprising since proline contributes to the structural integrity of a protein and any alteration in this residue should correspondingly alter the properties of the protein. This was evident not only in this enzyme's stability but in its fluorescence spectra, which revealed a shift of maximum from 360 to 340 nm. While the H157V enzyme was reduced about 80% in activity, it was as stable at 40°C as the wild type or C156S enzymes, but also demonstrated a blue shift in its spectrum indicating that its structure had been perturbed. A comparable change in the *E. coli* synthase (H147V) was reported recently but its activity was found to be only about 7% that of the wild type (*142*), perhaps reflecting the difference in specific activities of the *E. coli* and T4-phage synthases. Thus, of the three changes in the active site, only C156S was not structurally altered, but its activity was modified because the cysteinyl nucleophile is essential for catalysis. However, the other mutants reveal changes that are related to structural perturbations in the enzyme protein.

It is of interest to note that the H157V change did not result in an even greater loss in activity, which could be expected if it was involved in abstracting the H from the C5 position of dUMP. That this is probably not so, is seen in the case of the ϕ3T dTMP synthase, which contains a valine in this position (Table II) and yet is the most active synthase described to date (*143*). In a similar vein, the modification of amino acids in the folate-binding region appear to verify the requirement for a lysine residue at residue 48. As we indicated in our folylpolyglutamate fixation studies with the *L. casei* synthase (*144*), either lysine 50 or 51 contributes to the binding. Since, in the T4-phage synthase, lysines 48 and 49 correspond to *L. casei* lysines 50 and 51, it appears that the former residue is primarily involved in the binding, most probably via charge–charge interactions. Similar to C156S, neither the stability of the modified enzyme nor the fluorescence spectra were affected by the change, in contrast to K49R where both were.

While substitutions at the first lysine in the folate binding site can obviously impact on the enzyme's activity, recent studies have shown that amino-acid changes near this site can also have dramatic effects on enzyme activity. This was seen with a mutant of *E. coli* in which cysteine 50, adjacent to K48-R49 (Table III), was replaced with a tyrosine (*145*), resulting in a 99.8% loss in enzyme activity. Although the binding of folate derivatives was impaired, so was nucleotide binding. However on replacing this tyrosine with phenylalanine, the activity was improved 25-fold (*146*). Computer-graphic analysis of the substitution at this position revealed that the tyrosyl hydroxyl at residue 50 may share its proton with the carboxyl of folate or, if ionized, share the proton associated with the ϵ amino of lysine 48. This is supported in part by the fact that the phenylalanine mutant is so much more active. However, it is still only one-twentieth as active as the wild-type enzyme, which in effect could be due to the bulk of the phenylalanine ring causing a change in the enzyme's conformation.

Finally, arginines 218, and 179 are involved in promoting the fixation of the substrate and its analogs, as well as inorganic phosphate, most probably by ionic binding (*124*). These residues correspond to arginines 176 and 137 in the T4-phage synthase. As indicated recently (*140*), R176K is almost completely inactive, while R137K still retains 30% of its activity. In these cases where a sharp loss in activity was obtained, the structures were perturbed as indicated by blue shift in their fluorescence spectra, but not in R137K, which appeared as stable or more so than the wild-type enzyme. It appears from these results that R176K, which corresponds to arginine 218 of *L. casei*, is more vital to the binding of the phosphate of dUMP and FdUMP than the arginine 179 of *L. casei*.

It is evident from mutagenesis studies that much can be learned, in clarifying the roles of specific amino acids in substrate binding and their contributions to the catalytic reaction, particularly when used in conjunction with X-ray defined structures of proteins. It is anticipated therefore, that within the next year or two that the dTMP synthase reaction mechanism will be resolved in its entirety.

III. Concluding Remarks

We have attempted to present an overview of two critical enzymes involved in providing substrate precursors for DNA synthesis, with particular emphasis on our contributions to these areas of research. As a consequence we have no doubt neglected to cite numerous publications and for this we offer our apologies. As we have described, dCMP deaminase and dTMP synthase appear to be intimately associated both in their association with the mitotic process and in maintaining a flux of nucleotides into the pools of dCTP and dTTP.

It was perhaps intuitive on our part to study dTMP synthesis in conjunction with the newly discovered dCMP deaminase, since it was felt that if one enzyme provides substrate for another, particularly at a rate-limiting step in DNA synthesis, something would come of these studies; and it did. In the course of studying the properties of dCMP deaminase it was found to be an exquisitely regulated enzyme, controlled to a fine degree by the end products of its metabolic pathway, dCTP and dTTP. While the former nucleotide appears to be the sole allosteric activator of the deaminase, the latter can inhibit allosterically at least two other enzymes involved in providing dTMP to the cell, thymidine kinase and ribonucleoside 5′-diphosphate reductase (EC 1.17.4.1).

Thymidylate synthase on the other hand, appears to be regulated by the availability of its substrates, dUMP and $5,10$-CH$_2$H$_4$PteGlu. Since the formation of dUMP is critical to the survival of the cell and dCMP is so crucial to this process it might be instructive to determine, in a coupled enzyme system, the extent to which dCTP and dTTP influence dTMP formation. Analogs of these nucleotides or inhibitors of dCMP deaminase could act as potential chemotherapeutic agents by limiting the synthesis of dUMP, particularly in combination with other purine and pyrimidine inhibitors of DNA synthesis.

Despite all that has been learned regarding the two enzymes described in this review, there is still much to be learned with respect to the mechanism of their catalytic processes and the subtle nuances of their regulation within and outside of the cell. Hopefully, we will continue to contribute to the resolution of these fascinating problems as we mature along with them.

Acknowledgments

This work was supported in part by grants from the National Cancer Institute (CA44355), United States Public Health Service, Department of Health and Human Services, and the National Science Foundation (DMB86-16273). We would like to express our sincere appreciation to the numerous investigators, who by their efforts, made this review possible. We would also like to thank Judith Valentino for her patience and expertise in typing this manuscript.

References

1. F. Maley and S. Ochoa, *JBC* **233**, 1538 (1958).
2. G. F. Maley and F. Maley, *JBC* **234**, 2975 (1959).
3. E. Scarano, *BBA* **29**, 459 (1958).
4. M. Friedkin and A. Kornberg, *in* "The Chemical Basis of Heredity" (W. D. McElroy and B. Glass, eds.), p. 609. John Hopkins Univ. Press, Baltimore, Maryland, 1957.
5. F. Maley and G. F. Maley, *Cancer Res.* **21**, 1421 (1981).
6. F. Maley and G. F. Maley, *JBC* **235**, 2968 (1960).
7. P. Reichard, Z. N. Canellakis and E. S. Canellakis, *JBC* **236**, 2514 (1961).
8. R. L. Miller and N. Ressler, *Clin. Chim. Acta* **26**, 405 (1969).
9. G. F. Williams and D. D. Jones, *Br. Med. J.* **2**, 10 (1975).

10. G. F. Maley and F. Maley, *JBC* **237**, PC3311 (1962).
11. E. Scarano, G. Geraci, A. Polzella and E. Companile, *JBC* **238**, PC1556 (1963).
12. J. C. Gerhart and A. B. Pardee, *JBC* **237** 891 (1962).
13. J. Monod, J.-P. Changeaux and F. Jacob, *JMB* **6**, 306 (1963).
14. G. F. Maley and F. Maley, *JBC* **243**, 4506 (1968).
15. F. Maley and G. F. Maley, *Bchem* **1**, 847 (1962).
16. G. F. Maley and F. Maley, *BBA* **68**, 293 (1963).
17. G. F. Maley, D. U. Guarino and F. Maley, *JBC* **247**, 931 (1972).
18. J. Monod, J. Wyman and J.-P. Changeaux, *JMB* **12**, 88 (1965).
19. R. Nucci, C. A. Raia, C. Vaccaro, S. Sepe, E. Scarano and M. Rossi, *JMB* **124**, 133 (1978).
20. C. Raia, R. Nucci, C. Vaccaro, S. Sepe, R. Rella and M. Rossi, *JMB* **157**, 557 (1982).
21. F. Maley and G. F. Maley, *JBC* **257**, 11876 (1982).
22. G. A. O'Donovan, G. Edlin, J. A. Fuchs, J. Neuhard and E. Thomassen, *J. Bact.* **105**, 666 (1971).
23. J. Neuhard and E. Thomassen, *J. Bact.* **105**, 657 (1971).
24. G. R. Greenberg and R. L. Somerville, *PNAS* **48**, 247 (1962).
25. G. F. Maley, D. U. Guarino and F. Maley, *JBC* **242**, 3517 (1967).
26. W. H. Fleming and M. J. Bessman, *JBC* **242**, 353 (1967).
27. J. J. Scocca, S. R. Panny and M. J. Bessman, *JBC* **242**, 363 (1967).
28. H. Mollgaard and J. Neuhard, *JBC* **253**, 3536 (1978).
29. M. Nishihara, A. Chrambach and H. U. Aposhian, *Bchem* **6**, 1877 (1967).
30. H. A. Rolton and H. M. Keir, *BJ* **143**, 403 (1974).
31. S. Kit, R. A. deTorres and D. R. Dubbs, *Cancer Res.* **27**, 1907 (1967).
32. R. Dulbecco, L. H. Hartwell and M. Vogt, *PNAS* **53**, 403 (1965).
33. E. Königk, *Bull. W. H. O.* **55**, 249 (1977).
34. D. H. Hall and I. Tessman, *Virology* **29**, 339 (1966).
35. M. D. Dechamps, B. R. de Saint Vincent, C. Evrard, M. Sassi and G. Buttin, *Exp. Cell Res.* **86**, 269 (1974).
36. B. R. de Saint Vincent, M. Dechamps and G. Buttin, *JBC* **255**, 162 (1980).
37. G. Weinberg, B. Ullman and D. W. Martin, *PNAS* **78**, 2447 (1981).
38. S. Eriksson, S. Skog, B. Tribukait and K. Jäderberg, *Exp. Cell Res.* **155**, 129 (1984).
39. K. Bhalla, M. Birkhofer, L. Gongrong, S. Grant, W. Maclaughlin, J. Cole, G. Graham and D. J. Volsky, *Blood* **74**, 1923 (1989).
40. G. F. Maley and F. Maley, *JBC* **241**, 2176 (1966).
41. L. E. Bertani, A. Häggmark and P. Reichard, *JBC* **238**, 3407 (1963).
42. R. Labow and F. Maley, *BBRC* **29**, 136 (1967).
43. L. K. Moen, M. L. Howell, G. W. Lasser and C. K. Mathews, *J. Mol. Recognition* **1**, 48 (1988).
44. A. J. Mileham, H. R. Revel and N. E. Murray, *MGG* **179**, 227 (1980).
45. G. F. Maley, B. W. Duceman, A.-M. Wang, J. Martinez and F. Maley, *JBC* **265**, 47 (1990).
46. G. F. Maley, D. U. Guarino and F. Maley, *JBC* **258**, 8290 (1983).
47. S. Nikolnikov, G. Posfai and B. Sain, *Gene* **30**, 261 (1984).
48. E. Kutter and W. Rugger, *in* "Bacteriophage T4" (C. K. Mathews, E. M. Kutter, G. Mosig and P. B. Berget, eds.), p. 277. Am. Soc. Microbiol., Washington, D.C., 1983.
49. A. Larsson and P. Reichard, *This Series* **7**, 303 (1987).
50. P. O. Dwyer, S. A. King, D. F. Hoth and R. Leyland-James, *Cancer Res.* **47**, 3911 (1987).

51. F. W. Studier and B. A. Moffet, *JMB* **189**, 113 (1986).
52. E. M. McIntosh and R. H. Haynes, *MC Biol* **6**, 1711 (1986).
53. G. F. Maley and F. Maley, *Bchem* **21**, 3780 (1982).
54. W. Rode, D. J. Dolnick and J. R. Bertino, *Biochem. Pharmacol* **29**, 723 (1980).
55. P. H. Ellins, A. Y. Kao and B. A. Chabner, *JBC* **256**, 6335 (1981).
56. T. R. Cech, *Science* **230**, 1532 (1987).
57. M. Y. Lorenson, G. F. Maley and F. Maley, *JBC* **242**, 3332 (1987).
58. C. Heidelberger, N. K. Chandhuri, P. Dannenberg, D. Mooren, L. Griesbach, R. Duschinsky, R. J. Schnitzer, E. Pleven and J. Scheiner, *Nature* **179**, 663 (1957).
59. S. S. Cohen, J. G. Flaks, H. D. Barner, M. R. Loeb and J. Lichtenstein, *PNAS* **44**, 1004 (1958).
60. S. Spiegelman, R. Sawyer, R. Nayak, E. Ritzi, R. Stolfi and D. Martin, *PNAS* **77**, 4966 (1980).
61. F. Maley and G. F. Maley, *Adv. Enzyme Regul.* **8**, 55 (1970).
62. A. J. Wahba and M. Friedkin, *JBC* **236**, PC11 (1961).
63. H. H. Daron and J. L. Aull, *JBC* **253**, 940 (1978).
64. Y. -Z. Lu, P. D. Aiello and R. G. Mathews, *Bchem* **23**, 6870 (1984).
65. J. H. Galivan, G. F. Maley and F. Maley, *Bchem* **15**, 356 (1976).
66. A. L. Pogolotti, Jr., P. V. Danenberg and D. V. Santi, *J. Med. Chem.* **29**, 478 (1986).
67. R. B. Dunlap, N. G. L. Harding and F. M. Huennekens, *Bchem* **10**, 88 (1971).
68. R. P. Leary and R. L. Kisliuk, *Prep. Biochem.* **1**, 47 (1971).
69. J. H. Galivan, G. F. Maley and F. Maley, *Bchem* **14**, 338 (1975).
70. P. V. Danenberg, R. J. Langenbach and C. Heidelberger, *Bchem* **13**, 1073 (1974).
71. D. V. Santi, C. S. McHenry and H. Somer, *Bchem* **13**, 471 (1974).
72. R. L. Bellisario, G. F. Maley, J. H. Galivan and F. Maley, *PNAS* **73**, 1848 (1976).
73. A. L. Pogolotti, K. M. Ivanetich, H. Sommer and D. V. Santi, *BBRC* **70**, 972 (1976).
74. G. F. Maley, R. L. Bellisario, D. U. Guarino and F. Maley, *JBC* **254**, 1301 (1979).
75. C. M. Baugh and C. L. Krumdiek, *Ann. N.Y. Acad. Sci.* **186**, 7 (1971).
76. R. L. Kisliuk, Y. Gaumont, E. Lafer, C. M. Baugh and J. A. Montgomery, *Bchem* **20**, 929 (1981).
77. Y. S. Shin, M. A. Williams and E. L. R. Stockstad, *BBRC* **47**, 35 (1972).
78. R. L. Kisliuk, Y. Gaumont and C. M. Baugh, *JBC* **249**, 4100 (1974).
79. R. L. Kisliuk, Y. Gaumont, C. M. Baugh, J. H. Galivan, G. F. Maley and F. Maley, *in* "Chemistry and Biology of Pteridines" (R. L. Kisliuk and G. M. Brown, eds), p. 431. Elsevier/North-Holland, Amsterdam, 1979.
80. Y.-C. Cheng, G. E. Dutshman, M. C. Starnes, M. H. Fisher, N. T. Nanavathi and M. G. Nair, *Cancer Res.* **45**, 598 (1985).
81. J. H. Galivan, F. Maley and C. M. Baugh, *BBRC* **71**, 527 (1976).
82. J. H. Galivan, F. Maley and C. M. Baugh, *ABB* **184**, 346 (1977).
83. J. L. Aull, R. B. Loeble and R. B. Dunlap, *JBC* **249**, 1167 (1974).
84. R. Labow, G. F. Maley and F. Maley, *Cancer Res.* **29**, 366 (1969).
85. R. J. Bonney and F. Maley, *Cancer Res.* **35**, 1950 (1975).
86. M. Belfort, G. F. Maley and F. Maley, *PNAS* **80**, 1858 (1983).
87. M. Belfort, A. Moelleken, G. F. Maley and F. Maley, *JBC* **258**, 2045 (1983).
88. M. Belfort, G. F. Maley, J. Pedersen-Lane and F. Maley, *PNAS* **80**, 4914 (1983).
89. G. F. Maley, F. Maley and C. M. Baugh, *JBC* **254**, 7485 (1979).
90. F. K. Chu, G. F. Maley, F. Maley and M. Belfort, *PNAS* **81**, 3049 (1984).
91. B. M. Sjoberg, S. Hakare, C. Z. Mathews, C. K. Mathews, K. N. Rand and M. J. Gait, *EMBO J.* **5**, 2031 (1986).
92. J. G. Gott, D. A. Shub and M. Belfort, *Cell* **47**, 81 (1986).

93. J. Tomaschewski and W. Ruger, *NARes* **15**, 3632 (1987).
94. D. A. Shub, M.-Q. Xu, J. M. Gott and A. Zeeh, *CSHSQB* **52**, 193 (1987).
95. S. Purohit and C. K. Mathews, *JBC* **257**, 6201 (1984).
96. F. K. Chu, G. F. Maley, D. K. West, M. Belfort and F. Maley, *Cell* **45**, 157 (1986).
97. R. B. Waring and R. W. Davies, *Gene* **28**, 277 (1984).
98. T. R. Cech, *Gene* **73**, 259 (1988).
99. F. K. Chu, G. F. Maley and F. Maley, *FASEB J.* **2**, 216 (1988).
100. F. K. Chu, G. F. Maley and F. Maley, *Bchem* **26**, 3050 (1987).
101. A. Zaug, J. R. Kent and T. R. Cech, *Science* **224**, 574 (1984).
102. D. K. West, M. Belfort, G. F. Maley and F. Maley, *JBC* **261**, 13466 (1988).
103. J. Lazowaska, C. Jacq and P. P. Slonimski, *Cell*, 333 (1980).
104. D. K. West, L.-M. Changchien, G. F. Maley and F. Maley, *JBC* **246**, 10343 (1989).
105. L. Colleaux, L. D'Auriol, F. Galibert and B. Dujon, *PNAS* **85**, 6022 (1988).
106. J. M. Wenzlau, R. L. Saldanbe, R. A. Butow and P. S. Perlman, *Cell* **56**, 421 (1989).
107. A. Delahodde, V. Goguel, A. M. Becam, F. Greusot, J. Perea, J. Banroques and C. Jacq, *Cell* **56**, 431 (1989).
108. S. M. Quirk, D. Bell-Pedersen and M. Belfort, *Cell* **56**, 455 (1989).
109. D. H. Hall, Y. Liu and D. A. Shub, *Nature* **340**, 574 (1989).
110. K. Takeishi, S. Kaneda, D. Ayusawa, K. Shimizu, O. Grotoh and T. Seno, *NARes* **13**, 2035 (1985).
111. S. M. Perryman, C. Rossana, T. Deng, F. F. Vanin and L. F. Johnson, *Mol. Biol. Eval.* **3**, 313 (1986).
112. R. W. Honess, W. Bodemer, K. R. Cameron, H. H. Niller, B. Flekenstein and R. E. Randall, *PNAS* **83**, 3604 (1986).
113. J. Richter, I. Puchter and B. Fleckenstein, *J. Virol.* **62**, 3530 (1988).
114. S. M. Beverley, T. E. Ellenberger and J. S. Cordingley, *PNAS* **83**, 2584 (1986).
115. R. Grumont, W. L. Washtien, D. Caput and D. V. Santi, *PNAS* **83**, 5387 (1986).
116. U. Edman, J. C. Edman, B. Lundgren and D. V. Santi, *PNAS* **86**, 6503 (1989).
117. R. Thompson, R. W. Honess, L. Taylor, J. Moran and A. J. Davison, *J. Gen. Virol.* **68**, 1449 (1987).
118. D. E. Hughes, D. A. Shonekan and L. Simpson, *Mol. Biochem. Parasitol.* **34**, 155 (1989).
119. G. R. Taylor, P. A. Logaosky, R. K. Storms and R. H. Haynes, *JBC* **222**, 5298 (1987).
120. E. Kenny, T. Atkinson and B. S. Hartley, *Gene* **34**, 335 (1985).
121. D. J. Bzik, W. L. Li, T. Horii and J. Inselburg, *PNAS* **84**, 8360 (1987).
122. S. C. Singer, C. A. Richards, R. Ferone, D. Benedict and P. Ray *J. Bact.* **171**, 1372 (1989).
123. M. Iwakura, M. Kawata, K. Tsuda and T. Tanka, *Gene* **64**, 9 (1988).
124. L. W. Hardy, J. S. Finer-Moore, W. R. Montfort, M. A. Jones, D. V. Santi and R. M. Stroud, *Science* **235**, 448 (1987).
125. A. Lockshin and P. V. Danenberg, *Bchem* **19**, 4244 (1980).
125a. W. R. Monfort, K. M. Perry, E. B. Fauman, J. S. Finer-Moore, G. F. Maley, L. Hardy, F. Maley and R. M. Stroud, *Bchem*, in press (1990).
126. C. A. Lewis, Jr., P. D. Ellis and R. B. Dunlap, *Bchem* **19**, 116 (1980).
127. H. Donato, Jr., J. L. Aull, J. A. Lyon, J. W. Reinsch and R. B. Dunlap, *JBC* **251**, 1303 (1976).
128. D. M. Mittelstaedt and M. I. Schimerlik, *ABB* **245**, 417 (1986).
129. R. K. Sharma and R. L. Kisliuk, *BBRC* **64**, 648 (1975).
130. K. D. Danenberg and P. V. Danenberg, *JBC* **254**, 4345 (1979).
131. K. L. Cipollo and R. B. Dunlap, *BBRC* **81**, 1139 (1978).

132. M. Belfort, G. F. Maley and F. Maley, *ABB* **204,** 340 (1980).

133. D. Rosson, H. B. Otwell and R. B. Dunlap, *BBRC* **97,** 500 (1980).

134. R. P. Leary, N. Beaudette and R. L. Kisliuk, *JBC* **250,** 4864 (1975).

135. J. Galivan, J. Noonan and F. Maley, *AAB* **184,** 336 (1977).

136. H. H. Caron and J. L. Aull, *BBA* **658,** 132 (1981).

137. N. V. Beaudette, N. Langerman and R. L. Kisliuk, *ABB* **200,** 410 (1980).

138. P. G. Plese and R. B. Dunlap, *JBC* **252,** 6139 (1977).

138a. S. Climie and D. V. Santi, *PNAS* **87,** 633 (1990).

139. V. Frasca, L. LaPat-Polasko, G. F. Maley and F. Maley, *in* "Proceedings of the 1988 Miami–Biotechnology Winter Symposium" (K. Brew *et al.*, eds.), p. 149. IRL Press, Baltimore, Maryland, 1988.

140. B. Demple, B. Sedgwick, P. Robins, N. Totty, M. D. Waterfield and T. Lindahl, *PNAS* **82,** 2688 (1985).

141. I. K. Dev, B. B. Yates, J. Leong and W. S. Dallas, *PNAS* **85,** 1472 (1988).

142. I. K. Dev, B. B. Yates, J. Atashi and W. S. Dallas, *JBC* **264,** 19131 (1989).

143. G. F. Maley and F. Maley, *Adv. Enzyme Regul.* **29,** 181 (1989).

144. G. F. Maley, F. Maley and C. M. Baugh, *ABB* **216,** 551 (1982).

145. G. F. Maley and F. Maley, *JBC* **263,** 7620 (1988).

146. F. Maley, L. LaPat-Polasko, V. Fransca and G. F. Maley, *in* "Chemistry and Biology of Pteridines" (S. Ghisla, ed.), in press. de Gruyter, Berlin, 1990.

Stable DNA Loops *in Vivo* and *in Vitro*: Roles in Gene Regulation at a Distance and in Biophysical Characterization of DNA

GREGORY R. BELLOMY† AND
M. THOMAS RECORD, JR.‡

Departments of Biochemistry†‡ and Chemistry‡
University of Wisconsin
Madison, Wisconsin 53706

In 1961, Jacob and Monod proposed the operon model, the paradigmatic model for the regulation of gene expression at the level of transcription initiation, to explain the lactose-dependent expression of the genes involved in lactose metabolism in the bacterium *Escherichia coli* (1, 2). Though this simple, elegant model has served as the paradigm in the study of gene regulation, it is now clear that genetic regulation of this and other operons is more complex than the simple operon model initially proposed. Regulation of bacterial operons often involves multiple proteins binding to multiple sites on the DNA, both

Progress in Nucleic Acid Research
and Molecular Biology, Vol. 39

upstream and downstream from the promoter site at which transcription initiates. Recently, the lactose operon and its component parts have served as one of the primary systems for investigation of the complexities of genetic regulation.

One of the pervasive themes of studies of gene expression in the last decade has been the existence of regulatory DNA sequences that act at great distances (hundreds or even thousands of base-pairs) to affect gene expression. It is important to understand the biophysical basis of this effect and its implications for the physical properties of DNA and DNA-binding proteins *in vivo*. This article surveys the quantitative information available regarding action-at-a-distance in a variety of systems (primarily prokaryotic) in which the formation of stable DNA loops has been proposed as the mechanism of the effect (for other reviews, see 3–7). Our primary focus is on the use of quantitative studies of the length dependence of action-at-a-distance to investigate the physical properties of DNA *in vivo*. In addition, we discuss the biophysical basis of two mechanisms proposed to explain regulatory effects of DNA looping: local concentration (direct) effects and topological (indirect) effects.

I. Historical Perspective

By the mid-1970s, the classical example of operon control by repressor binding (i.e., regulation of the lactose operon by *lac* repressor) was showing signs of additional complexity (cf. 2,7, and references therein). *In vitro* studies of the binding of *lac* repressor to λp*lac* phage DNA and to partial deletions of the *lac* operon showed that a DNA sequence downstream from the transcription start site (within the *lacZ* gene) bound *lac* repressor specifically, albeit with a binding constant one-to-two orders of magnitude less than that of the intact *lac* operon (8). The purpose of this second repressor binding site (O_2), referred to as a "pseudo operator," was unknown. This site was thought to represent an evolutionary relic, or a remnant left by a DNA duplication event. Further study of the *lac* operon control region discovered yet a third repressor binding site (O_3), located upstream from the transcription start site at the end of the *lacI* gene, with an affinity for *lac* repressor less than that of the O_2 pseudo operator (9). Figure 1 and Fig. 2 summarize the locations and sequences of these and other *lac* operator sites. Because the affinity of repressor for the pseudo operators is lower than for the primary operator sequence (O_1), and because the concentration of free *lac* repressor in the cell is low, these sites originally

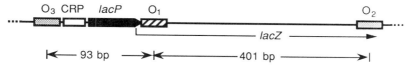

FIG. 1. Schematic of the wild-type *lac* operon. Center-to-center distances between the primary *lac* operator (O_1) (hatched box) and the O_2 and O_3 pseudo operators (shaded boxes) in their natural context are shown. The *lac* promoter (*lac* P) and the binding site for the CRP protein are indicated, as in the *lacZ* transcript (thin arrow).

appeared to be unlikely candidates for integral roles in the mechanism of repression of the *lac* operon, prior to consideration of regulation by action-at-a-distance.

Concurrently, a theoretical and molecular description of facilitated diffusion was being developed (*10–13*) to interpret the observation that the second order rate constant for binding of *lac* repressor to the *lac* operator on λp*lac* DNA exceeds the estimated upper (diffusion) limit for a collisional process in solution by 10- to 100-fold for some choices of ion concentrations (*14–16*). The proposed facilitating mechanism involves an initial step in which repressor binds nonspecifically to the DNA molecule and subsequent transfer steps within the domain of the DNA flexible coil by which repressor locates the operator. Several mechanisms were proposed for these transfer steps. One involves random movement ("sliding") of the repressor along nonspecific DNA sequences until it contacts the operator, at which point the protein adopts its specific operator-binding conformation and forms a stable complex (*10–13*). The sliding mechanism increases the rate of operator binding by reducing the dimensionality of the diffusional process (*17*)

```
                    +1        +8
O₁        ...TGTGTGGAATTGTGAGCGGATAACAATTTCACACA...

Oᶜ8G      ...TGTGTGGAATTGTGgGCGGATAACAATTTCACACA...

O₂        ...caacattAAaTGTGAGCGagTAACAAcccgtcgga...

O₃        ...gaaagcGggcaGTGAGCGcAacgCAATTaatgtga...

Oₛᵧₘ      ...---cTaGAATTGTGAGC-GcTcACAATTctAg---...
```

FIG. 2. Sequences of selected *lac* operators. See text for explanation of operator designations and references. Lower case symbols (agct) represent differences from the sequence of the wild-type primary operator. The transcription start site of the *lacP1* promoter is at +1 (top line). G (at + 11) is the center of partial twofold symmetry. (For O_{sym}, this position is deleted.) Underlined bases (O_1) are those protected from DNase-I cleavage by bound *lac* repressor.

from three-dimensional diffusion in solution to one-dimensional diffusion on the DNA chain.

A second model invokes a transient ring closure event that brings a nonspecifically bound repressor molecule into contact with a distant (generally nonoperator) region of the same flexibly coiling DNA chain, allowing transfer of the bidentate *lac* repressor protein to that region of the DNA (*10, 13*). This direct transfer mechanism for facilitated diffusion is closely related to the DNA looping process that is the subject of this article. The observation that *lac* repressor is able to bind to two DNA molecules simultaneously (e.g., *18–20*) demonstrates the feasibility of this direct transfer mechanism. Direct transfer involves **transient** formation of an unstable ternary complex between one *lac* repressor tetramer and two regions of (generally nonoperator) DNA.

Despite significant differences, the direct transfer model was the conceptual precursor of the DNA looping models proposed subsequently to explain "action-at-a-distance." "Direct transfer" is a kinetic model, in which the transient ternary complex is an unstable intermediate. DNA looping in *lac* systems differs in that it involves formation of a thermodynamically stable complex between repressor and two specific binding sites on DNA. The formation of DNA loops (transient in one case, stable in the other) is the key feature linking the two models. The ability of DNA to form loops arises from the fact that although DNA is locally a stiff polymer it is not infinitely stiff. Consequently there is a reasonable probability that distant regions along the molecular chain may contact one another by looping.

The intrinsic stiffness of DNA is characterized by its persistence length. The persistence length (or alternatively the statistical segment length, which is exactly twice the persistence length) is the fundamental parameter of statistical mechanical theories that predict the probability of cyclization (or loop formation) of linear polymers. For helical DNA in aqueous solution at 0.2 M Na$^+$, the persistence length is approximately 150 bp (*21, 22*). The probability of interaction of two distant sites on an isolated DNA molecule exhibits a relative maximum when they are separated by approximately 3.6 persistence lengths, or approximately 500 bp under standard *in vitro* conditions (cf. Section II).

Action-at-a-distance in gene expression *in vivo* was first observed for enhancer sequences in mammalian viruses, and subsequently in mammalian genomes (cf. *23* and references therein). Enhancers are DNA sequences, located hundreds to thousands of base-pairs from the transcription start-site, that activate transcription as much as 100-fold. They can activate transcription from heterologous promoters (although they may be tissue specific) when present in either orientation, either upstream or downstream, and at distances up to several thousand base-pairs. Enhancer sequences may represent binding sites for specific enhancer-binding proteins that activate transcription by direct protein–protein interaction with the transcription machinery mediated by "looping out" of the intervening DNA (cf. *24*).

The discovery of enhancer activity in eukaryotes was followed by the observation that distant sequences in prokaryotes are involved in modulation of repression of certain operons. A DNA site located 114 bp downstream (center-to-center distance) of the classical *gal* operator appears necessary for normal repression of the *gal* operon of *E. coli* (*25*). A similar situation was observed in the *ara* operon, where a distant site is essential for the normal repression of the *ara*P_{BAD} promoter (*26*). In both cases, the distant sites appear to be brought into close proximity by looping of the intervening DNA, so that the proteins bound at the sites can interact directly (*26, 27*). This represented the beginning of a very active research area in prokaryotic gene expression. Since these initial studies, DNA loop formation has been invoked to explain: (*i*) modulation of repression of transcription in numerous operons and model control systems; (*ii*) activation of site-specific recombination; (*iii*) the control of plasmid copy number; and (*iv*) the activation of transcription of certain genes in enteric bacteria.

This review first summarizes the principles of DNA cyclization theory in order to develop a framework within which to interpret the DNA looping data. A variety of systems in which loop formation appears to play a fundamental role in action-at-a-distance are then surveyed. We summarize the information on the physical properties of DNA *in vivo* obtained by quantitative investigation of the DNA looping process. Finally, we discuss the direct and indirect mechanisms by which loop formation appears to act to modulate gene expression *in vivo*.

II. DNA Cyclization as a Model for Looping

The process of formation of stable DNA loops involves bringing distant segments of DNA into close proximity. This process is in many ways analogous to DNA cyclization, or ring closure. Because DNA cyclization has been so thoroughly investigated, it is logical to draw on this work as a primitive model for the DNA looping process. The theory of DNA cyclization provides the basis for estimates of the physical properties of DNA *in vivo* from quantitative studies of the looping process as a function of the contour length of the loop (cf. Section IV).

Jacobson and Stockmayer (28) applied random chain statistics to describe the probability of cyclization of chain polymers with reactive termini as a function of chain length. The Jacobson–Stockmayer factor, or j-factor, is the effective local concentration of one end of a polymer molecule in the vicinity of the other. In a polymerization reaction, the j-factor is equal to the concentration of free monomer at which the rate of addition of monomers to the end of the chain is equal to the rate of unimolecular cyclization.

Several refinements of the original theory and its application to DNA led to the Shimada–Yamakawa theory of the twisted wormlike chain (29). This theory treats DNA as a series of straight segments in the limit of infinitesimal segment length, so as to approximate a uniformly deformable yet stiff chain. The theory predicts a maximum in the cyclization probability as a function of polymer chain length. For sufficiently long DNA molecules (longer than approximately four persistence lengths), the probability of cyclization decreases with increasing chain length due to the entropic cost of constraining the DNA chain to assume a configuration with the ends in close proximity to one another, rather than the myriad of other configurations available to it. As the chain gets longer, the total number of possible configurations increases much more rapidly than the number compatible with cyclization, resulting in a net increase in the entropic barrier to cyclization. For long DNA chains the j-factor is proportional to $N^{-3/2}$, where N is the length of the polymer chain (28). On the other hand, DNA molecules shorter than a few persistence lengths resist cyclization because the DNA is too stiff to bend in a circular trajectory. These two competing factors combine to give rise to an optimal length for cyclization of approximately 3.6 persistence lengths (29).

In addition to the requirement for localization of the two ends of a DNA molecule in the same volume element, the proper torsional alignment of the chain termini is required for ligation of the DNA strands. This gives rise to an oscillatory pattern of increased and decreased cyclization probability as the molecular length is increased in increments of single base-pairs (fractions of a helical repeat). The period of the oscillation reflects the helical repeat of the DNA, since addition of integral multiples of the helical repeat gives molecules with identical torsional alignments. For a specified loop size, the amplitude of the oscillation reflects the torsional rigidity of the DNA undergoing cyclization. The effect of the requirement for torsional alignment is most important for shorter molecules where the twisting necessary to overcome improper torsional alignment is distributed over the least DNA. Hence the amplitude decreases with increasing loop size. In summary, study of the cyclization process as a function of molecular length yields quantitative information regarding the persistence length, torsional rigidity, and helical repeat of DNA in solution.

Investigation of the probability of cyclization of the complementary single-stranded chain termini of phage λ DNA demonstrated the applicability of the Jacobson–Stockmayer theory to the DNA flexible coil in solution (30). Subsequent investigation of the length dependence of the probability of cyclization demonstrated agreement with the theoretical prediction (j proportional to $N^{-3/2}$) for molecules longer than approximately 1000 bp, whereas two shorter fragments cyclized less efficiently (31). With the advent of facile DNA manipulation by molecular cloning techniques, it became possible to study the cyclization process in more detail using DNA molecules of defined length. A series of "sticky-ended" restriction fragments between 100 and 1000 bp in length (with some fragments differing in length by only a few base-pairs) were used in ligation reactions to evaluate the cyclization probability as a function of length and to evaluate the DNA length corresponding to maximal cyclization probability (32, 33). Figure 3A (33) shows that this optimal length is approximately 500 bp for DNA *in vitro*. Quantitative analysis of these data yields a persistence length of approximately 140 bp for DNA *in vitro* (29). This value for the persistence length is in good agreement with values determined by other methods (21, 22). Figure 4 is a schematic illustration of analogous process of DNA loop formation for various lengths of DNA between the interacting sites.

Superimposed on the envelope of cyclization probabilities as a function of DNA length is a periodic oscillation resulting from the requirement for torsional alignment of the chain ends. This was demonstrated using a series of short DNA molecules differing by fractions of a helical repeat. Figure 3B shows that the probability of cyclization is a periodic function of length, with a period equal to the DNA helical repeat. This arises from the requirement for covalent joining of the overlapping "sticky ends" of restriction fragments. From the periodic variation in cyclization probability as a function of length, values of the DNA helical repeat of 10.54 bp (34) and 10.45 bp (35) were obtained. These values are very similar to those determined using the "Gaussian center" and "band shift" methods (36, 37).

In addition to the persistence length and helical repeat, the torsional rigidity constant C of the DNA is obtained by analysis of the amplitude of the periodic oscillation in the cyclization probability. For example, the ratio of the maximum to the minimum cyclization probabilities within a period (for molecules differing in length by one helical

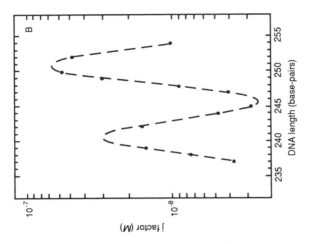

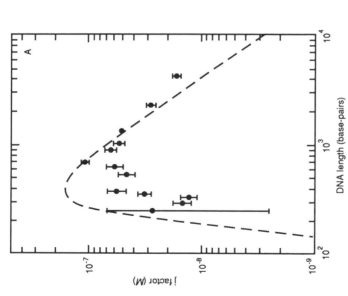

FIG. 3. Probability of DNA cyclization *in vitro* as a function of molecular length. (A) Log–log plots of experimental and theoretical cyclization probabilities of DNA fragments [expressed as local molar concentrations (j) of one chain terminus in the vicinity of the other] as a function of contour length (bp). The dashed theoretical curve neglects the requirement for torsional alignment, and demonstrates a relative maximum in j at a contour length of ~3.6 persistence lengths. At the maximum, the local concentration (j) is ~0.15 μM for the solution conditions investigated. (B) Log plot of experimental cyclization probabilities j of a series of DNA fragment length (bp), demonstrating the consequence of the requirement for proper torsional alignment of the chain termini for ligation. The dashed theoretical curve is the fit to a harmonic twisting potential with a torsional force constant $C = 2.4 \times 10^{-19}$ erg cm (33). [From Shore and Baldwin (33).]

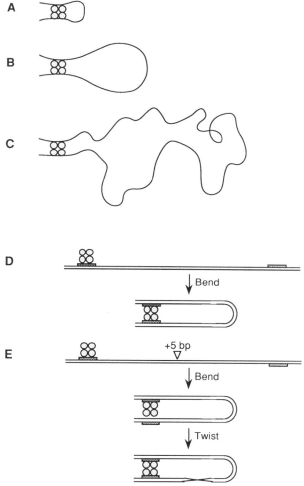

FIG. 4. (A–C) Effect of loop size (neglecting requirement for torsional alignment). (A) For very short distances between sites, the difficulty in bending the rigid DNA helix is the primary consideration limiting loop formation. (B) For intermediate intersite distances (approximately 500 bp for DNA cyclization *in vitro*) loop formation is optimal. (C) For large intersite distances, the entropic cost of bringing the sites on the chain molecule together increases with increasing intersite distance, reducing the probability of loop formation. (D–E) Effect of requirement for torsional alignment. An additional unfavorable step, twisting, is required for loop formation when DNA sites are not optimally torsionally aligned. The operators are shown as boxes and the looping protein as a tetramer. For this illustration, it is assumed that both DNA sites must be on the same helical "face" for optimal torsional alignment. (D) DNA sites that lie on the same face of the DNA helix need only bend in order to form a loop. (E) DNA sites that are initially out of phase (here illustrated for +5 bp) must undergo an unfavorable twisting process prior to loop closure.

turn) may be interpreted as the equilibrium constant for the process of insertion of one half-helical turn of twist prior to cyclization. For molecules in the 240-bp size range, this ratio is approximately 20. From these data (Fig. 3B), a torsional rigidity constant of $C = 2.4 \times 10^{-19}$ erg-cm is obtained for DNA involved in cyclization *in vitro (33)*. This value is within the range of values determined by other methods (*38–40*).

III. Survey of Some Regulatory Systems in Which Stable DNA Loops Are Implicated in Action-at-a-Distance

A. Prokaryotic Transcription Initiation

1. THE *lac* OPERON

a. Introduction. The *lac* operon is one of the most extensively studied systems of genetic regulation. Action-at-a-distance has been examined both in the context of the wild-type *lac* operon and in synthetic constructs involving *lac* operators. The *lac* operon consists of three genes involved in lactose metabolism that are repressed by the *lac* repressor–operator interaction and activated by the cyclic AMP receptor protein (CRP) (cf. Fig. 1). The operator overlaps the start-site of transcription, but more than competitive binding (steric occlusion) of *lac* repressor and RNA polymerase at the promoter may be involved in repression of transcription initiation (*41–43*). [One recent study proposes that *lac* repressor may stimulate the initial binding of RNA polymerase, though it represses transcription initiation by interfering with the subsequent isomerization of the polymerase into a transcriptionally competent open complex (*43*).] The repressor–operator interaction behaves as if under thermodynamic control *in vivo*, whereby the degree of repression correlates with the equilibrium level of occupancy of the primary operator (O_1) (*10*). Any increase in the extent of binding of repressor at O_1 resulting from the presence of a distant operator should cause an increase in the extent of repression.

b. The lac Repressor Tetramer Contains Two DNA-Binding Sites. The potential of *lac* repressor to bind simultaneously to two DNA sites has been recognized since the initial structural work by Steitz *et al.* (44). Electron microscopy and powder diffraction analysis of microcrystals of *lac* repressor indicate that the protein is a somewhat elongated plane rectangular tetramer with three twofold axes (D_2 symmetry). Given the partial twofold symmetry of the operator sequence, this suggests that the tetramer has two DNA binding sites (*44*). Experiments with fusion proteins consisting of the amino-terminal portions of the *lac* repressor protein fused to β-galactosidase are consistent with this proposal, and indicate that only two repressor subunits are necessary to interact with operator DNA (*18, 45, 46*). (For reviews of the properties of *lac* repressor, see *2, 10, 47–50*.)

Investigation of the binding of small synthetic DNA fragments containing the *lac* operator sequence to *lac* repressor demonstrates the existence of complexes with two operator fragments bound per tetramer (*19, 20*). These studies were subsequently extended to show that *lac* repressor tetramers can simultaneously interact with two large DNA molecules containing *lac* operator sites (*51*). The weight of experimental evidence indicates that *lac* repressor exists in solution as a stable tetramer at or above picomolar concentrations , although extrapolation of pressure-induced dissociation data to one atmosphere suggests that the tetramer may be unstable at subnanomolar concentrations (*52*).

c. Evidence for Looping in lac Constructs. Recombinant DNA technoloy was used to clone *lac* operators at various locations in other operons. Such experiments led to the discovery that *lac* operators can inhibit transcription even when removed from the immediate vicinity of the transcription start site. *Lac* operators cloned upstream and downstream from the *trp* promoter of *E. coli* give rise to a modulation of *trp* promoter activity by *lac* repressor (*53*). Repression was more efficient when both upstream and downstream *lac* operators were present. These experiments were performed to reproduce with *lac* operators the mode of repression reported for the *gal* operon (*25*), where two operators, neither of which overlaps the transcription start site, are responsible for repression.

Analogous experiments involving a *lac* promoter without a primary operator also showed that the combination of an upstream and downstream operator was sufficient for repression (*54*) (Fig. 5). Direct contact with the start site of transcription therefore is not essential for repression by *lac* repressor. Another role of looping, perhaps similar to

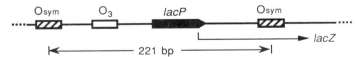

FIG. 5. An artifical *lac* control system without a primary control site (*54*). The O_{sym} sites (hatched boxes) are strong-binding *lac* operator variants (cf. Fig. 2). The black box represents the wild-type *lac* promoter, and the white box is the O_3 pseudo operator. Not shown is the *lac* O_2 pseudo operator located 402 bp downstream from the transcription start site.

that utilized in the *gal* system (see Section III,A,7 below), appears to be involved.

In a related experiment, *lac* operators were cloned upstream and downstream from two *res* sites, the DNA sequence elements involved in the recombination reaction catalyzed by Tn3 resolvase (55). Recombination was inhibited in the pressure of *lac* repressor only when two operators flanked one of the *res* sites. *Lac* repressor bound to a single operator between the *res* sites did not inhibit recombination, suggesting that a *lac* repressor-mediated loop caused the topological isolation of one of the *res* sites, and in this way inhibited recombination (55).

d. Quantitative Studies of Looping in lac Constructs. Results obtained from *in vitro* studies of the thermodynamics of binding of *lac* repressor to isolated constitutive operator mutants (i.e., removed from the context of the *lac* operon) indicate the importance of action-at-a-distance in the *lac* operon (56). Binding constants for certain isolated O^c mutant sites were approximately 10^{-3} that of O_1 (56). These reductions in affinity were much larger than those predicted from the decrease in repression *in vivo* resulting from the introduction of these mutations at the primary (O_1) operator site in the *lac* operon (57).

One possible explanation was that the *lac* pseudo-operators were masking the effect of the O^c mutations through cooperative interactions like those observed between operator sites in the *gal* and *ara* operons (see below). To test this hypothesis, a wild-type primary operator was placed at various locations upstream from a *lac* control element containing a constitutive operator mutation (O^c8G) (see Fig. 2). The presence of the upstream operator significantly increased repression of the regulated gene *in vivo*. The closest placement of the upstream operator to the constitutive operator (118 bp center-to-center distance) exhibited the smallest increment in repression (twofold). Operators located at greater distances upstream (185 and 283 bp) increased repression about 40-fold (58).

Two possible explanations for the reduced effect of the upstream site at the smaller interoperator distance were proposed, both involving looping. Either the DNA is too stiff to bend laterally into such a tight turn (cf. Fig. 4), or an alteration of the relative orientation of operators on the DNA makes looping unfavorable (Figure 3B). Of course, a combination of the two effects is also possible. The first possibility involves the lateral flexibility of DNA while the second involves the torsional flexibility. Both possible explanations have ample precedent in DNA cyclization experiments (33–35), as discussed previously and shown in Fig. 3.

In order to determine which of the two explanations is correct, a series of DNA molecules was constructed differing in interoperator distance by fractions of a helical turn, in order to observe the helical periodicity of repression, if any. The results indicate that it is primarily the dependence on proper torsional alignment that gives rise to the small increment in repression for the most proximal (118 bp) upstream operator (59, 60) (Fig. 6).

The ability of *lac* repressor to form stable loops in DNA molecules containing two strong binding operators *in vitro* has been investigated (61). In these experiments "symmetric" *lac* operator sequences (62, 63) (cf. Fig. 2) were cloned into two locations in a plasmid. The distance between the two operators was varied in increments of one or more

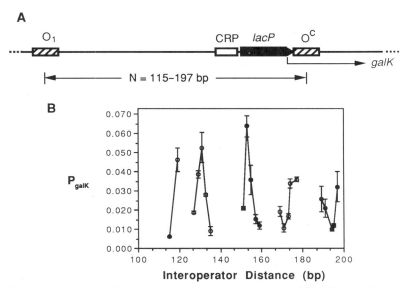

FIG. 6. Action-at-a-distance in a *lac*-based construct (59, 60). (A) Schematic representation of the artificial *lac* control system in which galactokinase (galK) expression is monitored as a function of the distance (N) between an upstream strong-binding (O_1) operator and a weak-binding (O^c8G) operator at the start-site for transcription of the galK gene. (N = 115, 119, 127, 129, 131, 133, 135, 151, 153, 155, 157, 159, 169, 171, 173, 174, 177, 189, 191, 194, 195, and 197). (B) Variation in fraction of maximal expression of galK (P_{galK}) with interoperator distance (N). Error bars represent the range or standard deviation of two or more determinations. The P value is defined as the ratio of galK activity in the repressed state to that in the induced state. Lines are drawn to illustrate the trends within each series of points. Analysis of the data yields a periodicity of 11.4–11.6 bp per turn, assumed to be the local helical repeat of this region of supercoiled plasmid DNA *in vivo*.

base-pairs to create a series of molecules with interoperator distance between 153 and 168 bp. Extensive evidence was obtained that *lac* repressor forms looped complexes with these pairs of *lac* operators *in vitro*, including visualization of looped structures by electron microscopy, observation of periodic variation of looping with increased interoperator distance by gel-shift binding assays, and observation of increased sensitivity to DNase I of the DNA between the operators involved in loop formation (*61*).

An altered pattern of DNase sensitivity of tightly looped DNA has also been observed in other systems (*64, 65*), and represents strong evidence (as does the helical periodicity) for loop formation. Gel-shift binding assays demonstrate that suboptimal torsional alignment prevents formation of the looped complex. Although the data are too tightly clustered to provide a precise value for the DNA helical repeat (without making an arbitrary assumption about the orientation of the two sites in the looped complex), they are consistent with a helical repeat of 10.5 bp per turn, as expected for linear DNA fragments *in vitro*.

In related work, operators were cloned at various distances from the primary operator to determine the dependence of complex stability on interoperator distance *in vitro* (*66*). Loop formation with linear DNA *in vitro* was more favorable for a 300 bp separation than for distances of 4100 or 99 bp (*66, 67*). However, on supercoiled DNA, large changes in the contour distance between the operators had little effect on looping *in vitro* (*67, 68*). A similar result was obtained in a study of loop formation between *lac* operators on small DNA circles, where increasing supercoiling resulted in a decreased dependence on interoperator distance (*69*).

e. Evidence for a Role of Looping in the Wild-type lac *Operon: Contributions of O_2 and O_3.* With the large amount of evidence suggesting that loop formation can occur between *lac* operators both *in vitro* and *in vivo*, the question naturally arises as to whether or not loop formation plays any functional role in the natural context of the *lac* operon *in vivo*. Initial filter-binding studies of repressor binding to λ p*lac* DNA deleted for either the O_2 or O_3 site showed little change in the stability of the repressor–operator complex, suggesting no functional role for the sites (*70*). Subsequent experiments using the same technique detected a fourfold increase in stability of repressor–operator complexes when both pseudo-operators were present (*51*). It was proposed that the O_2 pseudo-operator makes contact (via DNA loop formation) with a *lac* repressor tetramer bound at the primary operator to form a ternary complex of increased stability. On a supercoiled molecule ($\sigma = -0.06$) the presence of the O_2 site increased the stability of the repressor-operator complex more than 100-fold (71).

Experiments *in vivo* demonstrated that an isolated primary (O_1) operator gave less effective repression than the wild-type *lac* operon, thereby indicating a role for the naturally occurring pseudo operators (O_2, O_3) (72). To examine the role of the pseudo operators directly, site-directed mutagenesis was used to introduce multiple base-changes in the *lac* O_2 operator (73). The modified O_2 sequence, though incapable of repressor binding, utilized the degeneracies of the genetic code to retain the wild-type amino-acid sequence of β-galacto-sidase. Specific destruction of the O_2 site increased expression by a factor of five relative to the wild-type operon.

Two mechanisms of this effect of the O_2 operator were possible. Either the O_2 operator blocked transcription elongation and caused premature termination, and/or it acted via a looping mechanism to enhance occupancy of the primary site.

Subsequent experiments suggested that both effects might be in-volved (74). *In vivo* DMS footprinting demonstrated that the O_1 and O_2 operators each increased the extent of binding of repressor to the other, indicating that a long distance cooperative interaction might be occur-ring. A small but measurable effect on transcription elongation was also observed. Inactivation of O_2 increased expression by approxi-mately 50% over the basal level of the wild-type operon (74). Though the magnitude of the effect remains to be resolved, the O_2 operator appears to play a role in regression of the wild type *lac* operon, both by looping and by blocking transcription elongation.

The *lac* O_3 operator enhances binding to the O_1 operator *in vitro* only on supercoiled DNA (65). These experiments demonstrated that it was possible to form loops *in vitro* between the very weak O_3 and O_1 operators at a distance of only 93 bp (the natural O_3 to O_1 spacing), but that loop formation by the O_3 operator must be studied in a sequence background lacking the stronger O_2 site. The looped DNA *in vitro* exhibited a DNase-hypersensitive region, interpreted to mean that the DNA was "kinked" in the loop (65). This work also demonstrated a stoichiometry of one bridging repressor tetramer per looped complex, eliminating the possibility that tetramers bound at the individual oper-ators might interact via tetramer–tetramer contacts.

f. Summary. The *lac* repressor forms loops with *lac* operator sites both *in vitro* and *in vivo*. Methods used to demonstrate loop formation include direct electron-microscope visualization, altered nuclease sensitivity of DNA involved in loops, and a strong dependence of activity on the relative torsional phasing of operators both *in vitro* and *in vivo.* Studies of the natural *lac* operon show that loop formation is probably involved in modulation of *lac* expression, although the magnitude of the effect appears to be less than the effect of looping in many of the other systems described below.

2. THE *ara* OPERON

The arabinose operon of *E. coli* is also a well-studied example of loop formation as a mechanism in the regulation of gene expression. The *ara* operon consists of three genes involved in the utilization of arabinose, transcribed from the P_{BAD} promoter. This promoter is under both positive *and* negative control by the product of the *araC* gene, which is transcribed divergently from the *ara*P_C promoter located 120 bp upstream from the P_{BAD} transcription start site. In the course of studying deletion mutants to define the sequence elements necessary for proper regulation of the *ara*P_{BAD} promoter, it was found that a DNA site located 280 bp upstream from the start point of transcription (*ara*O_2) is important for repression of the P_{BAD} promoter by *araC* (26) (see Fig. 7).

Dimethyl sulfate protection studies on DNA in *E. coli* cells verified that the operators proposed to be involved in loop formation do in fact interact cooperatively *in vivo* (75). Insertion or deletion of small segments of DNA between O_2 and the P_{BAD} promoter gave rise to a cyclical increase and decrease in repression by AraC *in vivo* with a period consistent with the helical repeat of DNA, implying that the relative positions of the sites on the surface of the DNA are critical for activity. The dependence on proper torsional alignment and the ability to act at great distances support the proposal (26) that DNA loop formation is involved in the process. The proposed loop is between the *ara*O_2 and *ara*I operators, located 211 bp apart (76). The periodic modulating effect as a function of intersite distance (i.e., the requirement for proper torsional alignment) first observed in this system is a necessary (but not absolutely sufficient) condition for a mechanism

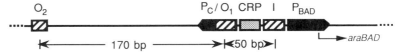

FIG. 7. The *ara* operon. The three arabinose operators are represented by hatched boxes, the divergent P_{BAD} and P_C promoters by black boxes, and the binding site for the CRP protein by the shaded box. Center-to-center distances are shown. The *araBAD* transcript is represented by a thin arrow. The *araC* transcript (not shown) proceeds leftward from the P_C promoter.

involving DNA loop formation, and has since been observed in several other systems, as reviewed in this section. Investigation of a large number of constructs *in vivo* demonstrated a modulatory effect of the upstream site at distances up to 500 bp between operators, and indicated that there is no lower limit to loop size (77). This was a surprising result given the strong decrease in the envelope of DNA cyclization probabilities of short lengths, especially below 200 bp (see Fig. 3). However the *ara* looping data indicated that the envelope of loop formation probabilities was length-invariant from 400 bp down to 36 bp. The periodicity of modulation of repression by the upstream site yields a helical repeat of this segment of plasmid DNA *in vivo* of approximately 11.1 bp per turn (discussed in Section IV).

Studies of transcription from P_{BAD} *in vitro* confirmed the looping mechanism proposed on the basis of the *in vivo* data (78). DNA supercoiling was found to be essential to the cooperative interaction between $araO_2$ and $araI$, since linearization of plasmid DNA was functionally equivalent to deletion of the $araO_2$ site (78). The requirement for supercoiling *in vitro* is a feature common to many DNA looping systems. One role of CRP protein in the regulation of the P_{BAD} promoter may be to disrupt the repression loop formed between the $araO_2$ and $araI$ sites (78). This suggestion is particularly interesting given that CRP–cAMP bends DNA when bound to its specific site (79). If the bend is oriented in the opposite direction from that needed for loop formation, loop formation probably would be disrupted by CRP–cAMP binding (see also Section V,C).

Rather than increasing the occupancy at the primary regulatory site ($araI$ in this case), loop formation instead causes a change to an active conformation of the protein already bound to its primary regulatory site even in the absence of loop formation (75, 78; see also Section III,A,4). Additional complexity arises from the observation that the $araO_1$ site, located near the $araP_C$ promoter, is also required for appropriate regulation of the arabinose operon, and that multiple competing looped structures (involving pairwise binding of AraC protein at all three sites) may exist (80, 81). Multiple competing looped structures are also possible in the *lac* (cf. Section III,A,1) and *deo* (cf. Section III,A,3) operons.

3. THE *deo* OPERON

The *deoCABD* operon encodes the genes for ribo- and deoxyribonucleoside catabolism (Fig. 8). Transcription is driven by two promoters, P_1 and P_2, separated by 599 bp. The P_2 promoter is under the control of both the *cytR* and *deoR* gene products, whereas the P_1 promoter is

Fig. 8. The *deo* operon. The solid boxes represent promoters, the shaded boxes the binding sites for CRP, and the hatched boxes the *deo* operators. Center-to-center distances between the operators are shown. The two transcripts of the *deoCABD* genes are represented by thin arrows.

regulated only by *deoR*. The DeoR protein binds to three sites, O_2 (located at the *deoP$_2$* start site,), O_1 (located at the *deoP$_1$* start site, 599 bp upstream), and O_E (located 878 bp upstream from *deoP$_2$*). The O_1 and O_2 sites are both necessary for proper DeoR-mediated repression (82, 83). The O_E site increases the extent of repression by a factor of three-to-four when present at its natural location (83).

Of particular importance is the observation that the effect of the O_2 site can be mimicked *in vivo* by supplying extra DeoR protein in *trans* (82). The same effect is seen in the case of the NR_I regulation of the *gln* operon (Section III,A,4), where adding excess protein *in vitro* can duplicate the effect of an upstream NR_I binding site (84). These results have significant implications for the mechanism of upstream activation in this system. They indicate that the primary role of the distant site is to increase the local concentration of the regulatory protein. If the mechanism of action required loop formation per se (e.g., topological constraints or alteration of the DNA structure due to loop formation), proper regulation would be unlikely in the absence of the distant site (see Section V).

Experiments where the spacing between the DeoR binding sites was varied showed that looping is possible when sites were separated by as few as 60 bp or as many as 5000 bp of intervening DNA (85). This is again similar to the distances reported for the *gln* operon (Section III,A,4), and different from results obtained with some other systems. The effectiveness of the distant site in repression decreased with increasing spacer length (e.g., from a 20-fold increase in repression at 1245 bp to a fivefold increase at 4000 bp), in approximate agreement with expectations based on the DNA cyclization model, suggesting to the authors that DNA loop formation was taking place.

In the course of isolation of DeoR, it was found that the protein associates to the level of octamers, in contrast to other DNA binding proteins which are typically dimers or tetramers (86). This suggests that the protein might be capable of binding to three or four operator sites simultaneously. Subsequently, electron microscopy showed that DNA molecules containing all three natural operator sites can form "double-loop" structures in which a single DeoR octamer simultaneously occupies all three operators (87).

4. REGULATION OF THE *glnALG* AND *nifLA* OPERONS BY THE NR_I PROTEIN

The *glnALG* operon of *E. coli* regulates the production of enzymes involved in nitrogen metabolism. The NR_I protein (also referred to as the NtrC protein) is a transcriptional activator that, when phosphorylated, binds to two sites 110 and 140 bp upstream from the promoter [and possibly a third site (88)] and enhances transcription by $E\sigma^{54}$ RNA polymerase of the *glnA* gene (the structural gene for glutamine synthetase) from the *glnA* P_2 promoter (cf. Fig. 9). The mechanism of this enhancement of transcription is apparently through facilitation of the isomerization of the initial RNA polymerase–promoter closed complex to the open complex, which is then competent for transcription initiation (84, 89).

Experiments on the binding of the proteins involved in *glnA* transcription *in vivo* show that $E\sigma^{54}$ is bound to the promoter at all times, even in the absence of NR_I, but that open complex formation requires activation by NR_I (88). The role of the distant site is to affect the activity of the bound protein, rather than to affect its extent of binding (84, 88). This is similar to the *ara* system, where AraC protein bound at the *araI* site is activated by loop formation, but is bound to the site regardless of looping (78; see also Section III,A,2).

In the *gln* system, the upstream site is involved in activation rather than repression of transcription. The mechanism of activation involves formation of a "heterotypic" loop, i.e., a loop involving contacts between two different proteins bound at the two sites. Action-at-a-distance in the *lac, ara,* and *deo* operons of *E. coli* involves formation of "homotypic" loops where a single protein (or oligomer thereof) interacts with the two sites at once. Transcriptional activation by the NR_I protein is possible even when the binding site is located over 1000 bp

FIG. 9. The *glnA* operon. Approximate locations (in bp) of the three NR_I (NtrC) binding sites utilized *in vivo* (88) are shown relative to the start site of transcription. The thin arrow represents the *glnA* transcript origination from the *gln* P_2 promoter.

either upstream or downstream from the promoter (90). These characteristics led to the designation of the NR_I system as a "bacterial enhancer".

In addition, NR_I is capable of activating transcription even in the absence of an upstream DNA binding site, as long as it is supplied at concentration four- to fivefold higher than that required in the case when the upstream site is present (84). This result indicates that loop formation per se is not essential for NR_I-dependent activation, and that the protein is capable of activating transcription both in *trans* (by a bimolecular binding process) and in *cis* (by a unimolecular looping process involving its distant binding site). This situation is similar to that seen for the DeoR-mediated repression of the *deoCABD* operon (Section III,A,3), where excess protein supplied in *trans* is sufficient to mimic the effect of a protein binding site in *cis*.

The NR_I protein is also involved in the regulation of transcription of the *nifLA* operon of *Klebsiella pneumoniae*. The products of the *nifLA* operon are necessary for the expression of several other nitrogen fixation operons. In this system, an upstream binding site in *cis* (located at approximately −150 relative to the start site of transcription) reduces the concentration of NR_I necessary for full transcriptional activity of the *nifL* promoter (91), as observed with the *deo* and *gln* operons discussed above. The necessity of proper torsional alignment of the upstream site relative to the promoter has been demonstrated in this system both *in vitro* and *in vivo* by insertion of 5, 11, 15, and 21 bp (92).

5. REGULATION OF THE *nifHDKY* OPERON BY THE NifA PROTEIN

In a system very closely related to the NR_I system previously discussed, the NifA protein of enteric bacterium *K. pneumoniae* activates transcription from the *nifH* promoter from its binding site at −136 relative to the start site of transcription (93–95). As with NR_I, activation by NifA takes place only at promoters transcribed by RNA polymerase holoenzyme containing the nitrogen gene sigma factor (σ^{54}), the product of the *rpoN* (*ntrA*) gene. The NifA protein, functionally and evolutionarily related to NR_I, can activate transcription *in vivo* when it is located in either orientation and at distances as great as 2000 bp upstream from the promoter, just like the NR_I protein (94). Investigation of constructs differing by small insertions (i.e., +5, +11, +15, and +21 bp) indicates that proper torsional alignment of the upstream NifA binding site (relative to the promoter) is essential for activity (95) and, therefore, that looping is the likely mechanism of action at a distance.

Deletions that bring the upstream site closer than the −90 position result in inactivity (95). To date, this appears to be the clearest example of a requirement for an intersite distance in excess of some minimum value, independent of effects of helical phasing. Since loop formation is thought to involve contact between the NifA transcriptional activator protein and RNA polymerase bound at the promoter, it is a heterotypic looping system, like the NR_I system discussed previously.

The upstream site binds the activator protein only when the corresponding promoter sequence is present in *cis (95)*, thereby demonstrating positive cooperativity between the binding of the activating protein to its specific site and the binding of $E\sigma^{54}$ RNA polymerase to the promoter. Since a binding site for IHF occurs between the *nifHDK* promoter and the upstream NifA binding site (96), it has been proposed that DNA bending caused by IHF bound to its site facilitates loop formation in this system, much as it appears to facilitate loop formation in several other systems (see Section V,C).

6. LAMBDA REPRESSOR

Although λ repressor is not thought to act at a distance in its natural context, this system has been used to create artificial constructs to study the DNA looping process *in vitro (64)*. The normal mode of action of λ repressor is to bind to three adjacent sites on a region of the phage λ genome between the P_R and P_{RM} promoters. When bound at these sites the protein activates its own synthesis from the P_{RM} promoter and inhibits transcription from the P_R promoter. Interactions of the λ repressor with two adjacent sites is cooperative, as a result of favorable protein–protein contacts. When two λ operators are separated by a distance too great to allow direct interaction as it normally occurs, contact between the bound λ repressor proteins is made by forming a loop in the intervening DNA. The strongest binding constructs (as measured by DNase I protection) were those with interoperator distances corresponding to integral multiples of the normal helical repeat of linear B-DNA *in vitro* (over the range 48–67 bp), suggesting that both operators must reside on the same face of the DNA helix to obtain high-affinity binding on linear DNA (64).

Additional evidence for looping in this system was provided by the discovery of alternating DNase-hypersensitive and DNase-resistant sites in the complexed (looped) DNA, with a period approximately that of the DNA helical repeat. This behavior is analogous to that observed in DNase cleavage of DNA cyclized into short rings, where the phenomenon is explained by proposing that helical grooves located on the inside surface of the loop are sterically occluded and that grooves on the outside are sites of enhanced DNase I cleavage (97). Yet another indication that the torsional alignment of the sites is the crucial factor came in an experiment where a short single-stranded "gap" was introduced between the operators (64, 98). The presence of this gap allowed molecules with any interoperator separation to form loops, and eliminated the pattern of DNase I hypersensitivity. It was proposed that the gap acts as a "swivel" to permit alignment of the two operators, and as a "kink" where bending of the looped DNA occurs without the distortion that led to the DNase I hypersensitivity (64). All of these results are consistent with the looping mechanism; electron-microscope visualization of looped complexes provided direct evidence for looping (98).

7. THE *gal* OPERON

Genetic analysis of the galactose operon of *E. coli* formed the basis for one of the first proposals for looping in a prokaryotic system. The *gal* operon consists of three genes involved in the catabolism of galactose. These genes are under the control of the galactose repressor protein (the product of the *galR* gene). The *gal* repressor protein binds to an operator site located about 60 bp upstream of the start point of transcription (known as O_E, or equivalently, O_1). However, galactose-constitutive mutations were isolated that mapped within the coding region of the first structural gene of the operon (*galE*), rather than at the classical gal operator locus (25). Investigation of the *gal* repressor binding ability of plasmid constructs *in vivo* and *in vitro* also indicated the importance of this second operator site, referred to as O_I (or equivalently, O_2) (99).

The O_E and O_I operators, which bracket the transcription start-site (Fig. 10), exhibit similar affinities for *gal* repressor (98). Binding studies *in vitro* indicated that the two sites bind *gal* repressor independently, and experiments *in vivo* provided no evidence for a cooperative interaction, since the effects of the two sites (measured by operator

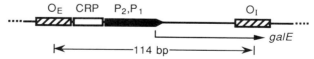

FIG. 10. The *gal* operon. Hatched boxes represent the O_E (O_1) and O_I (O_2) operators. The black box represents the two overlapping *gal* promoters, and the white box the binding site for CRP. The center-to-center distance between the operators is shown. The thin arrow represents the *galE* transcript.

titration) were approximately additive (99). Despite the apparent lack of cooperativity, DNA loop formation was proposed as a possible mechanism to utilize both operators to prevent transcription of the *gal* genes. In the *gal* system, neither operator site directly overlaps the promoter(s), making it unlikely that direct steric occlusion is the mechanism of repression. DNA looping may result in repression because the loop containing the promoter is refractory to transcription by RNA polymerase (27). The lack of a cooperative interaction between the two sites *in vitro* may reflect the importance of differences in helical repeat and/or lateral stiffness *in vivo* and *in vitro* (cf. Section IV).

Two subsequent experiments addressing the question of whether or not loop formation is involved in *gal* repression gave contradictory answers. Independent examination of transcription from both of the two overlapping *gal* promoters showed that only the upstream operator is necessary for full repression of the P_1 promoter. In contrast, the P_2 promoter required both operators for full repression. Given the lack of cooperativity and of direct evidence of obligatory interaction between repressors bound to the two operators, it was concluded that a looping mechanism is not necessarily involved (100). In another study, *gal* operators were replaced, one at a time, with *lac* operators, and the levels of repression *in vivo* resulting from the various combinations of operators and repressor proteins were assessed. Efficient repression was maintained when homologous operators were present, but heterologous operators were less effective at repression (101).

In other words, mere occupancy of both sites by different proteins is not sufficient for full repression. Specific interaction between the distant bound proteins is apparently required, which is strong evidence for looping. Further experiments will be required to resolve these apparently conflicting results regarding the role of loop formation in control of the *gal* operon.

8. THE *nar* OPERON

The *nar* operon of *E. coli* encodes the genes for nitrate reductase. The *fnr* gene of the operon is under the control of the NarL protein, which activates transcription in the presence of nitrate. A NarL binding site located at approximately −200 relative to the start site of transcription is essential for full transcriptional activation by nitrate (102). It is proposed that NarL protein bound at the −200 site interacts with another molecule of NarL bound at a site located at −55, resulting in formation of a 145-bp DNA loop. Small insertions and deletions between the sites result in periodic loss and recovery of transcriptional enhancement activity *in vivo* (with an amplitude corresponding to at least an eightfold variation), indicating that looping is the probable mechanism.

Since insertions or deletions of 20 bp abolish the effect, it was inferred that changes in intersite distance of two helical turns are not tolerated in this system (102). However, this conclusion was based on the assumption that the helical repeat of DNA on a supercoiled plasmid *in vivo* is approximately 10 bp per turn, which need not be the case. Looping experiments *in vivo* in two other systems indicate helical repeats in excess of 11 bp per turn (60, 77; cf. Section IV). Consequently the insertion or deletion of 20 bp may not represent a change of an integral number of helical turns in this system. If torsional constraints are important, proper allowance for this variable may permit sites to be moved closer together or farther apart without degradation of the ability to interact via looping.

9. THE *nrd* OPERON

The *nrd* operon of *E. coli* encodes the genes for ribonucleotide reductase; the operon is induced by thymine starvation. Two DNA regions, one upstream and one downstream from the promoter, are necessary for negative regulation of the *nrdA* gene, the first gene of the operon (103). Since the effects of mutations in the two sites are not simply additive, it is proposed that they interact cooperatively through formation of a 220-bp DNA loop. Though other interpretations are possible, the facts that neither site is in proximity to the promoter and yet both appear to be involved in repression of transcription make loop formation a likely explanation of these results.

B. Prokaryotic DNA Recombination

1. LAMBDA *Int*

The integrative recombination reaction of bacteriophage λ appears to involve loop formation between several *Int* binding sites found in the "core" region (which overlaps the sites of strand cleavage for the integration process) and sites to the left and right of the core (104, 105) (Fig. 11). The Int protein is capable of binding to two DNA sites simultaneously. But in contrast to other systems in which a protein can bind to multiple related sites due to oligomeric symmetry, the Int protein recognizes two distinct classes of sites and binds to these classes, using independent domains of the protein (106). An extensive series of insertion and deletion mutants revealed that the relative helical phasing of the core region and the left region (P1-H1, cf. Fig 11) is critical to recombinational activity *in vitro* (104).

FIG. 11. The attP region for integration of phage λ (*104*). Binding sites for Int are shown as striped and white boxes. The white boxes represent the "core" region, which overlaps the sites of strand cleavage during the integration. Binding sites for the DNA bending protein IHF are shown as shaded boxes. Numbers (in bp) represent the distances from the site of integration. DNA bending by the IHF protein bound at the H1 and H' sites is proposed to facilitate P1-core loop formation (*104*) and P'-core loop formation (*105*), respectively.

That the helical phasing is the critical factor was inferred in experiments using the unwinding ligand ethidium bromide. The binding of ethidium changes the relative torsional alignment of the regions of DNA adjacent to the bound dye. Hence, given the proper extent of binding of ethidium, two sites unable to form loops efficiently due to incorrect phasing in the absence of ethidium might form loops more efficiently in the presence of the dye. This was in fact observed, providing evidence that helical phasing is the reason for the observed behavior of the deletion mutants. Investigation of the length dependence indicated that insertions or deletions of more than two helical turns greatly decrease the recombinational activity.

Subsequent studies demonstrated the formation of yet another looped structure in this system, this one involving binding of Int protein, both to the core region and to Int binding sites in the region to the right (*105*; cr. Fig. 11). A requirement for proper torsional alignment was also demonstrated for formation of this loop. The DNA bending protein IHF (integration host factor) is thought to play an important role in formation of both loops. IHF-induced DNA bending appears to facilitate loop formation in other systems as well (see Section V,C).

2. THE *Hin* SYSTEM OF *Salmonella*

Another bacterial site-specific recombination system, the Hin-mediated recombinational enhancer of *Salmonella typhimurium,* also appears to involve loop formation. This element causes a 200-fold enhancement of inversion of a 993-bp DNA segment containing the promoter that controls transcription of the flagellin gene (*107*) (Fig. 12). This inversion event is responsible for the "phase variation" exhibited by *Salmonella.* The enhancer is located 122 bp downstream from the *hix*L recombination site and 871 bp upstream from the *hix*R site (*108*). The enhancer was active both *in vivo* and *in vitro* when located up to

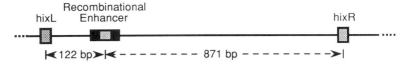

FIG. 12. The Hin site-specific recombination system. The binding sites for the Hin protein are represented as shaded boxes, and the two Fis binding sites as black boxes at the ends of the 60-bp long recombinational enhancer region. Distances are measured from the centers of the *hix* sites to the center of the recombinational enhancer region.

4000 bp from the nearest recombination site, and in either orientation outside of the recombined region. When the enhancer is placed 48 bp from a recombination site, it is inactive, which may result from either the lateral stiffness of the intervening DNA or the torsional misalignment of the two sites. In the latter case, the enhancer site should exhibit activity if shifted by one half a helical turn.

The recombinational enhancer contains two Fis protein binding sites (Fig. 12). Studies of variants with altered distances between the two sites show that the activity of the enhancer requires a specific relative torsional phasing of the sites, and that insertions or deletions of more than one or two helical turns are detrimental (*107*). The optimal orientation of the bound Fis proteins is, however, on opposite sides of the DNA helix. This result emphasizes the fact that a dependence on torsional alignment does not imply that the interacting sites or proteins must reside on the same face of the DNA, but only that some specific relative orientation is required (*109*).

A model to account for the observed dependence of recombination on torsional alignment of the Fis binding sites is that the Fis proteins bound at the two sites within the recombinational enhancer form loops with the flanking *hix* sites (cf. Fig. 12) to bring both *hix*R and *hix*L into the proper alignment for recombination (*107*). The proposed structure consists of two DNA loops, one of approximately 100 bp comprised of the left most Fis protein binding site and the *hix*L site, and the other of approximately 850 bp between the right most Fis protein binding site and the *hix*R site. The "double-loop" model proposed here is somewhat analogous to that proposed for the simultaneous interaction of DeoR repressor with its three known binding sites (87).

In these *in vitro* studies, the *E. coli* histone-like protein HU increased the activity of recombinational enhancers located closer than 200 bp from a recombination site (*108*). Apparently the HU protein increases the flexibility of DNA to allow loop formation at intersite distances where the required DNA bending would otherwise be unfavorable (*108*), a conclusion consistent with the observation that HU facilitates cyclization of DNA fragments too short to cyclize in its absence (*110*).

C. Prokaryotic Origins of DNA Replication

1. REPLICATION OF PLASMID R6K

Replication of the R6K plasmid of *E. coli* from the ori-β site is facilitated by the presence of the ori-γ site in *cis*, which is composed of seven tandem binding sites for the "initiator protein" (*111, 112*). These sites bind the initiator protein tightly and are then thought to interact cooperatively with the α and β origins of replication, located 2000 and 1200 bp away, respectively (*112, 113*). The ori-γ site acts as an "enhancer" of replication; the mechanism of this effect appears to be the formation of a DNA loop. DNA cyclization is enhanced when the initiator protein is bound to two sites (ori-β and ori-γ) located at opposite ends of the DNA molecule, implying that the binding of the initiator protein brought the two ends of the molecule into close proximity. Loop formation was also confirmed using exonuclease-III protection to assay for extent of occupancy of the weaker ori-β site with and without the ori-γ site present in *cis*. The ori-β site was efficiently bound only when ori-γ was present, indicating cooperative interaction at a distance.

The most direct evidence for loops came from electron microscopy, which showed a significant increase in looped structures on addition of the initiator protein to molecules containing both β and γ sites. Chemical footprinting (dimethyl sulfate) confirmed that cooperativity exists between the two sites, as there was protection of the β site when a γ site was present on the same molecule, but not on a molecule lacking the γ site.

Experiments with a plasmid containing a single γ site showed that it is possible for initiator protein bound at a site on one plasmid to form a bridge to a site on another DNA molecule, providing strong evidence for the bidentate character of the initiator protein, a prerequisite for loop formation (*114, 115*). This was demonstrated by treating complexes with T4 topoisomerase II, which forms catenated circles with molecules held together by the initiator protein, but does not in the absence of the protein. By holding the two plasmids in close proximity, the initiator protein greatly increases the chances of fortuitously interlinking the two molecules in the course of the double-strand cleavage and religation reactions characteristic of type II topoisomerases. The ability to form such intermolecular site–site complexes may not be just an *in vitro* artifact, since a multicopy plasmid in an *E. coli* cell is present at a concentration of approximately 150 nM, high enough to allow intermolecular complex formation. Loop formation may be facilitated by DNA bending by an IHF protein bound between the interacting replication origins (*116*). This is similar to proposals that IHF-induced DNA bending is involved in several other systems involving loop formation (cf. Section V,C).

2. THE LAMBDA O PROTEIN

Another system involving replication and loop formation is found in the bacteriophage λ where the O protein mediates formation of loops (*117*). In order to study the formation of the "O-some," two λ origins were cloned approximately 1000 bp apart in a plasmid. In this way, any interaction between a protein bound at one origin and a protein bound at the other would give rise to a 1000-bp loop, readily visualized by electron microscopy. Such looped structures were in fact observed at the expected locations.

The DNA within the loop was more thermostable than the un-looped DNA in the tails (*117*). This was interpreted to mean that the DNA within the loop is topologically isolated as a result of tight binding of O protein, and that the increased thermal stability of the loop is analogous to the increased thermal stability of closed circular DNA relative to linear DNA. Loops formed in other systems that involve high affinity interactions between proteins and DNA would also be expected to be topologically isolated on a physiologically relevant time scale. Topological isolation implies that the loop represents a separate domain that may have a superhelix density significantly different from the bulk value.

DNA loop formation mediated by the O protein was incorporated into a model for O-some formation that entails loop formation between two of the four tandem O-protein binding sites (called iterons) clustered in the λ replication origin. According to this model, the O-protein first binds to the inner two iterons, which bend the DNA around themselves. At that point, the proteins bound to the outer two iterons close the loop via protein–protein interactions. The end result is an octameric complex of O-protein monomers around which is wrapped a 90-bp loop of DNA. The demonstration of loop formation between distant O-protein binding sites provides the precedent for the protein–protein contacts between O proteins bound at the outer two iterons, which are proposed to close the 90-bp loop in the natural context (*117*).

D. Eukaryotic Control Elements

1. *Drosophila* HEAT-SHOCK CONSENSUS ELEMENTS

Drosophila melanogaster heat-shock genes are activated by the binding of a protein (the heat-shock transcription factor) to DNA sites (heat-shock elements) located upstream from the transcription start site. These elements require proper helical phasing, indicating that looping may be involved (*118*). An extensive series of insertion mutations was made to increase the spacing between the heat-shock elements and the transcription start-site from their normal locations about 55 and 80 bp upstream. Transcription was maximal when integral ($\pm$ 1 bp) numbers of helical turns were inserted, but was significantly reduced (to between 1/4 and 1/15 of the original level) when nonintegral multiples of the helical repeat were inserted. The dependence on helical phasing appeared to decrease gradually as the number of helical turns inserted as increased from one to three turns, and disappeared with the insertion of 27 helical turns (*118*). This was interpreted by analogy to DNA cyclization, where the amplitude of the periodic variation in cyclization probability decreases with increasing molecular length, becoming negligible above approximately four or five persistence-lengths.

2. THE SV40 EARLY PROMOTER

The SV40 early-early and late-early promoters are regulated by at least three sets of proteins and upstream binding sites. There is a periodic loss and recovery of activity that depends on helical phasing of these sequence elements (*119*). This suggests that DNA looping may be involved in the function of these sequence elements.

3. REGULATION OF THE UTEROGLOBIN GENE BY THE PROGESTERONE RECEPTOR

Expression of the uteroglobin gene is regulated by upstream sequences called "hormone responsive elements." Two such elements are located approximately 2400 and 2660 bp upstream from the transcription start site. Electron microscopy of complexes of purified rabbit progesterone receptor and DNA fragments containing these sites shows loop formation between the sites (*120*). Although it is not known whether the receptor–receptor interaction plays any role in the functioning of the receptor *in vivo*, it is clear that the potential for loop formation exists.

4. REGULATION OF YEAST MATING TYPE BY RAP-1

Transcriptional "silencers" in the yeast *S. cerevisiae* keep "silent copies" of the mating-type genes from being expressed. Silencers work in either orientation and at distances up to 2600 bp (*121, 122*). The RAP-1 protein binds to these silencers, and causes DNA loop formation when bound to DNA fragments containing the sequences *in vitro* (*123*). Loop formation has been confirmed by direct observation by electron microscopy, and by an increased rate of DNA cyclization for molecules containing the silencer sequences in the presence of the RAP-1 protein. The increase in rate of cyclization was approximately twofold, approximately the same as that seen in cyclization of DNAs containing the ori-β and ori-γ sequences from the plasmid R6K of *E. coli* (*113*; Section III,C,1). The increased rate of cyclization provides evidence for DNA bending or loop formation caused by the RAP-1 protein. The loop represents an isolated topological domain that can be modified to keep genes contained within it from being expressed.

5. YEAST RIBOSOMAL PROTEIN GENES

Upstream sequence elements are involved in enhancing the efficiency of transcription of the yeast ribosomal protein genes. The upstream activating sequences (UAS_{rpg}) are effective when located 390 bp from the start site of transcription but ineffective at a distance of 120 bp from the start site (*124*). This feature suggests loop formation, since no other model predicts a decrease in activity as a distant site is moved closer to its point of action. The data, however, are insufficient to distinguish between torsional effects and DNA bending stiffness as the cause of the decreased activity at a distance of 120 bp, and do not provide evidence for a minimum distance requirement for loop formation.

IV. Interpretation of the Length Dependence of DNA Looping

The effect of varying the contour distance between the two interacting sites in systems capable of loop formation has been investigated *in vivo* and *in vitro*, and provides quantitative information not only about the helical repeat but also the lateral (bending) and torsional (twisting) behavior of the DNA (and of the linking protein) in the specified environment. No other physical method provides such information *in vivo*. Loop formation involving a single DNA molecule can in principle be distinguished from formation of "sandwich structures" (*61*) involving two DNA molecules by the lack of a dependence of the effect on DNA molecule concentration, and by the existence of an extremum in the envelope of the effect as a function of intersite distance (*109*). (If sandwich structures are formed in studies of action-at-a-distance on high-copy-number plasmids *in vivo*, the helical repeat and the torsional stiffness of the DNA can be determined by analysis of the length dependence of action-at-a-distance, but the lateral stiffness of the DNA will play only a minor role.) The following section reviews the information about DNA structure and properties *in vivo* and *in vitro* derived from studies of the length dependence of action-at-a-distance.

A. Helical Repeat

1. THE HELICAL REPEAT *in Vivo* DIFFERS FROM ITS *in Vitro* VALUE

As discussed in Section II, studies of the cyclization probability of DNA as a function of length *in vitro* (Fig. 3B) led to values of the DNA helical repeat of 10.45 bp per turn (*35*) and 10.54 bp per turn (*34*). These values are similar to the helical repeat determined by several other methods (*36, 37, 125–127*).

The binding of λ repressor to molecules containing operators separated by five to seven turns of the DNA helix has been studied *in vitro* (*64*). The periodic oscillation of loop formation was consistent with the implicit assumption that the helical repeat of the DNA was 10.5 bp per turn. *In vitro* investigation of looping involving *lac* repressor and linear DNA yielded a periodicity consistent with the known "random sequence" value of 10.5 bp per turn (*61*).

On the other hand, *in vivo* determinations of the helical repeat of DNA by analysis of the length dependence of modulation of expression by a distant site yield values of 11.1 bp per turn (*77*) and 11.4–11.7 bp per turn (*59, 60*; cf. Fig. 5). Fourier analysis (*125*) of the periodicity of modulation of expression in the *ara* system on a plasmid *in vivo* as a function of interoperator distance indicated a helical repeat of the intervening DNA of 11.1 bp per turn (*77, 128*). In this case, the altered helical repeat was interpreted by proposing that the linking number deficit (negative supercoiling) *in vivo* was expressed primarily as a twist deficit (increased helical repeat) instead of writhe.

Initial investigation of the modulation of expression by an upstream site in a *lac* construct on a plasmid *in vivo* demonstrated that the effect of the upstream site on repression is greatly reduced at a small interoperator distance (118 bp) (*58*). Further investigation of the modulation of expression as a function of the distance between operators in this system indicated that the decrease in repression at 118 bp is due to effects of torsional phasing, since deletion of three base-pairs from the 118 bp construct to obtain an interoperator distance of 115 bp dramatically increased the extent of repression. Selected additional constructs in the range of 115 to 177 bp exhibited an oscillatory variation of repression with interoperator distance (59). The choice of constructs, i.e., two sets of five different spacings clustered within a eight base-pair region, made it possible to define two local extrema in the oscillating curve representing repression as a function of interoperator spacing. Surprisingly, these extrema were incompatible with a helical repeat of 10.5 bp per turn for the DNA involved in the loop. Because the observed local maximum and minimum in repression were located approximately 40 bp apart, two possible helical repeats, 9.0 ± 0.3 bp per turn and 11.7 ± 0.3 bp per turn, were most consistent with the data. Examination of additional constructs with interoperator distances specifically chosen to eliminate this ambiguity showed the helical repeat to be 11.6 ± 0.3 bp per turn (60; cf. Fig. 6).

The helical repeat is the most reliable of the physical properties of DNA deduced from looping data. This results from the fact that one loop is directly compared with a loop of another size. Any complications arising from details of the process of loop formation per se should cancel out in the comparison of the two interoperator distances. (Indeed the result is independent of whether loops or sandwich structures are the mechanism of action-at-a-distance.) It should also be noted that the value of the helical repeat applies only to the DNA segment used to vary the interoperator distance. Thus the properties of the invariant DNA region (e.g., the distortion of DNA by bound proteins such as CRP) have no effect on the calculated value of the helical repeat.

2. POSSIBLE EXPLANATIONS FOR THE ALTERED HELICAL REPEAT *in Vivo*

In analyzing why the *in vivo* helical repeat of DNA appears to differ so dramatically from its *in vitro* value, the differences between the *in vivo* and *in vitro* experiments should first be considered. Measurements of the helical repeat *in vitro* are performed with linear or (relatively) relaxed circular DNA, whereas DNA *in vivo* is supercoiled. In addition, *in vitro* experiments are carried out at high dilution with highly purified DNA, whereas the cellular milieu is a crowded environment with a collectively high concentration of biopolymers. Although no experimental evidence is available regarding the role of the *in vivo* solution environment, several studies have examined the role of supercoiling. These investigations indicate that the topological state of the DNA is a major factor in the altered helical repeat observed *in vivo*.

The effect of supercoiling *in vitro* on *lac*-repressor-mediated loop formation was examined with small closed-circular DNA molecules containing two symmetric operators located at various distances from each other (69). Supercoiling shifted the interoperator distance at which loop formation was optimal from its value on nonsupercoiled DNA. This was interpreted as a shift in the helical repeat due to supercoiling. The helical repeat increased from approximately 10.3 to 10.7 bp per turn as the superhelix density was altered from $\sigma = +0.023$ to $\sigma = -0.023$ (69).

Constructs with systematic variations in the distance between *ara* operators, used to determine the helical repeat of 11.1 bp per turn *in vivo*, were utilized to examine the effect of supercoiling *in vivo* directly. A shift in the optimal interoperator spacing was observed in a DNA-gyrase-deficient *E. coli* strain. The alteration in the helical repeat was consistent with the hypothesis that high negative supercoiling favors a higher value for the helical repeat (77). However, it is necessary that the entire *in vivo* linking number deficit ($\sigma \sim -0.06$) be expressed as altered twist in order to obtain the helical repeat observed *in vivo*.

Two factors complicate this analysis of the effect of supercoiling density on DNA twist (and thus helical repeat). The first is that "restrained" supercoils will not contribute to an alteration of twist. Restrained supercoils are those that are not eliminated when a topological "swivel" is introduced. They are thought to be the result of associations of proteins that alter DNA topology within the cell, but that are removed during DNA isolation. Approximately half of the total superhelix density is thought to be unrestrained *in vivo* (129–133). A second consideration is that some of the superhelical stress may be expressed as writhe rather than twist. For long DNA molecules, it has been estimated that approximately one-third to two-thirds of total superhelical stress is expressed as writhe (34, 134, 135).

As a result of the probable existence of restrained supercoiling *in vivo*, and the partitioning of unrestrained supercoiling between twist and writhe, it is possible that as little as one-quarter of the total observed linking number deficit is available for alteration of the DNA helical repeat. For a reasonable estimate of the total superhelix density of a plasmid *in vivo* ($\sigma \sim -0.06$), the expected shift in helical repeat is from 10.50 to 10.66 bp per turn, far below the range of values observed in looping experiments *in vivo* (11.1–11.7 bp per turn).

3. TRANSCRIPTIONALLY INDUCED SUPERCOILING

One possible explanation of the altered helical repeat determined in looping studies *in vivo* may be that transcription can induce negative supercoiling in the DNA upstream from the promoter (*133, 136–145*; see also *146*). Transcription [e.g., of the *tet* gene from its natural promoter or the *galK* gene from the tac promoter (*143*)] can cause a dramatic local linking deficit behind, and local linking excess in front of, a transcribed gene. Transcription on the plasmid pBR322 creates regions of increased and decreased (negative) supercoiling in the locations predicted by the transcription-induced supercoiling model (*147*). Divergent transcription should give rise to a still higher local linking deficit since the two transcription complexes will inhibit the rotation of the DNA necessary for mutual annihilation of the positive and negative supercoiling regions (*137*). The plasmid used in the *lac*-based looping system (Fig. 6) has just such an arrangement of transcriptional promoters, and the helical repeat measurement applies to a region of DNA located between the divergent *lac* and *bla* promoters (*60*). The plasmids used in the *ara*-based system (Fig. 7) are of similar design (*77*). It is thus possible that the helical repeat is measured for DNA located in a domain of large local linking deficit, and that it is this large local linking deficit (expressed as a local twist deficit) that gives rise to the observed anomalous helical repeat.

This hypothesis is consistent with the proposal that small topological domains of DNA (i.e., one persistence length, or approximately 150 bp for DNA *in vitro*) express a moderate linking number deficit as an altered twist, and that writhe is observed only after approximately two superhelical turns have been absorbed as twist (*148, 149*). The domain of excess negative supercoiling in the plasmid described above may be as small as 400 bp, the distance between the two promoters. Such a small domain may not allow significant writhe, so that the majority of the topological unwinding may be reflected directly as an increased helical repeat.

Experimental data also suggest a relatively small writhe component in small supercoiling domains. Study of loop formation in 452-bp DNA minicircles showed that the entire linking number deficit was expressed as an altered twist with little or no writhe (*69*). DNA cyclization data indicate that writhe no longer occurs with DNA loops smaller than approximately 1000 bp (*35*), although other results disagree with this conclusion (*34*).

If writhe in fact does not occur for such small DNA loops, and thus presumably for small topological domains (e.g., 6), it is possible that transcriptionally induced local linking deficits will be expressed primarily as altered helical repeats. Such a situation could give rise to a very large increase in the helical repeat of the DNA in the region between the promoters in the plasmid described earlier. The absence of writhe is important because it allows helical repeats as large as those observed (11.4–11.6) with attainable superhelix densities. For example, in the absence of writhe, a superhelix density of $\sigma = -0.087$ would give rise to a helical repeat of 11.5 bp per turn. Further experiments are required to resolve this question, but transcriptionally induced local linking deficits are probably at least a part of the explanation of why the helical repeat differs *in vivo* and *in vitro* (60, 77).

B. Force Constants for Lateral (Bending) and Torsional (Twisting) Deformations

In addition to the helical repeat, quantitative analysis of looping experiments provides other information regarding the physical properties of DNA *in vivo*. Quantitative information may be extracted from looping data by pursuing the analogy between the looping and DNA cyclization processes. Theoretical analysis (29) of DNA cyclization data (33, 35) yielded the helical repeat, torsional rigidity, and persistence length of DNA *in vitro*. The values obtained are all in good agreement with independent determinations of the same quantities, lending confidence that the theory is an adequate description of the cyclization process. Although DNA loop formation and DNA cyclization differ in important ways (109), the overall similarity of the processes makes this approach a good first approximation. Independent analysis of DNA looping data (109) yields estimates of the helical repeat and torsional rigidity constant in agreement with those obtained using the Shimada–Yamakawa theory (29). [These estimates remain valid even if formation of sandwich structures (61) instead of single loops is the principal mechanism of action-at-a-distance on high copy number plasmids *in vivo* (109). On the other hand, the role of lateral stiffness (persistence length) is very different in the two mechanisms.]

Differences between loop formation and cyclization include the fact that the loop includes a bridging protein of non-negligible size and that the protein may be capable of bending to aid the looping process. In addition, the required orientation of the two interacting DNA segments would generally differ in the two cases. However, none of these differences is expected to affect the observed helical periodicity.

The torsional rigidity estimated from this analysis will be a lower estimate since protein flexibility may allow sites that are somewhat torsionally misaligned to interact as readily as perfectly aligned sites.

For example, the flexibility of the GAL4 transcriptional activator protein of yeast (or the lack of specificity of the contact between its "acid blob" region and the downstream transcription factor) appears to eliminate any requirement for proper torsional alignment (*150*). Similarly, recent studies of fine-scale deletion mutants in a model *deo* operator system show little dependence on relative helical phasing for operators from 171 to 66 bp apart (*151*). Such an effect could be due to a highly flexible protein, or may reflect the fact that DeoR exists as an octamer with four DNA binding sites (*86*).

The accuracy of the estimate of persistence length is affected by all the factors cited above, so that knowledge of the precise helical trajectory of the DNA in the loop will be required to determine the intrinsic bending stiffness of DNA *in vivo*. The binding of CRP–cAMP to its site between the two operators probably influences loop formation, since CRP–cAMP has been shown to bend DNA when bound at its specific site in the *lac* control region (*79*). Bending in the appropriate direction could significantly enhance loop formation, giving rise to an anomalously low apparent persistence length. Precedent for just such an effect of site-specific protein-induced DNA bending is found in studies of looping mediated by λ Int protein, where bending and the relative phasing of multiple bends are important for loop formation (*152, 153*). In addition, the histone-like protein HU of *E. coli* is observed to increase the extent of binding of certain proteins to DNA (*154*) and to increase DNA flexibility, allowing cyclization of DNA molecules shorter than 100 bp that are too small to cyclize in the absence of the protein (*110*). An apparent facilitation of loop formation by HU protein *in vitro* is also observed for the Fis-mediated recombination involved in phase variation in *Salmonella* (Section III,B,2). This effect is particularly noteworthy when the recombinational enhancer is within 200 bp of the recombination site.

The apparent persistence length calculated from the *lac* looping data using the quantitative cyclization theory is 30 bp, or approximately one-fifth of the accepted *in vitro* value (*21, 22*). This *in vivo* value results from the fact that action-at-a-distance remains efficient at an interoperator distance of 115 bp (the smallest distance that could be examined). Since the efficiency of DNA cyclization *in vitro* decreases strongly for molecules shorter than approximately two persistence lengths, application of the cyclization model to the *in vivo lac* looping data requires that the *in vivo* persistence length be much less than 115 bp. In most studies of looping, there is no evidence for an extremum in the envelope of the effect as a function of inter-site distance. Nor is a minimum distance for loop formation generally observed.

Loop formation *in vitro* on linear DNA by the λ repressor occurs at intersite distances of less than 60 bp on a linear DNA fragment (*64*); looping *in vivo* between arabinose operators occurs at distances of less than 40 bp (*77*); looping is possible down to a separation of 66 bp between DeoR operators *in vivo* (*151*); and looping has been reported for the *lac* system at a distance of 63 bp, using two symmetric *lac* operators (*61*; see below). Only in *nif*H activation of transcription by the NifA protein has there been a systematic demonstration of a minimum distance below which looping does not occur. In this system, distances of less than 90 bp between sites result in inactivity regardless of torsional orientation (*95*).

Other systems in which an apparent minimum distance has been observed have not eliminated torsional effects as the cause of poor looping at short distances (*90, 107, 124*). No minimum distance is observed in *ara, deo, cI,* and *lac*. In general, it appears that action-at-a-distance need not exhibit a minimum distance for activity, although the quantitative model for looping based on cyclization theory predicts that an effective minimum should be observed. In studies involving high-copy-number plasmids *in vivo*, the lack of a minimum intersite distance may indicate that sandwich structures (*61*) play a role in action-at-a-distance.

The lack of a minimum distance for loop formation in the *ara* system was addressed by use of an analog technique involving a metal spring of appropriate length bent into the shape of a loop (*77*). A realistic estimate for the size of the protein bridging the loop was incorporated into the model. The model assumed that interactions between proteins bound at the two sites were equally efficient regardless of the relative orientation of the sites. In other words, the proteins were assumed to be totally flexible, thus requiring no specific orientation of DNA sites but merely that they be within a certain distance of one another. For this analog model, it was found that the work required to bend the DNA into a loop actually decreased sharply below a distance of separation of sites of approximately 100 bp. (This predicted efficiency of loop formation at very short distances is not observed in the data. In the context of the model, this result may be interpreted to mean that the protein is not totally flexible, so that it cannot bind to any two sites separated by the width of an AraC protein regardless of all other geometric considerations).

The metal spring analogy represents an important alternative to comparisons with DNA cyclization, which necessarily include the very strict geometric requirements for ring closure. A general model for loop formation would encompass the totally rigid and totally flexible protein situations as limiting cases. Different proteins presumably will exhibit different flexibilities, but all should fall within the limits set by the totally rigid and totally flexible models described above.

It has often been proposed that protein flexibility accounts for a significant amount of the bending in formation of small loops (e.g., 3, 59, 77). However, if this is correct, the protein must be sufficiently flexible in one plane to allow small loops to form, but must be sufficiently inflexible in another plane to give rise to the preferences for a particular torsional orientation of the interacting sites. If it is assumed that only the DNA is flexible, then the torsional rigidity constant C may be evaluated as described in Section II. The result obtained from Shimada–Yamakawa analysis of the *in vivo lac* looping data (59, 60) ($C = 1.1 \pm 0.3 \times 10^{-19}$ erg-cm) is in good agreement with values obtained for DNA *in vitro (29, 33, 38–40)*. The *in vivo* value must be considered to be a lower estimate, because of the possible contribution of protein flexibility. It is also possible that the data, which necessarily consist of interoperator distances that are integral numbers of basepairs, do not include the maximum and minimum torsional effects, and thus underestimate the true amplitude as a function of intersite distance.

Studies of loop formation on supercoiled DNA *in vitro* indicate that supercoiling greatly reduces or eliminates the dependence of loop formation on the distance between interacting sites (69, 71). This result is paradoxical, since studies of loop formation *in vivo* with plasmid DNA (presumably negatively supercoiled) show a strong dependence of looping on interoperator distance (59, 60, 77). One might expect *a priori* that the *in vivo* result would more closely resemble *in vitro* results on supercoiled rather than linear DNA, but that does not appear to be the case.

V. The Local Concentration Model and Topological Models for Regulatory Effects Involving DNA Looping

A large body of evidence indicates that looping of DNA plays an important role in many gene regulatory systems. The next logical question is then, how does looping exert its influence? The models proposed to answer that question fall into two classes, the local concentration model and topological models.

A. The Local Concentration Model

The basic idea behind the local concentration model is that the DNA acts as a relatively flexible and/or deformable tether, thereby effectively increasing the local concentration of a distant bound protein in the vicinity of its site of action. This increased local concentration then drives binding at the target site farther toward completion than would otherwise be possible at the specified concentration (activity) of free protein. This thermodynamic local concentration model is distinct from kinetic facilitation mechanisms (e.g., sliding or direct transfer), which provide a mechanism for facilitation of both binding and dissociation with no participation of the distant site in the final complex, and thus provide no increase in the equilibrium extent of occupancy of target site.

Record *et al.* (58, 59, 60, 155) have interpreted increased repression in their *lac* constructs *in vivo* in terms of an increased local concentration of *lac* repressor at the site of repression due to the upstream site. The effective (local) repressor concentration (R_e) is expressed as the sum of the free repressor concentration (activity) (R_f) and an additional contribution from repressor bound at an upstream site N bp away (R_N): $R_e = R_f + R_N$. The value of R_N is equal to the product of the fractional occupancy of the distant site and the probability that the upstream site is in the vicinity of the target site (expressed by analogy to the j-factor). In order for the local concentration from looping to play an important regulatory role in a particular operon, this local concentration (R_N) must be comparable to or exceed the concentration (or, more precisely, activity) of the free protein (R_f). For DNA-binding proteins present in small numbers of copies per cell, the concentration variable R_N has clear evolutionary advantages over R_f, since R_N as a function of N exhibits a wide range of closely separated values, which can be varied by subtle changes in the properties of the intervening DNA (155).

An analogy to metal chelators has been used to describe the effect of upstream operators on the binding of the DeoR protein (82). Direct evidence in support of the local concentration model was obtained from experiments where the effect of an upstream binding site in *cis* was mimicked merely by increasing the concentration of free protein in the absence of an upstream site (82, 84). The fact that excess protein added in *trans* is effective precludes any mechanism invoking a role for DNA distortion or topological constraint. In these cases, the increased local concentration is apparently acting by mass action to drive occupancy at the target site toward saturation.

B. Topological Models

A different class of mechanisms of regulation by DNA loop formation are those in which the loop per se is the important factor in activity. Pairs of *lac* operators placed so as to bracket a target region inhibit transcription initiation or recombination involving sites within that region (53–55). This contrasts with the normal action of *lac* repressor, which inhibits transcription initiation by binding at a site overlapping the promoter. Switching *lac* and *gal* operators in positions upstream and downstream of (but not directly overlapping) the *gal* promoter yielded full repression only when pairs of identical operators were present (*101*). Constructs with one type of operator at the upstream site and the other type of operator downstream were less effective in repression. This experiment demonstrated that looping is in and of itself sufficient for repression, since even the totally heterologous system of two flanking *lac* operators was sufficient to repress the *gal* promoter in the presence of the *lac* repressor protein. A related observation is that the binding of CRP to its site in the *lac* operon may be inhibited by the formation of an O_1–O_3 93-bp loop due to the constraints that this small loop places on the DNA (*156*).

The formation of loops could exert its indirect effect in two ways, by distorting the DNA within the loop and thus altering the binding characteristics of the target site (e.g., *25, 27, 65*), or by formation of an isolated topological domain containing the target site (e.g., *6, 55, 71, 123*). Precedents exist for both of these effects in sufficiently small loops. Consistent with the first possibility, an altered DNA conformation induced by the severe bending involved in loop formation has been demonstrated *in vitro* by observation of increased and/or decreased DNase sensitivity of DNA involved in loops (*64, 65*).

Precedent for formation of a topologically isolated domain consistent with the alternative role for loops involving formation of topologically altered domains is found in experiments that demonstrate a greatly increased melting temperature (T_m) for DNA crosslinked into a loop (*117*). This elevated T_m for the DNA of a loop is similar to the behavior of covalently closed circular DNA in which the two DNA strands are topologically linked and thus cannot easily undergo the unwinding normally associated with DNA melting. Topological isolation would affect processes that require significant unwinding. In addition, a small isolated domain might exhibit an altered superhelix density as a result of the action of topoisomerases. Since topoisomerases have preferred sites of binding, a small isolated domain may contain an unusual ratio of gyrase to topoisomerase I binding sites, and thus exist in a state of unusual superhelix density.

C. The Role of Protein-Induced DNA Bending in Loop Formation

Protein-induced bending of DNA is necessary for efficient loop formation in a number of looping systems. Bending of DNA by the IHF protein may facilitate the interaction between distant sites involved in the integrative recombination reaction of phage λ (*105;* Section III,B,1), the replication of the plasmid pSC101 (*157*), replication of the R6K plasmid of *E. coli* (*114;* Section III,C,1), and regulation of the *nifHDK* operon by NifA in *Klebsiella* (*96;* Section III,A,5). IHF is essential for efficient loop formation by Int during the integrative recombination reaction of phage λ. IHF may function by bending of the DNA at a site between the two Int binding sites. In this way IHF can exert its effect without the necessity for specific protein–protein contacts (*105*). The hypothesis that the DNA-bending activity of IHF is the source of its effect was confirmed in recent experiments where one of the three IHF-binding sites was replaced with either a CRP protein-binding site or a segment of intrinsically curved DNA (*152*). Both experiments indicated that bending per se (at the location of the IHF binding site) is sufficient to enhance recombination.

Another recent experiment showed that the distance between the IHF binding sites, and hence the phasing of the bend centers, is critical to stable Int-mediated loop formation (*153*). A similar potential for protein-induced DNA-bending to influence DNA loop formation is found in both the *ara* (*78*) and *lac* (*59*) looping systems, where a bound CRP may influence looping *in vivo* (Sections III,A,1 and 2).

A related phenomenon is the requirement for HU protein for activity of recombinational enhancers located less than 300 bp from a recombination site (*108;* Section III,B,2). The protein is thought to bind without sequence specificity to DNA between the enhancer and recombination sites and thereby increase the flexibility of the DNA to allow loop formation, which would otherwise be inhibited by the bending-stiffness of naked DNA.

Consistent with this hypothesis of increased flexibility, HU enhances the cyclization of DNA molecules too short to cyclize in its absence (*110*). The HU-mediated effect differs from the effects of IHF and CRP in that HU increases flexibility rather than introducing a static bend. In addition, HU does not exhibit the degree of sequence specificity demonstrated by IHF and CRP, and thus should facilitate any process where significant DNA bending is required. Both the HU and IHF/CRP type of facilitation of loop formation are mechanisms to overcome the intrinsic stiffness of DNA in the process of loop formation. Bending induced by site-specific DNA-binding proteins provides a way of varying the contribution of the distant site to the local concentration of the effector of protein at the site of action [i.e., a means of varying the concentration R_N (Section V,A) at constant N], and hence of modulating gene expression.

VI. Conclusions

In principle, "action-at-a-distance" may be either a "through-space" or a "through-bond" effect, in the jargon of two-dimensional NMR spectroscopy. Formation of stable DNA loops (DNA looping), the subject of this review, is a "through space" effect, involving two regions of DNA distant along the contour of the molecule, and one or more proteins that contact these two regions simultaneously via bending and/or curvature of the intervening DNA sequence. Possible "through-bond" (along the DNA contour) thermodynamic models for action at a distance have also been considered, including the long-range effects of changes in DNA secondary structure induced by changes in supercoiling, as well as long-range cooperativity of protein binding and/or DNA structure. ["Through bond" and "through space" effects merge in the formation of cooperative looped nucleoprotein assemblies (e.g., *158*).]

Strong evidence exists for protein-mediated formation of DNA loops in regulatory systems or constructs both *in vitro* and *in vivo*. Electron microscopy, nuclease sensitivity, and DNA cyclization have all been used to demonstrate loop formation *in vitro*. The existence of a periodic modulation of activity with small changes in intersite distance has been observed in several systems both *in vitro* and *in vivo*. Such periodicity, determined by the local DNA helical repeat, is expected in any system involving sufficiently short lengths of a DNA loop. However, since loops involving both a single DNA molecule and sandwich structures (*61*) involving two DNA molecules will exhibit periodicity in action-at-a-distance, periodicity is not uniquely diagnostic for loop formation at high DNA concentrations. (It is, however, likely that any system forming sandwich structures at high concentrations will exhibit looping at lower DNA concentrations.)

The variety of organisms, genetic systems, and possible mechanisms of loop formation shows that looping is a general strategy in the modulation of gene expression. Systems ranging from bacteria to vertebrates exhibit looping, in processes ranging from the repression or enhancement of transcription to genetic recombination and DNA replication. Both heterotypic (e.g., *gln*) and homotypic (e.g., *lac, gal, ara*) classes of loops are observed. The distinction between these classes is important, because heterotypic loop formation requires specific interaction between two different proteins rather than simply the potential for oligomerization of a given protein.

Two general control mechanisms involving stable loop formation appear operative: (i) "direct," in which a bivalent regulatory protein, present at a high local concentration as a result of interaction at a distant site, interacts directly with the target site, and (ii) "indirect," in which either the topological constraint or local structural distortion of DNA caused by loop formation results in altered properties of the target sequence. The finding in the *deo* and *gln* systems that addition of excess regulatory protein in *trans* is able to mimic the effect of a distant binding site in *cis* provides strong evidence for the direct, local-concentration model in these systems. However, studies in model *lac*-repressor-mediated control systems indicate that, at least in certain situations, loop formation per se can cause repression.

In most cases, looping is proposed to act by increasing the local concentration R_e of regulatory protein in the vicinity of the target site by the amount of R_N resulting from formation of a DNA loop of size N (cf. 58, 59, 150, 159). The increase in R_e increases the occupancy of the target site. However, in the *ara* and *gln* systems looping acts not by increasing occupancy of a site but by allosterically altering the activity of a protein already bound at the site as a result of a protein–protein interaction driven by the concentration R_N. This distinction further illustrates the wide variety of qualitatively different mechanisms by which loop formation modulates gene expression.

Numerous fundamental questions remain regarding loop formation and its role in genetic regulation. For example, why do some systems exhibit looping *in vivo* over distances of several thousands of base-pairs (*gln* and *deo*) whereas others exhibit no effect at a distance of 500 base-pairs (*ara*). Part of the answer may be that both the free concentration (activity) R_f and the concentration from looping R_N contribute to the effective concentration R_e of the regulatory protein at the target site (58–60, 155). If values of R_f differ significantly for different regulatory proteins, the distances N at which looping ceases to contribute (i.e., distances at which R_N is much less than R_f) will also differ. (Of course the value of R_f also affects R_N by determining the level of occupancy of the sites.) Both of the systems capable of action at distances of several thousand base-pairs are ones to which the local concentration model probably applies, since an increase in protein concentration supplied in *trans* is sufficient to mimic a distant DNA site in *cis*.

It will be important to determine whether values of R_f for the DeoR and NR_I proteins are significantly smaller than for the LacR and AraC proteins under conditions where action at great distances is observed in the *deo* and *gln* systems, but not in *lac* and *ara*. Of course, it is unlikely that any extensive region of DNA within the cell will behave simply like a flexible coil, in view of its condensed state and its interactions with the myriad of other DNA-binding proteins.

Other important questions concern the extent of variation of the helical repeat *in vivo,* and the reasons for the differences from the *in vitro* value. Global effects of DNA supercoiling are probably involved, but local effects must also be invoked. Local linking deficits induced by transcriptional activity are a plausible explanation of the large helical repeats observed in *ara* and *lac*-based looping systems *in vivo.*

ACKNOWLEDGMENTS

We gratefully acknowledge comments from Drs. R. Gourse, S. Leirmo, M. Mossing, and W. Ross and from J. H. Ha and S. Law on sections of this article, and the assistance of Sheila Aiello in its preparation. Work from this laboratory was supported by NSF grant CHE-8803673.

REFERENCES

1. F. Jacob and J. Monod, *JMB* **3**, 318 (1961).
2. J. H. Miller and W. S. Reznikoff (eds.), "The Operon." CSH Lab, Cold Spring Harbor, New York, 1980.
3. M. Ptashne, *Nature* **322**, 697 (1986).
4. R. Schleif, *Nature* **327**, 369 (1987).
5. R. Schleif, *Science* **240**, 127 (1988).
6. J. C. Wang and G. N. Giaever, *Science* **240**, 300 (1988).
7. J. D. Gralla, *Cell* **57**, 193 (1989).
8. W. S. Reznikoff, R. B. Winter and C. K. Hurley, *PNAS* **71**, 2314 (1974).
9. W. Gilbert, J. Majors and A. Maxam, *in* "Dahlem Workshop on Organization and Expression of Chromosomes" (V. G. Allfrey, E. K. F. Bautz, B. J. McCarthy, R. T. Schimke and A. Tissières, eds.), p. 167. Dahlem Konf., Berlin, 1976.
10. P. H. von Hippel, *in* "Biological Regulation and Development" (R. Goldberger, ed.), p. 279. Plenum, New York, 1979.
11. P. H. Richter and M. Eigen, *Biophys. Chem.* **2**, 255 (1974).
12. O. G. Berg and C. Blomberg, *Biophys. Chem.* **4**, 367 (1976).
13. O. G. Berg, R. B. Winter and P. H. von Hippel, *Bchem* **20**, 6929 (1981).
14. A. D. Riggs, S. Bourgeois and M. Cohn, *JMB* **53**, 401 (1970).
15. M. D. Barkley, *Bchem* **20**, 3833 (1981).
16. R. B. Winter, O. G. Berg and P. H. von Hippel, *Bchem* **20**, 6961 (1981).
17. G. Adam and M. Delbrück, *in* "Structural Chemistry and Molecular Biology" (A. Rich and N. Davidson, eds.), p. 198. Freeman, San Francisco, California, 1968.
18. J. Kania and B. Müller-Hill, *EJB* **79**, 381 (1977).
19. R. B. O'Gorman, M. Dunaway and K. S. Matthews, *JBC* **255**, 10100 (1980).

20. F. Culard and J. C. Maurizot, *NARes* **9**, 5175 (1981).
21. P. J. Hagerman, *Biopolymers* **20**, 1503 (1981).
22. P. J. Hagerman, *Annu. Rev. Biophys. Biophys. Chem.* **17**, 265 (1988).
23. E. Serfling, M. Jasin and W. Schaffner, *Trends Genet.* **1**, 224 (1985).
24. P. Robbins and M. Botchan, *in* "Eukaryotic Transcription: The Role of cis and trans-Acting Elements in Initiation" (Y. Gluzman, ed.), p. 41 CSH Lab, Cold Spring Harbor, New York, 1985.
25. M. H. Irani, L. Orosz and S. Adhya, *Cell* **32**, 783 (1983).
26. T. M. Dunn, S. Hahn, S. Ogden and R. F. Schleif, *PNAS* **81**, 5017 (1984).
27. A. Majumdar and S. Adhya, *PNAS* **81**, 6100 (1984).
28. H. Jacobson and W. H. Stockmayer, *J. Chem. Phys.* **18**, 1600 (1950).
29. J. Shimada and H. Yamakawa, *Macromolecules* **17**, 689 (1984).
30. J. C. Wang and N. Davidson, *JMB* **19**, 469 (1966).
31. J. E. Mertz and R. W. Davis, *PNAS* **69**, 3370 (1972).
32. D. Shore, J. Langowski and R. L. Baldwin, *PNAS* **78**, 4833 (1981).
33. D. Shore and R. L. Baldwin, *JMB* **170**, 957 (1983).
34. D. S. Horowitz and J. C. Wang, *JMB* **173**, 75 (1984).
35. D. Shore and R. L. Baldwin, *JMB* **170**, 983 (1983).
36. J. C. Wang, *CSHSQB* **43**, 29 (1978).
37. J. C. Wang, *PNAS* **76**, 200 (1979).
38. M. D. Barkley and B. H. Zimm, *J. Chem. Phys.* **70**, 2991 (1979).
39. J. C. Thomas, S. A. Allison, C. J. Appellof and J. M. Schurr, *Biophys. Chem.* **12**, 177 (1980).
40. D. P. Millar, R. J. Robbins and A. H. Zewail, *J. Chem. Phys.* **76**, 2080 (1982).
41. B. Chen, B. de Crombrugghe, W. Anderson, M. Gottesman, I. Pastan and R. L. Perlman, *Nature NB* **233**, 67 (1971).
42. A. Schmitz and D. J. Galas, *NARes* **6**, 111 (1979).
43. S. B. Straney and D. M. Crothers, *Cell* **51**, 699 (1987).
44. T. A. Steitz, T. J. Richmond, D. Wise and D. Engelman, *PNAS* **71**, 593 (1974).
45. J. Kania and D. T. Brown, *PNAS* **73**, 3529 (1976).
46. N. Geisler and K. Weber, *PNAS* **73**, 3103 (1976).
47. S. Bourgeois and M. Pfahl, *Adv. Protein Chem.* **30**, 1 (1976).
48. K. Beyreuther, *in* "The Operon" (J. H. Miller and W. S. Reznikoff, eds.), p. 123. CSH Lab, Cold Spring Harbor, New York, 1980.
49. M. Dunaway, S. P. Manly and K. S. Matthews, *PNAS* **77**, 7181 (1980).
50. B. Müller-Hill, T. Fanning, N. Geisler, D. Gho, J. Kania, P. Kathmann, H. Meissner, M. Schlotmann, A. Schmitz, I. Triesch and K. Beyreuther, *in* "Protein-Ligand Interactions" (H. Sund and G. Blaver, eds.), p. 211. Walter de Gruyter, Berlin, 1975.
51. P. A. Whitson and K. S. Matthews, *Bchem* **25**, 3845 (1986).
52. C. A. Royer, G. Weber, T. J. Daly and K. Matthews, *Bchem* **25**, 8308 (1986).
53. G. L. Herrin and G. N. Bennett, *Gene* **32**, 349 (1984).
54. M. Besse, B. von Wilcken-Bergmann and B. Müller-Hill, *EMBO J.* **5**, 1377 (1986).
55. R. Saldanha, P. Flanagan and M. Fennewald, *JMB* **196**, 505 (1987).
56. M. C. Mossing and M. T. Record, Jr., *JMB* **186**, 295 (1985).
57. A. Jobe, J. R. Sadler and S. Bourgeois, *JMB* **85**, 231 (1974).
58. M. C. Mossing and M. T. Record, Jr., *Science* **223**, 889 (1986).
59. G. R. Bellomy, M. C. Mossing and M. T. Record, Jr., *Bchem* **27**, 3900 (1988).
60. G. R. Bellomy and M. T. Record, Jr., submitted for publication (1990).
61. H. Krämer, M. Niemöller, M. Amouyal, B. Revet, B. von Wilcken-Bergmann and B. Müller-Hill, *EMBO J.* **6**, 1481 (1987).

62. J. R. Sadler, H. Sasmor and J. L. Betz, *PNAS* **80**, 6785 (1983).
63. A. Simons, D. Tils, B. von Wilcken-Bergmann and B. Müller-Hill, *PNAS* **81**, 1624 (1984).
64. A. Hochschild and M. Ptashne, *Cell* **44**, 681 (1986).
65. J. A. Borowiec, L. Zhang, S. Sasse-Dwight and J. D. Gralla, *JMB* **196**, 101 (1987).
66. W.-T. Hsieh, P. Whitson, K. S. Matthews and R. D. Wells, *JBC* **262**, 14583 (1987).
67. A. E. Chakerian and K. S. Matthews, *Int. J. Biochem.* **20**, 493 (1988).
68. P. A. Whitson, W.-T. Hsieh, R. D. Wells and K. S. Matthews, *JBC* **262**, 14592 (1987).
69. H. Krämer, M. Amouyal, A. Nordheim and B. Müller-Hill, *EMBO J.* **7**, 547 (1988).
70. M. Pfahl, V. Gulde and S. Bourgeois, *JMB* **127**, 339 (1979).
71. P. A. Whitson, W.-T. Hsieh, R. D. Wells and K. S. Matthews, *JBC* **262**, 4943 (1987).
72. D. Vidal-Ingigliardi and O. Raibaud, *NARes* **13**, 5919 (1985).
73. E. Eismann, B. von Wilcken-Bergmann and B. Müller-Hill, *JMB* **195**, 949 (1987).
74. Y. Flashner and J. D. Gralla, *PNAS* **85**, 8968 (1988).
75. K. Martin, L. Huo and R. F. Schleif, *PNAS* **83**, 3654 (1986).
76. S. Hahn, T. Dunn and R. Schleif, *JMB* **180**, 61 (1984).
77. D.-H. Lee and R. Schleif, *PNAS* **86**, 476 (1989).
78. S. Hahn, W. Hendrickson and R. Schleif, *JMB* **188**, 355 (1986).
79. H.-M. Wu and D. M. Crothers, *Nature* **308**, 509 (1984).
80. E. P. Hamilton and N. Lee, *PNAS* **85**, 1749 (1988).
81. L. Huo, K. Martin and R. Schleif, *PNAS* **85**, 5444 (1988).
82. G. Dandanell and K. Hammer, *EMBO J.* **4**, 3333 (1985).
83. P. Valentin-Hansen, B. Albrechtsen and J. E. Løve Larsen, *EMBO J.* **5**, 2015 (1986).
84. A. J. Ninfa, L. J. Reitzer and B. Magasanik. *Cell* **50**, 1039 (1987).
85. G. Dandanell, P. Valentin-Hansen, J. E. Løve Larsen and K. Hammer, *Nature* **325**, 823 (1987).
86. L. Mortensen, G. Dandanell and K. Hammer, *EMBO J.* **8**, 325 (1989).
87. M. Amouyal, L. Mortensen, H. Buc and K. Hammer, *Cell* **58**, 545 (1989).
88. S. Sasse-Dwight and J. D. Gralla, *PNAS* **85**, 8934 (1988).
89. D. L. Popham, D. Szeto, J. Keener and S. Kustu, *Science* **243**, 629 (1989).
90. L. J. Reitzer and B. Magasanik, *Cell* **45**, 785 (1986).
91. P-K. Wong, D. Popham, J. Keener and S. Kustu, *J. Bact.* **169**, 2876 (1987).
92. S. D. Minchin, S. Austin and R. A. Dixon, *EMBO J.* **8**, 3491 (1989).
93. S. E. Brown and F. M. Ausubel, *J. Bact.* **157**, 143 (1984).
94. M. Buck, S. Miller, M. Drummond and R. Dixon, *Nature* **320**, 374 (1986).
95. M. Buck and J. Woodcock, *Mol. Microbiol.* **1**, 243 (1987).
96. E. Santero, T. Hoover, J. Keener and S. Kustu, *PNAS* **86**, 7346 (1989).
97. H. R. Drew and A. A. Travers, *JMB* **186**, 773 (1985).
98. J. Griffith, A. Hochschild and M. Ptashne, *Nature* **322**, 750 (1986).
99. H.-J. Fritz, H. Bieknäse, B. Gleumes, C. Heibach, S. Rosahl and R. Ehring, *EMBO J.* **2**, 2129 (1983).
100. G. Kuhnke, A. Krause, C. Heibach, U. Gieske, H.-J. Fritz and R. Ehring, *EMBO J.* **5**, 167 (1986).
101. R. Haber and S. Adhya, *PNAS* **85**, 9683 (1988).
102. S. F. Li and J. A. DeMoss, *JBC* **263**, 13700 (1988).
103. C. K. Tuggle and J. A. Fuchs, *EMBO J.* **5**, 1077 (1986).
104. J. F. Thompson, U. K. Synder and A. Landy, *PNAS* **85**, 6323 (1988).
105. L. Moitoso de Vargas, S. Kim and A. Landy, *Science* **244**, 1457 (1989).
106. L. Moitoso de Vargas, C. A. Pargellis, N. M. Hasan, E. W. Bushman and A. Landy, *Cell* **54**, 923 (1988).

107. R. C. Johnson, A. C. Glasgow and M. I. Simon, *Nature* **329**, 462 (1987).
108. R. C. Johnson, M. F. Bruist and M. I. Simon, *Cell* **46**, 531 (1986).
109. G. R. Bellomy and M. T. Record, Jr., *Struct. Organ. Aspects Metab. Regul. New Ser.* **134**, 307 (1990).
110. Y. Hodges-Garcia, P. J. Hagerman and D. E. Pettijohn, *JBC* **264**, 14621 (1989).
111. D. M. Stalker, R. Kolter and D. R. Helinski, *JMB* **187**, 225 (1986).
112. M. Filutowicz, E. Uhlenkopp and D. R. Helinski, *JMB* **187**, 225 (1986).
113. S. Mukherjee, H. Erickson and D. Bastia, *Cell* **52**, 375 (1988).
114. S. Mukherjee, H. Erickson and D. Bastia, *PNAS* **85**, 6287 (1988).
115. M. McEachern, M. Bott, P. Tooken and D. R. Helinski, *PNAS* **86**, 7942 (1989).
116. M. Filutowicz and K. Appelt, *NARes* **16**, 3829 (1988).
117. M. Schnös, K. Zahn, F. R. Blattner and R. B. Inman, *Virology* **168**, 370 (1989).
118. R. S. Cohen and M. Meselson, *Nature* **332**, 856 (1988).
119. K. Takahashi, M. Vigneron, H. Matthes, A. Wildeman, M. Zenke and P. Chambon, *Nature* **319**, 121 (1986).
120. B. Théveny, A. Bailly, C. Rauch, M. Rauch, E. Delain and E. Milgrom, *Nature* **329**, 79 (1987).
121. K. Nasmyth and D. Shore, *Science* **237**, 1162 (1987).
122. A. H. Brand, L. Breeden, J. Abraham, R. Sternglanz and K. Nasmyth, *Cell* **41**, 41 (1985).
123. J. F.-X. Hofmann, T. Laroche, A. Brand and S. M. Gasser, *Cell* **57**, 725 (1989).
124. L. P. Woudt, W. H. Mager, R. T. M. Nieuwint, G. M. Wassenaar, A. C. van der Kuyl, J. J. Murre, M. F. M. Hockman, P. G. M. Brockhoff and R. J. Planta, *NARes* **15**, 6037 (1987).
125. D. Rhodes and A. Klug, *Nature* **286**, 573 (1980).
126. T. D. Tullius and B. A. Dombroski *Science* **230**, 679 (1985).
127. I. Goulet, Y. Zivanovic and A. Prunell, *NARes* **15**, 2803 (1987).
128. R. Schleif, *J. Cell. Biochem.* **S11C**, L004 (1987).
129. D. E. Pettijohn and O. Pfenninger, *PNAS* **77**, 1331 (1980).
130. R. R. Sinden, J. O. Carlson and D. E. Pettijohn, *Cell* **21**, 773 (1980).
131. R. R. Sinden, S. S. Broyles and D. E. Pettijohn, *PNAS* **80**, 1797 (1983).
132. J. B. Bliska and N. R. Cozzarelli, *JMB* **194**, 205 (1987).
133. W. Zacharias, A. Jaworski, J. E. Larson and R. D. Wells, *PNAS* **85**, 7069 (1988).
134. A. V. Vologodskii, V. V. Anshelevich, A. V. Lukashin and M. D. Frank-Kamenetskii, *Nature* **280**, 294 (1979).
135. S. A. Wasserman, J. H. White and N. R. Cozzarelli, *Nature* **344**, 448 (1988).
136. G. J. Pruss and K. Drlica, *PNAS* **83**, 8952 (1986).
137. L. F. Liu and J. C. Wang, *PNAS* **84**, 7024 (1987).
138. H.-Y. Wu, S. Shyy, J. C. Wang and L. F. Liu, *FASEB J.* **2**, 2764 (1988).
139. H.-Y. Wu, S. Shyy, J. C. Wang and L. F. Liu, *Cell* **53**, 433 (1988).
140. G. N. Giaever, L. Snyder and J. C. Wang, *Biophys. Chem* **29**, 7 (1989).
141. N. Figueroa and L. Bossi, *PNAS* **85**, 9416 (1988).
142. K. Drlica, R. J. Franco and T. R. Steck, *J. Bact.* **170**, 4983 (1988).
143. J. K. Lodge, T. Kazic and D. E. Berg, *J. Bact.* **171**, 2181 (1989).
144. Y.-P. Tsao, H.-Y. Wu and L. F. Liu, *Cell* **56**, 111 (1989).
145. A. Jaworski, J. A. Blaho, J. Larson, M. Shimizu and R. D. Wells, *JMB* **207**, 513 (1989).
146. G. J. Pruss and K. Drlica, *Cell* **56**, 521 (1989).
147. A. R. Rahmouni and R. D. Wells, *Science* **246**, 358 (1989).
148. M. LeBret, *Biopolymers* **18**, 1709 (1979).

149. M. LeBret, *Biopolymers* **23**, 1835 (1984).
150. D. M. Ruden, J. Ma and M. Ptashne, *PNAS* **85**, 4262 (1988).
151. G. Dandanell and K. Hammer, *Molecular Genetics of Bacteria and Phages: Prokaryotic Genetic Regulation,* 211 (1989).
152. S. D. Goodman and H. A. Nash, *Nature* **341**, 251 (1989).
153. U. K. Snyder, J. F. Thompson and A. Landy, *Nature* **341**, 255 (1989).
154. Y. Flashner and J. D. Gralla, *Cell* **45**, 713 (1988).
155. M. T. Record, Jr., and M. C. Mossing, *in* "RNA Polymerase and Regulation of Transcription" (W. Reznikoff, R. Burgess, J. Dahlberg, C. Gross, M. Record and M. Wickens, eds.), p. 61 Elsevier, New York, 1987.
156. S. Sasse-Dwight and J. D. Gralla, *JMB* **202**, 107 (1988).
157. T. T. Stenzel, P. Patel and D. Bastia, *Cell* **49**, 709 (1987).
158. H. Echols, *Science* **233**, 1050 (1986).
159. G. R. Bellomy, Ph.D. thesis. Univ. of Wisconsin, Madison, 1989.

Mitochondrial Aminoacyl-tRNA Synthetases

ALEXANDER TZAGOLOFF,
DOMENICO GATTI AND
ALEXANDRA GAMPEL

Department of Biological Sciences
Columbia University
New York, New York 10027

Aminoacyl-tRNA synthetases (amino acid—tRNA ligases, EC subsubclass 6.1.1) are important components of the translational machinery of all cells. Bacteria have at least 20 different synthetases, each designed to acylate its cognate tRNA isoacceptors with a single amino acid (*1*). In eukaryotes, the situation is more complex. Animals and fungi synthesize proteins in two physically separate cellular compartments, the cytoplasm and mitochondria. The contribution of mitochondria to the total cellular protein pool is minor both in terms of the number of proteins and their relative mass. Nonetheless, mitochondria have their own complete set of aminoacyl-tRNA synthetases, as well as

Progress in Nucleic Acid Research
and Molecular Biology, Vol. 39

tRNAs, ribosomes, and all the accessory factors necessary for chain initiation, elongation, and termination. In plants, the synthesis of proteins encoded in chloroplast DNA has necessitated the retention of still a third system of protein synthesis.

Virtually all our knowledge about the structure and function of aminoacyl-tRNA synthetases has come from studies of different bacterial and eukaryotic cytoplasmic enzymes. These topics have been discussed in a number of recent reviews (1–4). Undoubtedly, the same enzymes will continue to serve as models for probing the most fundamental issues of the catalytic mechanism and the accuracy of tRNA and amino-acid selection.[1] However, there are several reasons why aminoacyl-tRNA synthetases of such specialized organelles as mitochondria and chloroplasts are of special interest. Studies of the organelle-specific synthetases enlarge the number of examples of this enzyme family and hence provide a more complete compilation of data for evaluating the evolutionary derivations of its individual members. Second, mitochondria use modified genetic codes that have necessitated corollary changes in the tRNAs and in some instances in the aminoacyl-tRNA synthetases. Some mitochondrial synthetases have diverged in their primary sequences from the homologous cytoplasmic and bacterial enzymes. These changes can highlight domains critical for the formation of the catalytic core structure of a particular synthetase. Finally, there is increasing evidence pointing to a secondary role of certain aminoacyl-tRNA synthetases in the splicing of mitochondrial RNA.

This review emphasizes different aspects of the structure and function of mitochondrial aminoacyl-tRNA synthetases. Some of the discussion will also speculate on the broader question of how this family of enzymes may have evolved.

I. Genetic System of Yeast Mitochondria

Before engaging in a discussion of the mitochondrial aminoacyl-tRNA synthetases it may be helpful to review briefly some of the unique features of the genetic system of this organelle.

A. Genetic Code

The mitochondrial genomes of higher and lower eukaryotes code for the endogenous ribosomal and transfer RNAs and for a limited number of proteins that participate in electron transport and in oxida-

---

[1] See Rogers and Sölll in this volume regarding mischarging [Eds].

tive phosphorylation. These genomes differ in size, in the structure of their genes, and even in their genetic content (5–7). In addition to the variations in the molecular organization of their DNA, mitochondria of different organisms display a wide range of novel mechanisms for decoding their genetic information. Most mitochondria so far examined operate with a modified genetic code. Animal and fungal mitochondria make use of UGA as a tryptophan codon (5, 8) and of AUA as a methionine codon (9). There are other deviations from the universal code as well. In mammalian mitochondria, AGA and AGG act as translational stops (8), and in yeast, the four codons of the CUN family specify threonine instead of leucine (10).

B. Mitochondrial tRNAs

There are 24 tRNA genes in yeast mitochondria (11). Because of the somewhat unusual rules governing codon recognition, this number of tRNAs is sufficient to decode the entire genetic code. Thus, codon families for single amino acids normally requiring two different tRNAs are read by a single mitochondrial tRNA with U in the wobble position of the anticodon. Presumably, this U is capable of base-pairing with all four nucleotides in the 3' position of the codon (12). As a consequence, only one tRNA is required for each amino acid except methionine, arginine, serine, and threonine. The two methionine tRNAs function respectively in initiation and chain elongation. Serine and arginine each require two tRNAs because their codons are split between two different families. The existence of two codon families for threonine (ACN, CUN) also accounts for the presence of two threonine tRNAs (13).

Unlike animal mitochondrial tRNAs, whose D and TΨC loops are abnormally small (14), the tRNAs of fungal mitochondria have structures not especially different from those of bacteria and eukaryotic cells (11, 12). They have normal-size loops and the expected nucleotides in the loop and stem structures. The only exception is one of the two yeast mitochondrial threonine tRNAs, whose aberrant structure is described later (Section IV).

Some yeast mitochondrial tRNAs (tyrosine, tryptophan, serine, and leucine tRNAs) are efficiently charged by E. coli aminoacyl-tRNA synthetases in vitro (15, 16). There is also evidence that bacterial synthetases may be substituted for the mitochondrial enzymes in vivo (17). A construct coding for the E. coli tyrosyl-tRNA synthetase fused to a mitochondrial import leader sequence complements a yeast mutant lacking the mitochondrial synthetase. The mutant is complemented by the E. coli tyrosyl-tRNA synthetase even when the gene fusion was introduced on a single-copy plasmid, indicating the interchangeability of the two enzymes (17).

C. Mitochondrial Protein Synthesis

Although the tRNAs and the two ribosomal RNAs of yeast mitochondria are encoded in mitochondrial DNA, most other components of the translational apparatus—including the aminoacyl-tRNA synthetases, initiation and elongation factors, and all but one of the ribosomal proteins—are products of nuclear genes (6, 7, 9). These proteins are translated on cytoplasmic ribosomes and are subsequently imported into the matrix compartment, the site of mitochondrial protein synthesis.

Mitochondria and bacteria share many common attributes in the way they synthesize proteins. Translation of mitochondrial mRNAs is initiated with a formylmethionine which remains at the amino terminus of the mature proteins (18). Yeast mitochondria have a prokaryotic type of initiation factor, IF-2, suggesting that formation of the initiation complex depends on the same sequence of events as in bacteria. A further point of analogy concerns mitochondrial ribosomes, which are more closely related to bacterial than to eukaryotic cytoplasmic ribosomes. Mitochondrial ribosomes are sensitive to the same spectrum of antibiotics that inhibit bacterial, but not cytoplasmic, ribosomes (19). However, in other ways, the two translation systems are quite distinct. Yeast mitochondrial mRNAs do not have a Shine–Dalgarno ribosome attachment site, nor is the homologous sequence evident in the small ribosomal RNA (20). Mammalian mitochondrial mRNAs have no 5′ leader (21). There are also significant differences in the protein compositions of mitochondrial ribosomes. For example, some subunits of yeast mitochondrial ribosomes have no homologs in bacterial ribosomes (22, 23).

Some of the more remarkable findings to have emerged from studies of mitochondria from plant, animal, and fungal sources are (1) the diversity of their genetic codes; (2) the organization of the genomes; and (3) the ways in which genetic information is processed (5–7, 24, 25). The same diversity can also be discerned in the machineries that translate the mRNAs into the final protein products. In this respect, mitochondria show a much greater imagination than other genetic systems, including those of chloroplasts, whose operational principles have remained fairly fixed across phylogenetic boundaries. In a sense, mitochondria demonstrate the inherent plasticity of nucleic acids as vehicles for expressing genetic information. The reason why mitochondria chose to adopt such a multiplicity of solutions to achieve essentially the same end result remains a puzzle.

II. Mitochondrial Aminoacyl-tRNA Synthetases

A. Purification

Mitochondrial aminoacyl-tRNA synthetases are much less abundant than their cytoplasmic counterparts. Purification of these enzymes has been difficult and consequently not much is known about their physical and enzymatic properties. One of the few exceptions is the methionyl-tRNA synthetase of yeast mitochondria, which has been isolated as a homogenous protein (26). The purification of this particular enzyme was facilitated by virtue of its tendency to bind to polyanions and to various affinity columns (26). The purified synthetase has a specific activity 1000 times that of the crude mitochondrial extract. Approximately the same degree of purification has been reported for the phenylalanyl-tRNA synthetase of hen liver mitochondria (27). Since the water-soluble protein components represent 20 to 30% of the mitochondrial protein mass, the overall purification of these enzymes is another fivefold higher. Therefore, the methionyl- and phenylalanyl-tRNA synthetases represent at most 0.02% of the mitochondrial proteins. This is probably a fairly reasonable estimate of the concentrations of the other mitochondrial synthetases. Unlike the bacterial methionyl-tRNA synthetase, which exists as an α_2 homodimer, the mitochondrial synthetase behaves as a 65-kDa monomer (26). In contrast, the phenylalanyl-tRNA synthetases of yeast and hen liver mitochondria, like the bacterial synthetase, have an $\alpha_2\beta_2$ structure (27, 28).

Cytoplasmic aminoacyl-tRNA synthetases of mammalian cells are organized in large complexes with molecular weights exceeding 10^6 (29). The functional significance of the macromolecular assemblies still awaits clarification. Such large complexes have not been observed in bacteria; rather, the enzymes behave as discrete monomers (1). Based on the limited information available, this appears also to be true of the mitochondrial synthetases.

B. Enzymatic Properties

Bacterial and eukaryotic aminoacyl-tRNA synthetases acylate their tRNAs by first forming the activated aminoacyladenylate intermediate (1, 4). In the ensuing reaction, the amino acid is transferred to the 3' hydroxyl of the tRNA with the simultaneous release of AMP. There is nothing to suggest that this basic mechanism of tRNA acylation is in any way different in mitochondria. The mitochondrial enzymes are also probably endowed with an "editing" function to ensure high-fidelity selection of the appropriate amino acids. At present, however, the mitochondrial phenylalanyl-tRNA synthetase is the only mitochondrial synthetase shown to possess an editing mechanism (30).

The relative efficiency with which mitochondrial synthetases acylate tRNAs from different sources has been examined for the phenylalanyl-, methionyl-, and leucyl-tRNA synthetases (*31*). The yeast enzymes charge *E. coli* and yeast cytoplasmic tRNAs but with slower rates (*31*). Similar results have been obtained with the phenylalanyl-tRNA synthetase of bovine liver mitochondria (*32*). The K_m of the bovine enzyme is about the same for the mitochondrial and *E. coli* tRNAs, but is almost a tenth that of the yeast cytoplasmic tRNA (*32*). A comparison has also been made of the kinetic properties of yeast mitochondrial and cytoplasmic methionyl-tRNA synthetases (*26*). The K_m values were assayed for both the tRNA and the amino acid. Both synthetases have similar K_ms for the two substrates and show only marginal differences in their turnover numbers. Unfortunately, in this study the *E. coli* methionine tRNA was used as the substrate for the mitochondrial enzyme. It is interesting that while the mitochondrial synthetase is capable of acylating both the initiator and elongator methionine tRNAs of yeast mitochondria, the cytoplasmic synthetase acylates only the elongator tRNA (*26*). Outside of these few studies, not much is known at present about the enzymatic properties of mitochondrial aminoacyl-tRNA synthetases.

C. Aminoacyl-tRNA Synthetase Genes

It was evident from earlier biochemical studies that some of the yeast mitochondrial and cytoplasmic homologs are encoded by different genes. The leucyl-, phenylalanyl-, and methionyl-tRNA synthetases of yeast mitochondria are separable by chromatography from the cytoplasmic enzymes (*31*). The existence of two different genes for some of the yeast isoenzymes has been confirmed genetically. At least eight synthetases of yeast mitochondria are products of genes distinct from those coding for the cytoplasmic synthetases. They are the lysyl-, aspartyl-, phenylalanyl-, tyrosyl-, threonyl-, tryptophanyl-, leucyl-, and methionyl-tRNA synthetases (*33–39*). Mutations in each of these mitochondrial synthetases induce a respiratory-deficient phenotype but do not affect the ability of yeast to grow on fermentable substrates. Even though none of the mitochondrial enzymes have been sequenced directly, the primary structures deduced from the gene sequences suggest that each of the eight synthetases is synthesized as a precursor with an amino-terminal import signal. In every case, the primary translation product has a sequence rich in basic and hydroxylated amino acids at its amino-terminal end (Fig. 1), a feature characteristic of mitochondrial precursors (*40*). The routing of these enzymes to mitochondria is probably achieved by the same mechanism responsible for

```
              +   +                   +  +       -        -            + + +
Asp    M L A R S R V C L Q T I T R R L A D F P E A N A I K K K F L
                +  + +                     +          +     +      +     +
Lys    M N V L L K R R S L T F A P R W L W C K C R S S R S R P Y S
              +              +         +  +                +   -   +              -
Trp    M S N K Q A V L K L I S K R W I S T V Q R A D F K L N S E A
              -    +                      +  +
Tyr    M L E L R S C S N L V N S S R R L V P L V T Y S G L S A I T
              -                       +       +   +         +                 +
Phe    M E V T S M F L N R M M K T R T G L Y R L Y S T L K V P H V
        +            +              +                +              +  +        +
Thr    M K I Q L V R W H C S R N A L W N R A F Y S T R K A T K N A
              +              +            +  +                 +  +          -  +
Leu    M L S R P S S R F L S T K R G P G P A V K K L I A I G E K W
              +              +         +                                     +
Met    M Q C R S I V H R L Y S K I S H V T T P I F Y P N A K P H L
        +                        +               +                 +  +
Val    M N K W L N T L S K T F T F R L L N C H Y R R S L P L C O N
              +              +              +            +
His    M L S R S L N K V V T S I K S S S I I R M S S A T A A A T S
```

Fig. 1. Amino-terminal sequences of mitochondrial aminoacyl-tRNA synthetases. Only the first 30 amino-terminal residues encoded by the genes are reported. The basic and acidic residues have been marked by plus and minus signs, respectively.

the transport of other mitochondrial constituents to the matrix compartment.

While most mitochondrial synthetases appear to be products of distinct genes, there are two examples of a single gene coding for the identical cytoplasmic and mitochondrial enzymes (41, 42). The yeast *HTS1* and *VAS1* genes code for both the mitochondrial and cytoplasmic forms of histidyl- and valyl-tRNA synthetases, respectively (41, 43). The mechanism by which the two products of *HTS1* are targeted either to mitochondria or to the cytoplasmic compartment has been clarified (41). An analysis of the *HTS1* transcripts revealed the existence of two distinct size classes of mRNAs. The longer transcripts have 5′ termini clustering in a region 85 to 130 nucleotides upstream from the first in-frame AUG codon. These full-length transcripts code for the mitochondrial enzyme with a basic amino-terminal import sequence. A second more abundant class of transcripts have 5′ termini centering approximately 10 nucleotides downstream from the first AUG codon. The shorter transcripts lacking the first methionine codon are used to initiate translation from the second AUG located 60 nucleotides downstream from the first AUG. The resultant translation product is 20 amino acids shorter and lacks all or part of the amino terminal signal essential for mitochondrial import. It has been proposed that differential transcription of the gene accounts for the sequestration of the shorter product in the cytoplasm and transport of the longer protein into mitochondria (*41*). Evidence supporting this proposal was obtained by eliminating the first ATG from the *HTS1* reading frame. The substitution of the mutant for the wild-type gene caused the cells to become respiration-deficient but did not eliminate their ability to grow on glucose. Similar evidence has been adduced for the intracellular sorting of the two valyl-tRNA synthetase products of *VAS1* (*42*).

The discovery of two classes of aminoacyl-tRNA synthetases in yeast, those selectively employed in mitochondrial protein synthesis and others shared with the cytoplasmic system, raises intriguing questions related to the functional necessity of maintaining separate genes for a subset of the mitochondrial enzymes. Obviously, mitochondrial and cytoplasmic enzymes originating from common genes will have identical structures and catalytic properties. Other synthetases encoded by different genes, even though they may be homologous and have the same basic core structure, are likely to exhibit differences in tRNA preference, turnover, and perhaps regulation of their catalytic activities. Such factors may be important from the standpoint of the catalytic efficiency of the compartment-specific enzymes. For example, differences in the mitochondrial and cytoplasmic concentrations of amino acids and tRNAs may be compensated for by the intrinsic K_ms of the aminoacyl-tRNA synthetases for these substrates.

Other circumstances as well, such as the structures of the cytoplasmic and organellar tRNAs, may also have dictated the need to have separate sets of aminoacyl-tRNA synthetase genes. With the exception of the studies cited above, the specificities of the mitochondrial and cytoplasmic enzymes for their respective tRNAs have not been examined in detail. This problem has been difficult to address experimentally because of cross-contamination by the more abundant cytoplasmic enzymes.

D. Role of Mitochondrial Aminoacyl-tRNA Synthetases in RNA Splicing

A substantial number of mitochondrial genes in *Saccharomyces cerevisiae* and *Neurospora crassa* contain introns that, depending on their primary/secondary structures and mechanism of splicing, have been classified as group I and group II introns (*44, 45*). Some, but not all, group I and group II introns catalyze their own excision *in vitro* in the absence of protein factors and energy sources. Only the sequential two-step transesterification mechanism employed by group I introns

(46) will be reviewed here. The first transesterification step involves a nucleophilic attack of a guanine nucleotide on the 5' splice site resulting in a covalent attachment of the guanine nucleotide to the 5' hydroxyl of the intron and the release of the 5' exon. The free 3' hydroxyl of the 5' exon then initiates a second attack on the 3' splice site. The end products of the second transesterification are the free intron with the nonencoded guanine nucleotide and the ligated exons.

Even though group I introns are catalytic RNAs, there is compelling evidence indicating that under *in vivo* conditions, splicing of many mitochondrial pre-mRNAs containing group I introns is strictly dependent on accessory protein factors (47–50). This evidence comes largely from studies of mutants of yeast and of *N. crassa*. In yeast, processing of group I introns can be blocked by mutations in both mitochondrial and nuclear genes. The mitochondrial mutations are often localized in introns coding for *trans*-acting factors (51). These observations provided the first indication for the existence of intron-encoded splicing factors ("maturases") and led to the proposal of the maturase model of RNA processing (52). A large number of splicing-defective mutants of yeast and *N. crassa* have also been described in which the mutations are in nuclear genes. Such mutants may be arrested in splicing of a single (47, 48, 53) or of multiple (50) introns. At present only a few of the nuclear-encoded splicing proteins have been characterized and their precise role in promoting the catalytic activity of the RNA remains poorly understood. The general presumption is that they stabilize a catalytically competent conformation of the RNA (54). Remarkably, two such splicing proteins have turned out to be aminoacyl-tRNA synthetases (55, 56).

The participation of a mitochondrial aminoacyl-tRNA synthetase in splicing of group I introns was first reported by Lambowitz and co-workers (55), who found that conditional *cyt18* mutants of *N. crassa*, when grown at the nonpermissive temperature, have severely reduced mitochondrial protein synthetic activity and accumulate unspliced precursors of the large rRNA and of the cytochrome *b* mRNA (54, 57). When the wild-type *CYT18* gene was cloned and its sequence determined, the encoded product was discovered to be homologous to the tyrosyl-tRNA synthetases of *Escherichia coli* and of *Bacillus stearothermophilus* (55). The following evidence supported the conclusion that the splicing-deficient phenotype of *cyt18* mutants is caused by mutations in the structural gene for the mitochondrial tyrosyl-tRNA synthetase: (1) complementation of the *cyt18* mutants was lost when the amino-terminal coding region of the gene was deleted; (2) *cyt18* mutants have missense mutations in the tyrosyl-tRNA synthetase gene; (3) antibodies directed against a fusion protein of the *CYT18*-encoded product inhibit acylation of the tyrosine tRNA by wild-type mitochondrial synthetase extracts. Even though these observations unambiguously demonstrate that mutations in the mitochondrial tyrosyl-tRNA synthetase are responsible for the RNA processing defect, a direct role of the protein in splicing has not been established. Specifically, the phenotype of *cyt18* mutants could be an indirect effect of mutations in the tyrosyl-tRNA synthetase if splicing is dependent on some mitochondrial translation product.

Several lines of evidence support the idea of a direct involvement of the synthetase in the splicing reaction. Mitochondrial lysates and ribonucleoprotein (RNP) preparations from wild-type cells promote excision of the intron from the native 35-S precursor of the rRNA and from an *in vitro* transcribed RNA containing the intron (58). Comparable extracts obtained from *cyt18* mutants are fully active only when the cells are grown at the permissive temperature. Extensive fractionation of mitochondrial extracts indicate that the splicing activity cofractionates with the tyrosyl-tRNA synthetase (59). However, the interpretation of these studies was somewhat complicated by the fact that the synthetase elutes in two separate peaks on phosphocellulose, only one of which stimulates splicing of the ribosomal intron.

The strongest evidence for a direct role of the synthetase was obtained from studies of a partial revertant of a *cyt18* mutant. This revertant is able to process the RNAs normally even though it is impaired in mitochondrial protein synthesis (55). Furthermore, mitochondrial extracts from the revertant are not able to acylate the tyrosine tRNA. Together, these results point to two different activities in the tyrosyl-tRNA synthetase, one concerned with acylation of the tRNA and the other in promoting splicing of group I introns.

There is a somewhat analogous situation in yeast (56). The bI4 intron (fourth intron) of the cytochrome *b* gene and the aI4 intron in the gene coding for subunit 1 of cytochrome oxidase have ORFs in register with the reading frames of the respective upstream exons (52, 60–62). Excision of both introns requires the maturase encoded by the bI4 intron. Thus, mutations in bI4 block excision of both the bI4 and aI4 introns (52, 63). Even though the proteins encoded by aI4 and bI4 are homologous, only the latter appears to be an active maturase. However, the latent activity of the aI4 protein can be elicited by a single base change in the reading frame, causing the substitution of a lysine for a glutamic acid (64). Such mutations behave as mitochondrial suppressors of splicing-deficient bI4 mutants (64). There are also nuclear suppressors of bI4 splicing defective mutants (65, 66). One particular group of genetically linked mutations in a nuclear gene (named *NAM2*) act as allele specific suppressors (67). The nuclear gene (*NAM2*) responsible for suppressing the bI4 mutations was cloned and identified as the mitochondrial leucyl-tRNA synthetase (56). As in the case of the tyrosyl-tRNA synthetase, the dominant mutations conferring suppressor activity are in the leucyl-tRNA synthetase gene (56). Surprisingly, the wild-type *NAM2* gene from *Saccharomyces douglassi* acts as a natural suppressor of the bI4 deficiency (68). Unfortunately, because of the lack of an *in vitro* splicing assay for the bI4 intron, a direct demonstration for the involvement of the leucyl-tRNA synthetase in splicing has not yet been achieved.

III. Cloning of the Genes for Mitochondrial Aminoacyl-tRNA Synthetases

Based on their genetic code and tRNA composition, yeast mitochondria probably require 21 aminoacyl-tRNA synthetases for translating the dozen or so endogenous mRNAs. This estimate is one in excess of the customary 20 synthetases that are believed to be part of the eukaryotic and bacterial translational machineries (*1*). One extra synthetase must be invoked because the two threonine tRNAs of yeast mitochondria are each acylated by a different threonyl-tRNA synthetase.

A number of nuclear genes coding for the yeast mitochondrial enzymes have been cloned and their sequences determined. With a few exceptions, the genes were obtained by complementation of nuclear respiratory-deficient mutants of *Saccharomyces cerevisiae* (*33–39*). Mutants defective in mitochondrial aminoacyl-tRNA synthetases have been identified among a collection of *pet* strains selected for their inability to grow on nonfermentable carbon sources (69). Based on their biochemical properties, the *pet* mutants describe a number of different phenotypes, one of which is consistent with lesions in components necessary for mitochondrial protein synthesis. Such mutants are deficient in all the mitochondrial translation products and, as a result, are pleiotropically deficient in the respiratory chain enzymes (cytochrome oxidase, coenzyme QH_2-cytochrome c reductase, ATPase) some of whose subunit polypeptides are synthesized in mitochondria. Another important hallmark of this class of mutants is the instability of their mitochondrial DNA, which tends to acquire large deletions or may be totally lost (70). Consequently, strains defective in mitochondrial protein synthesis convert to rho^- and rho^0 mutants at a high frequency. The frequency with which the wild-type genome is lost in any particular mutants depends on the tightness of the *pet* mutation. For example, mutant constructs lacking a gene for a mitochondrial aminoacyl-tRNA synthetase or ribosomal protein convert quantitatively to rho^- and rho^0 derivatives (70). The requirement of mitochondrial protein synthesis in maintaining the wild-type genome is paradoxical, as there is no evidence that replication of the full-length circular DNA depends on a mitochondrially translated protein.

Two approaches have been used to recognize *pet* mutants with lesions in mitochondrial aminoacyl-tRNA synthetases. Individual mutants from complementation groups ascertained to be defective in mitochondrial protein synthesis have been tested for their ability to acylate different tRNAs. For these assays, crude extracts of mutant mitochondria are used to charge total tRNAs with labelled amino acids. The products are separated by reverse-phase chromatography to assess the acylation activities in the extracts. Alternatively, genes capable of complementing mutants defective in mitochondrial protein synthesis have been cloned by transformation with genomic libraries. The sequences of the genes and of the encoded products have been useful in identifying mutations in aminoacyl-tRNA synthetases in those instances when the protein sequence has turned out to be homologous to known bacterial or yeast cytoplasmic enzymes. Direct cloning of the gene and its characterization without prior knowledge of the reason for the translational defect of the *pet* mutant has been the most expedient way of identifying strains with lesions in mitochondrial synthetases, ribosomal proteins, and translation initiation and elongation factors.

The genes defined by *pet* mutants are needed solely for the expression of respiratory competent mitochondria and are therefore unlikely to provide a function necessary for cell viability. Aminoacyl-tRNA synthetase genes obtained by transformation of *pet* mutants can therefore code only for enzymes that function in mitochondrial but not in cytoplasmic protein synthesis. Mutations in genes coding for both the cytoplasmic and mitochondrial isoenzymes are lethal and therefore are unlikely to be represented in a *pet* mutant collection. A different strategy must be adopted to clone genes coding for enzymes shared by the two cellular compartments. The histidyl-tRNA synthetase gene *HTS1* was cloned by transformation of a temperature-sensitive *hts1* mutant (41). The *VAS1* gene for the valyl-tRNA synthetase, on the other hand, was obtained by screening a genomic library with an antibody against the purified protein (43).

IV. Threonyl-tRNA Synthetases of Yeast Mitochondria

There is currently one example of an aminoacyl-tRNA synthetase whose existence is explained by the idiosyncrasy of the mitochondrial genetic code. As indicated earlier, in yeast mitochondria threonine is encoded by both the conventional ACN and by CUN codons that normally designate leucine. The two sets of codons are read by two different tRNAs, one with a $(3')$UGU$(5')$ and the other with a $(3')$GAU$(5')$ anticodon (10, 11, 71). The tRNA^{GAU} has a number of unusual features, the most striking of which is an asymmetrically placed anticodon due to an extra nucleotide in the anticodon loop (20, 71). In addition, this tRNA has structural characteristics reminiscent of both leucine and threonine tRNAs. For example, its stem and loop structures have the invariant nucleotides of a leucine tRNA. The tRNA^{GAU}, however, lacks the long variable loop normally present in leucine tRNAs.

Because of its chimeric structure, it was not clear whether this tRNA is acylated by a leucyl- or a threonyl-type of synthetase. This question was resolved from studies of a group of *pet* mutants defective in charging the mitochondrial tRNA^{GAU}. Since the mutants showed normal acylation of the tRNA^{UGU}, it appeared that each threonine tRNA is acylated by a separate synthetase. The nuclear gene (*MST1*) responsible for the acylation of the tRNA^{GAU} was cloned by transformation of an *mst1* mutant with a yeast genomic library (34). The sequence of the gene revealed that the synthetase is homologous to the threonyl-tRNA synthetase of *E. coli*. Thus, even though the tRNA has a leucine anticodon, it is recognized as an appropriate substrate by a threonyl-specific synthetase. The mitochondrial threonyl-tRNA synthetase is considerably shorter than the bacterial and yeast cytoplasmic enzymes (72, 73), lacking some 200 residues from the amino-terminal end. This long amino-terminal sequence, therefore, must serve some function other than aminoacylation.

To date, the second threonyl-tRNA synthetase gene has not been cloned. It is unlikely that *THS1*, the gene for yeast cytoplasmic threonyl-tRNA synthetase (72,), also codes for the mitochondrial enzyme. The first in-frame ATG of this gene has been destroyed by *in vitro* mutagenesis and by frame-shifting. If the mitochondrial and cytoplasmic enzymes were both encoded by *THS1*, the mutant gene lacking the first ATG should complement *ths1*, but not *mst1* mutants. This was found not to be the case (A. M. Myers and A. Tzagoloff, unpublished).

The occurrence of CUN codons in yeast mitochondrial mRNAs is rare (62). Presumably, this codon family was appropriated to specify threonine at a time when the preferred codons for leucine were UUA and UUG. Furthermore, assuming some limited use of CUN codons for leucine, their replacement by threonine must have conferred some advantage to the cell. Two requirements had to be satisfied to implement the switch in the code. First is the appearance of a threonine tRNA with a (3')GAU(5') anticodon. The second requirement is an enzyme, which we now know to be a threonyl-tRNA synthetase, capable of charging the new tRNA with threonine.

It is possible to envision a number of evolutionary mechanisms of how this could have occurred. According to one such scenario, the original leucine tRNA^{GAU} acquired a mutation that reduced but did not completely prevent it from being charged by the leucyl-tRNA synthetase. Since the scheme assumes a low frequency of CUN codons this condition may have been tolerated despite the inefficient acylation of the mutant tRNA. To account for the two different mitochondrial enzymes, there must have been a duplication of a gene coding for a threonyl-tRNA synthetase. The deletion of the amino-terminal coding region in the new copy may have resulted concurrently with the duplication or by subsequent mutations. Two other events must be invoked: mutations in the duplicated gene allowing recognition of the tRNA as a proper substrate for the enzyme, and further modification of the tRNA leading to a loss of recognition by the leucyl-tRNA synthetase.

V. Degree of Sequence Conservation between Yeast Mitochondrial, Yeast Cytoplasmic, and Prokaryotic Aminoacyl-tRNA Synthetases

How similar are the mitochondrial to other bacterial and eukaryotic cytoplasmic aminoacyl-tRNA synthetases? The sequences of some dozen mitochondrial synthetases permits a partial answer to this question. Because none of the proteins have been sequenced directly, there is still some question regarding the amino termini of the mature proteins. As might be expected, the mitochondrial synthetases are homologous to both the yeast cytoplasmic and to the bacterial synthetases, indicating common ancestral origins. The extent of primary sequence similarities among the three groups of enzymes ranges from 21 to 52% (Table I). These values are based on the number of identical residues over the entire lengths of the polypeptide chains. Although the homology becomes more obvious when conservative substitutions are included in the calculations, they do not affect the basic conclu-

TABLE I

HOMOLOGY OF YEAST MITOCHONDRIAL TO YEAST
CYTOPLASMIC AND *E. coli* AMINOACYL-tRNA
SYNTHETASES[a]

Enzyme	Yeast cytoplasmic[b]	*E. coli*[b]
TyrRS	—	35
ValRS	100	41
LeuRS	—	36
MetRS	20	24
TrpRS	—	36
ThrRS	52	44
PheRS	—	23
AspRS	21	—
LysRS	31	22
HisRS	100	23

[a] The yeast mitochondrial aminoacyl-tRNA synthetases (RS) were aligned with the yeast cytoplasmic and *E. coli* homologs by the MFALGO program (85). The primary structure similarities are expressed as percentage of identical residues over comparable lengths of the polypeptide chains. The sequences were obtained from the following references: yeast mitochondrial TyrRS (J. Hill and A. Tzagoloff, unpublished), ValRS (42), LeuRS (36), MetRS (37), TrpRS (33), ThrRS (34), PheRS (35), AspRS (38), LysRS (39), HisRS (41); yeast cytoplasmic ValRS (42), MetRS (77), ThrRS (72), AspRS (81), LysRS (82), HisRS (41); *E. coli* TyrRS (74), ValRS (75), LeuRS (76), MetRS (78), TrpRS (79), ThrRS (73), PheRS (80), LysRS (83), HisRS (84).

[b] Percent of identical residues.

sions regarding the degree of divergence or conservation of any particular enzyme type.

The kind of changes incurred by mitochondrial synthetases can be seen in the dot matrices shown in Fig. 2. Some enzymes such as the tryptophanyl- and tyrosyl-tRNA synthetases have highly conserved sequences and very few insertions and deletions. Other synthetases have highly divergent sequences compared to the bacterial or eukaryotic enzymes. These include the aspartyl-, the α-subunit of the phenylalanyl-, the histidyl-, and the methionyl-tRNA synthetases. There are also examples of synthetases whose polypeptide chains have sustained

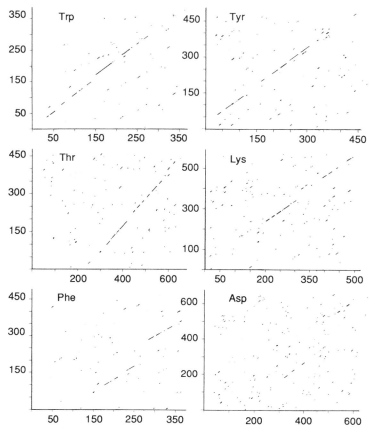

FIG. 2. Homology of yeast mitochondrial and *E. coli* aminoacyl-tRNA synthetases. The dot matrices were obtained with a program that scored a dot for every four identities in a window of nine residues. The mitochondrial synthetases (*y* axis) were compared to the homologous *E. coli* enzymes (*x* axis) except for the yeast mitochondrial aspartyl-tRNA synthetase, which was compared to the yeast cytoplasmic enzyme.

long deletions or insertions. A case in point is the threonyl-tRNA synthetase, which lacks some 200 residues at the amino-terminal region.

Based on the number of amino-acid identities and on their size, the yeast mitochondrial synthetases appear to be more similar to the bacterial than to the cytoplasmic synthetases (Table I). In the case of the methionyl-tRNA synthetase, the resemblance to the prokaryotic prototype is also evident in the absence of a long amino-terminal domain that is present only in the cytoplasmic synthetase (37, 77, 78). However, to conclude that mitochondrial synthetases as a group are close relatives of the bacterial synthetases seems unwarranted at present. A more tenable interpretation of the still fragmentary data is that some enzymes, because of structural constraints, tend to be more conserved than others, independent of their source.

VI. Homologous Proteins within the Aminoacyl-tRNA Synthetase Family

The primary structures of some 17 different aminoacyl-tRNA synthetases are now known. As of this writing the only sequences still missing are those of the asparaginyl-, prolyl-, and cysteinyl-tRNA synthetases. How related are the present-day members of this family? Do they owe their origin to disparate genetic elements that have undergone a process of convergent evolution, or are they products of a smaller number of ancestral genes that have followed a path of divergent evolution? These questions have some bearing on which enzymes may have common structures and may ultimately provide some basis for conjecture about the chemical compositions of early proteins.

The presence in a substantial number of synthetases of short homologous sequences was the first hint of possible evolutionary kinships. Thus the sequence His-Ile-Gly-His (HIGH) or variations of it were reported to occur near the amino termini of a diverse group of enzymes that included the methionyl-, tyrosyl-, isoleucyl-, glutamyl-, and glutaminyl-tRNA synthetases (2, 86). A second sequence Lys-Met-Ser-Lys (KMSK) was also found in some of the enzymes nearer to the carboxyl terminus (87). Chemical cross-linking experiments indicated that the latter element is part of the tRNA binding domain (88). Despite these observations, a case for homology in an evolutionary sense could not be made due to the absence of any obvious overall primary structure similarity. This situation persisted until the sequence of two enzymes, the valyl- and leucyl-tRNA synthetases, became available (34, 43, 75). These two synthetases share enough sequence similarity to permit an unambiguous alignment of their polypeptide chains (43, 75). The leucyl- and isoleucyl-tRNA synthetases were also noted to be homologous, establishing that these as well as the valyl-specific enzyme are derived from the same ancestral gene (36). The methionyl-tRNA synthetase qualifies as a fourth member of the leucyl subgroup. Even though the latter enzyme is somewhat different in size and is more divergent in primary sequence, it too has extensive regions of amino-acid conservation with the other three synthetases (36, 75, 89).

The notion of a common evolutionary line of descent of these synthetases is not surprising, considering that their amino-acid substrates
have similar sizes and chemical properties.

The above four aminoacyl-tRNA synthetases each have the HIGH
and KMSK motifs (36, 43, 75, 86). As discussed in more detail later, the
HIGH sequence is part of a loop in the nucleotide binding pockets of
the tyrosyl- and methionyl-tRNA synthetases that faces the adenine
moiety of ATP (90). Even though the amino-acid sequences of the
acyladenylate binding domain in the two synthetases are different
(exclusive of the HIGH sequence), the secondary structure elements
and the architecture of the sites are very similar (91). In fact, it is not
unreasonable to think that all aminoacyl-tRNA synthetases with the
HIGH motif may have the same general type of active site (89). There
are several explanations for the presence of structurally analogous
catalytic sites in enzymes with highly divergent sequences. The enzymes could have evolved independently from different genes. Alternatively, the absence of sequence homology may be indicative of very
early gene duplication events. The duplications could have occurred at
the level of the entire gene or of a domain encompassing the catalytic
site only.

All three explanations are tenable, and a clear choice among them
is not possible at present. Nonetheless, there is some basis for favoring
the notion that the nucleotide binding domain of the methionyl- and
tyrosyl-tRNA synthetases may have evolved from a common precursor.
These enzymes are only two examples of a larger group of synthetases
characterized by their possession of the HIGH sequence (Fig. 3). It is
difficult to imagine how this sequence could have arisen independently in so many proteins, particularly since there are examples of
other aminoacyl-tRNA synthetases lacking it. Also of some significance
is the fact that a search of the most current protein banks detects the
HIGH sequence only in the aminoacyl-tRNA synthetases. This motif,
therefore, really does appear to be a signature for this class of enzymes,
as suggested by Schimmel (2).

Assuming the HIGH motif to be a vestigial sequence derived from a
common genetic element, it was of interest to determine the extent to
which the primary sequence of this domain might have diverged in the
nine different synthetases listed in Fig. 3. The regions corresponding
to the β-α-β unit of the nucleotide binding pockets of tyrosyl- and
methionyl-tRNA synthetases and the analogous regions of seven other
enzymes with the HIGH motif were analyzed by the RDF2 program
(96, 97). This program evaluates the statistical significance of homology scores by comparing the values obtained with the real sequences

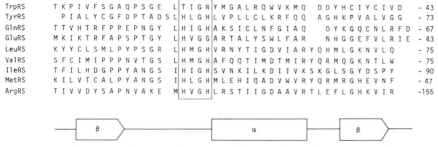

TrpRS	T K P I V F S G A Q P S G E	L	T I G N	Y M G A L R Q W V K M Q	D D Y H C I Y C I V D	- 43
TyrRS	P I A L Y C G F D P T A D S L	H L G H	L V P L L C L K R F Q Q	A G H K P V A L V G G	- 73
GlnRS	T T V H T R F P P E P N G Y	L	H I G H	A K S I C L N F G I A Q	D Y K G Q C N L R F D	- 67
GluRS	M K I K T R F A P S P T G Y	L	H V G G	A R T A L Y S W L F A R	N H G G E F V L R I E	- 43
LeuRS	K Y Y C L S M L P Y P S G R	L	H M G H	V R N Y T I G D V I A R Y Q H M L G K N V L Q	- 75
ValRS	S F C I M I P P P N V T G S	L	H M G H	A F Q Q T I M D T M I R Y Q R M Q G K N T L W	- 75
IleRS	T F I L H D G P P Y A N G S	I	H I G H	S V N K I L K D I I V K S K G L S G Y D S P Y	- 90
MetRS	K I L V T C A L P Y A N G S	I	H L G H	M L E H I Q A D V W V R Y Q R M R G H E V N F	- 47
ArgRS	T I V V D Y S A P N V A K E	M	H V G H	L R S T I I G D A A V R T L E F L G H K V I R	-155

Fig. 3. Alignment of aminoacyl-tRNA synthetases of *E. coli* containing the HIGH sequence. The amino-acid sequence of the tyrosyl-tRNA synthetase β-α-β domain (74) has been aligned with the comparable regions of the tryptophanyl- (79), glutaminyl- (92), glutamyl- (93), leucyl- (76), valyl- (75), isoleucyl- (86), methionyl- (78), and arginyl-tRNA (94) synthetases by the multiple alignment program of Lipman *et al.* (95). The secondary structure elements determined from the X-ray structure of the tyrosyl-tRNA synthetase of *B. stearothermophilus* (90) are shown in the lower part of the figure. The HIGH sequences of each enzyme are enclosed by the box.

to those obtained after scrambling one of the sequences by a Monte Carlo procedure (97). High scores with significant deviations above the mean score of the scrambled sequences were obtained in pairwise comparisons of the leucyl-, isoleucyl-, valyl-, arginyl-, and methionyl-tRNA synthetases (Table II). An appreciable homology was also detected between glutamyl- and glutaminyl-tRNA synthetases. The primary sequence similarity of the active site domains in the latter two enzymes is illustrated in Fig. 4, which shows the identities and conserved substitutions between three different glutaminyl-tRNA synthetases and the glutamyl-tRNA synthetase of *E. coli*.

Eight other aminoacyl-tRNA synthetases whose primary structures have been determined appear to be unrelated to the group with the HIGH motif. Alignments of their sequences have revealed an unambiguous homology of lysyl- and aspartyl-tRNA synthetases (38, 39). In addition, some suggestive sequence similarity has been detected between seryl- and threonyl-tRNA synthetases. The primary structure conservation between different lysyl- and aspartyl-tRNA synthetases is illustrated in Fig. 5. In this analysis, two different aspartyl-tRNA synthetases have been aligned with two lysyl-tRNA synthetases, using the multiple sequence alignment program of Lipman *et al.* (95), and the number of amino-acid identities and conservative replacements at each position averaged over a window of seven residues. Like the leucyl subgroup, the lysyl- and aspartyl-specific enzymes exhibit sev-

ALEXANDER TZAGOLOFF ET AL.

TABLE II

Homology of the Amino Terminal Regions of Synthetases Containing the HIGH Sequence[a]

	IleRS	LeuRS	ValRS	MetRS	ArgRS	GlnRS	GluRS	TyrRS	TrpRS
IleRS		6.4	8.8	10.8	−0.8	3.5	− 0.8	1.1	0.0
LeuRS	57		11.7	10.5	7.0	3.1	2.0	1.6	0.3
ValRS	63	91		10.0	4.4	3.8	1.7	1.8	0.8
MetRS	76	89	80		5.5	1.6	0.9	4.5	1.4
ArgRS	18	64	46	51		−0.1	1.5	−0.3	−1.0
GlnRS	40	40	41	28	18		12.4	2.3	1.2
GluRS	16	34	31	27	28	85		−0.6	−1.0
TyrRS	26	32	32	46	19	37	18		0.5
TrpRS	21	24	26	31	14	28	15	24	

[a] The domains with the His-Ile-Gly-His (HIGH) sequence of nine different *E. coli* aminoacyl tRNA synthetases presumed to fold into an β-α-β unit (see Fig. 3) were aligned and scored by the FASTA algorithm (97). The homology scores for each pair of synthetases are reported below the diagonal. The statistical significance of the scores was evaluated by the RDF2 program (96, 97). This is reported above the diagonal in the matrix and is expressed as standard deviation above (positive values) or below (negative values) the mean score derived from 400 pairwise comparisons in which one of the two sequences compared was shuffled by a Monte Carlo procedure. Significant values are indicated by the bold numbers.

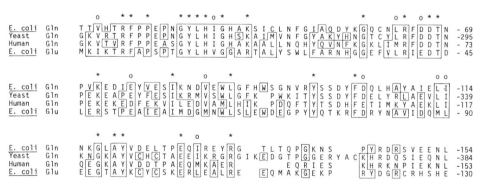

Fig. 4. Homology of glutamyl- and glutaminyl-tRNA synthetases. The indicated regions of the human (98), yeast (99), and *E. coli* (92) glutaminyl-tRNA synthetases and of *E. coli* glutamyl-tRNA synthetase (93) were aligned by the multiple alignment program of Lipman *et al.* (95). Positions with identical and conserved substitutions have been boxed only in those instances when there is a match between the glutamyl- and at least one glutaminyl-tRNA synthetase. The following were considered to be conservative amino-acid substitutions: I=L=M=V, F=Y, D=E, and R=K. Positions with identical residues in all four proteins are indicated by a star and with conserved replacements with an open circle.

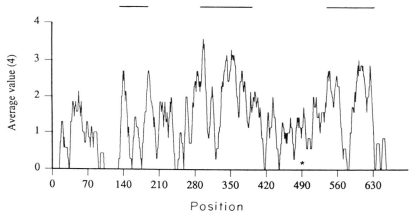

FIG. 5. Homology of aspartyl- and lysyl-tRNA synthetases. The yeast mitochondrial (39) and cytoplasmic (82) lysyl-tRNA synthetases were aligned with one another and with the yeast mitochondrial (38) and cytoplasmic aspartyl-tRNA synthetases by the multiple alignment program (95). The mitochondrial aspartyl-tRNA synthetase has a long insertion of 137 residues after Val-364 (marked with an asterisk) which was omitted from the analysis. The degree of sequence conservation in the four proteins was calculated by assigning a score of zero to regions not present in all the proteins or lacking any identity, and a score of one for each identical or quasiidentical amino acid (Ile=Val, Met=Leu, Tyr=Phe, Lys=Arg). A window of seven residues was used to scan the sequences and the scores at each position were averaged. Regions of high primary sequence conservation between the four synthetases are indicated by the bars.

eral long domains of high sequence conservation indicative of a derivation from a common ancestral gene. The most highly conserved domains are located in the central and carboxyl terminal regions of the polypeptide chains. These sequences are probably involved in forming the catalytic core structure, discussed in more detail in the next section. The common origin of these synthetases is unexpected in light of the amino-acid substrates that have different charges and are not frequently exchanged in homologous proteins.

As indicated above, computer searches suggest that the threonyl- and seryl-tRNA synthetases might also be distantly related to one another. An alignment of five different synthetases indicates a significant number of residues are identical or have conservative substitutions in a region proximal to their amino termini (Fig. 6). The primary sequence conservation, however, is borderline, and its significance is difficult to assess. We have provisionally assigned these two synthetases to another evolutionary subgroup of the family.

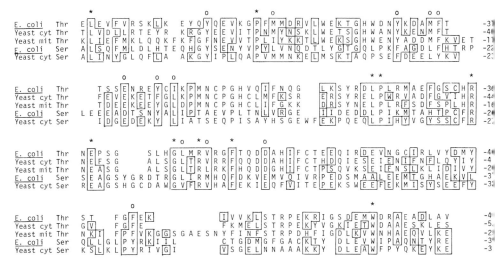

FIG. 6. Homology of threonyl- and seryl-tRNA synthetases. The yeast mitochondrial (34), yeast cytoplasmic (72), and E. coli (73) threonyl-tRNA synthetases have been aligned with the yeast cyoplasmic (100) and E. coli (101) seryl-tRNA synthetases with the multiple alignment program (95). Positions having at least one identity or conservative replacement (I=L=M=V, F=Y, D=E, and K=R) between the two different types of enzymes are boxed. Positions at which all five proteins have the same or conserved amino acids are marked by the asterisks and open circles, respectively.

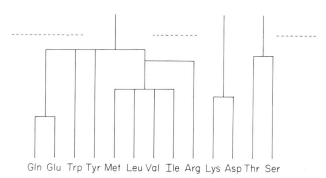

Gln Glu Trp Tyr Met Leu Val Ile Arg Lys Asp Thr Ser

FIG. 7. Evolutionarily related aminoacyl-tRNA synthetases. The distance between the branching points and the horizontal broken line is approximately proportional to the divergence in primary structure as determined from the homology scores and their statistical significance (see Table II). The horizontal broken line denotes an arbitrary time from which the relative time of divergences has been calculated.

A tentative scheme of how the synthetase family may have evolved is summarized in Fig. 7. Some enzymes, such as the lysyl- and aspartyl-tRNA synthetases, and the set represented by the leucyl-, isoleucyl-, valyl-, and methionyl-, and perhaps arginyl-tRNA synthetases are proposed to have arisen from common precursors as a result of gene duplications. Other synthetases within the group with the HIGH sequence are also viewed to be evolutionarily related. Their sequences, however, have undergone such profound changes that relationships are at the threshold of detection by primary structure criteria.

VII. Catalytic Sites of Aminoacyl-tRNA Synthetases

A. Aminoacyladenylate Site of Methionyl- and Tyrosyl-tRNA Synthetases

The three-dimensional (tertiary) structures of the tyrosyl- and methionyl-tRNA synthetases have been reported (90, 102, 103). Both enzymes contain the HIGH sequence motif, but otherwise have essentially different sequences. High-resolution X-ray diffraction data have also been obtained of tyrosyl-tRNA synthetase with bound tyrosyladenylate (90). The crystallographic analyses have led to a description of the topology of the active site and of the residues making contact with the aminoacyladenylate intermediate. A detailed account of the structure is not given here. Instead, we wish to emphasize the structural features common to both synthetases. The active site of the tyrosyl-tRNA synthetase fits the description of a cleft starting at the surface and terminating with a funnel in the interior part of the protein. The site is composed of secondary structural elements recruited from an amino-terminal region of the protein encompassing some 200 residues. The active site is defined by five apposed parallel β-strands on one side and by two α-helices on the opposite side of the cleft. The HIGH sequence is part of a long loop located near the rim of the cleft. The amino acid fits into the deepest level of the cleft, and during the catalytic cycle, must occupy the active site prior to the entry of ATP (90). The disposition of the tRNA in the three-dimensional model is still not known.

Although the interactions of ATP and of methionine with the methionyl-tRNA synthetase have not been determined with equal certitude, the active site is built on the same structural principles as the one in the tyrosyl-tRNA synthetase (89, 103). The same number and arrangement of helices and parallel β-strands are present in the methionyl-tRNA synthetase, altough their primary sequences are different. The exception to this is the HIGH sequence in the long loop near the surface of the cleft which is nearly superimposable with the analogous loop of the tyrosyl-tRNA synthetase (89, 91).

B. Glycine-rich Domain of Lysyl- and Aspartyl-tRNA Synthetases

Lysyl- and aspartyl-tRNA synthetases lack the HIGH motif. Analyses of four yeast and one *E. coli* enzymes indicate several highly conserved domains likely to be important in determining their core structures (36). It was of interest to see whether the available sequence information could be exploited to make some reasonable guesses about the nucleotide binding site. Two assumptions were made in attempting to identify regions involved in ATP binding. First, such regions were expected to have a larger number of amino-acid identities between lysyl- and aspartyl-tRNA synthetases than other domains involved in interaction with either the amino acid or the tRNA. The possibility also existed that the acyladenylate site of the synthetases might bear some resemblance to other ATP binding proteins and could therefore be identified on the basis of some characteristic sequence.

Comparisons of five different aspartyl- and lysyl-tRNA synthetases revealed a highly conserved domain near their carboxyl termini (36). This domain is defined by a stretch of 33 residues with ten identities and six conservative substitutions. A singular feature of the domain is the presence of four glycines with the canonical spacing Gly-Gly-X-Gly-X-Gly associated with the nucleotide binding site of numerous kinases, GTP binding proteins, and dehydrogenases (104–115) (Fig. 8). The structure of the nucleotide-binding pocket has been determined for a number of proteins, including adenylate kinase (114), H-Ras (116), and elongation factor EF-tu (117). In all cases, the four glycines occur in a loop that overhangs the nucleotide binding pocket. The sequences flanking the glycines form a β-α-β unit located in the active site with the glycine-rich loop connecting the first β-strand to the α-helix.

It is interesting to note that the topology of the nucleotide binding pocket of adenylate kinase is almost identical to the active site cleft of tyrosyl-tRNA synthetase (Fig. 9). Both sites are defined by a pleated sheet of five parallel β-strands. Two of the strands are recruited from the β-α-β unit (strands A,B, and b,c in Fig. 9). This unit also provides the loop with the HIGH sequence in the synthetase and the structurally analogous glycine-rich loop in adenylate kinase. Although the crystallographic data is still somewhat ambiguous with respect to the

```
EF-tu       I T G A A Q   M D G   A I -   L V V A A   T D G   (92-110)
F1          M A E K F R   D E G   R D -   V L L F V   D N I   (226-244)
ATP/ADP     W S N V L R   G M G   G A F   V L V L Y   D E I   (274-293)
H+-ATPase   A F A Q L R   K M G   I K -   T V M I T   G D N   (456-474)
PFK         G I E Q L K   K H G   I Q -   G L V V I   G G D   (82-100)
ADK         G E E F E R   K I G   Q P -   T L L L Y   V D A   (102-120)

Mit. LysRS  R I K S I R   F S G   Q K I   V F I D L   Y N G   (106-125)
Cyt. LysRS  R I H A K R   E S G   S K L   K F Y V L   H G D   (129-148)
Mit. AspRS  I E Q K P K   R V G   K N L   I F G L L   R D S   (56-75)
Cyt. AspRS  R V H N T R   Q Q G   A T L   A F L T L   R Q Q   (114-133)

              α        turn     β         loop
```

```
EF-tU                     G H V D H G   K T T L T A A I T T             (18-33)
H-Ras                     G A G G V G   K S A L T I Q L I Q             (10-25)
PFK                       G G N S P G   M N A A I R S V V R             (10-25)
F1                        G G A G V G   K T V N M M E L I R   N I A   I E H   (150-171)
ADH                       G L G G V G   L S V I M G C K A A   G A A   R I I   (199-220)
LDH                       G V G A V G   M A C A I S I L M K   D L A   D E V   (27-48)
ADK                       G G P G S G   K G T Q C E K I V Q   K Y G   Y T H   (15-36)

Mit. LysRS  Y G M P P V   G G F G L G   I D R L C M L F C D   K K R   I E E   (536-563)
Cyt. LysRS  Y G L P P T   G G W G C G   I D R L A M F L T D   S N T   I R E   (542-569)
Mit. AspRS  M G T P P H   A G F A I G   F D R M C A M I C E   T E S   I R D   (593-620)
Cyt. AspRS  Y G C P P H   A G G G I G   L E R V V M F Y L D   L K N   I R R   (517-544)

              loop                 α              turn   β
```

FIG. 8. Primary sequence comparison of aspartyl- and lysyl-tRNA synthetases and of various mono- and dinucleotide binding proteins. Two regions of the yeast mitochondrial lysyl-, and aspartyl-tRNA synthetases (38, 39), and of the yeast cytoplasmic enzymes (82) have been aligned with homologous regions of elongation factor [EF-tu (104)], β-subunit of F1 ATPase [F1 (105)], adenine nucleotide translocator [ATP/ADP (106)], plasma membrane ATPase [H+-ATPase (107)], phosphofructokinase [PFK (108)], adenylate kinase [ADK (109)],H-Ras protein [Ras (110)], alcohol dehydrogenase [ADH (111)], and lactate dehydrogenase [LDH (112)]. The predicted secondary structures derived from the average of the four different aminoacyl-tRNA synthetases are indicated under each set of sequences. The regions shown in the upper part of the figure correspond to the domain inferred to contribute the β-strand (strand D) shown in Fig. 9. The sequences shown in the lower part of the sequences are proposed to fold into the β-α-β unit with the long loop containing the glycine-rich motif. The sequence forming the first β strand of this unit is not included in the figure. The primary structure features common to the different proteins are boxed.

disposition of ATP in tyrosyl-tRNA synthetase and in adenylate kinase, it is consistent with the phosphate tail straddling the central part of the pocket and the adenine moiety protruding toward the outer boundary of the pocket near the loop structure.

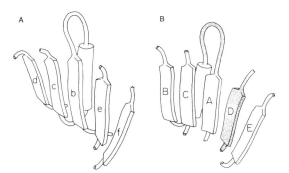

FIG. 9. Schematic representation of the secondary structure elements in the nucleotide binding site of (A) tyrosyl-tRNA synthetase and of (B) adenylate kinase (ADK). The β-strands are labelled in alphabetic order (lower case for the tyrosine enzyme and upper case for ADK) according to their position along the amino-acid sequence. Regions of adenylate kinase homologous to the lysyl- and aspartyl-tRNA synthetases are shaded.

Is the presence of a canonical glycine-rich sequence in the aspartyl- and lysyl-tRNA synthetases fortuitous, or does it herald the existence of an active site that might resemble at least in part the ATP binding pocket of adenylate kinase and other related enzymes? Two lines of evidence favor the latter conclusion. The secondary structure of the carboxyl-terminal domain of the aspartyl- and lysyl-tRNA synthetases has been analyzed by several programs designed to predict regions of α-helix, β-strand, and turns or loops in the polypeptide chain (118–120). Although the accuracy of the programs in predicting secondary structure does not exceed 50–60% when applied to isolated sequences (121), their reliability increases significantly if multiple homologous sequences are analyzed and the results averaged. Using this approach, it was inferred that the secondary structure of the carboxyl terminal domain consists of a β-α-β unit. The predicted average secondary structure of the carboxyl terminal domain places the glycines in an extended loop that bridges the first β-strand to its neighboring α-helix (Fig. 8). The overall length of the unit including the glycine-rich loop is not inconsistent with sizes reported for the comparable secondary structure elements of the mono- and dinucleotide binding pocket. The importance of the carboxyl terminal domain for the function of mito-chondrial lysyl-tRNA synthetase is supported by genetic evidence. Thus, deletion of a part of the *MSK1* gene coding for the last 20 residues yields an inactive protein that no longer complements *msk1* mutants (36).

A second characteristic feature of some ATP binding pockets is a β-strand with the general pattern Arg-X-X-Gly-X-X-(hydrophobic)$_{4-5}$-X-Asp (strand D in Fig. 9). This sequence folds into an α-β unit followed by a loop with the aspartic acid (114). A conserved domain fitting the criteria for this structural element is present in the amino-terminal half of the different aspartyl- and lysyl-tRNA synthetases (Fig. 8). Both the primary sequence and secondary structure prediction of the domain detected in the two types of synthetases conform to this general pattern with the exception of the mitochondrial lysyl- and cytoplasmic aspartyl-tRNA synthetases, which have an asparagine and glutamine, respectively, at the position of the aspartic acid (Fig. 8).

The proposed structural model of the ATP binding site in the lysyl- and aspartyl-tRNA synthetases implies that they represent an evolutionarily separate subset of the synthetase family. Furthermore, if the model has any validity, part of the active site may have been acquired from a gene for a protein with a glycine-rich type of ATP binding site.

ACKNOWLEDGMENT

Part of the research described in this article was supported by a National Science Foundation Research Grant PCM 8116680.

REFERENCES

1. P. Schimmel and D. Söll, *ARB* **48**, 601 (1979).
2. P. Schimmel, *ARB* **56**, 125 (1987).
3. P. Schimmel, *Bchem* **28**, 2747 (1989).
4. A. R. Fersht, *Bchem* **26**, 8031 (1987).
5. B. Dujon, *in* "Molecular Biology of the Yeast *Saccharomyces cerevisiae:* Life Cycle and Inheritance" (J. N. Strathern, E. W. Jones, and J. R. Broach, eds.), pp. 505–535. CSHLab, Cold Spring Harbor, New York, 1981.
6. A. Tzagoloff and A. Myers, *ARB* **55**, 249 (1986).
7. G. Attardi and G. Schatz, *Annu. Rev. Cell Biol.* **4**, 289 (1988).
8. S. Anderson, A. T. Bankier, B. G. Barrell, M. H. L. de Bruijn, A. R. Coulson, I. C. Eperon, D. P. Nierlich, B. A. Roe, F. Sanger, P. H. Schreier, A. J. H. Smith, R. Staden and I. G. Young, *Nature 290*, 457 (1981).
9. M. E. S. Hudspeth, W. M. Ainley, D. S. Shumard, R. A. Butow and L. I. Grossman, *Cell* **30**, 617 (1982).
10. M. Li and A. Tzagoloff, *Cell* **18**, 47 (1979).
11. S. G. Bonitz, R. Berlani, G. Coruzzi, M. Li, G. Macino, F. G. Nobrega, M. P. Nobrega, B. E. Thalenfeld and A. Tzagoloff, *PNAS* **77**, 3167 (1980).
12. J. E. Heckman, J. Sarnoff, B. Alzner-DeWeerd, S. Yin and U. L. RajBhandary, *PNAS* **77**, 3159 (1980).
13. N. C. Martin and M. Rabinowitz, *Bchem* **17**, 1628 (1978).
14. B. G. Barrell, S. Anderson, A. T. Bankier, M. H. L. de Bruin, E. Chen, A. R. Coulson, J. Drowin, I. C. Eperon, D. Nierlich, B. A. Roe, F. Sanger, P. H. Schreier, A. J. H. Smith, R. Staden and I. G. Young, *PNAS* **77**, 3164 (1980).

15. J. W. Casey, J. W. Hsu, G. S. Getz and M. Rabinowitz, *JMB* **88**, 735 (1974).
16. N. C. Martin and A. K. Hopper, *JBC* **257**, 10562 (1982).
17. H. Edwards and P. Schimmel, *Cell* **20**, 643 (1987).
18. A. E. Smith and K. A. Marcker, *JMB* **38**, 241 (1968).
19. G. D. Clark-Walker and A. W. Linnane, *BBRC* **25**, 8 (1966).
20. M. Li, A. Tzagoloff, K. Underbrink-Lyon and N. C. Martin, *JBC* **257**, 5921 (1982).
21. J. Montoya, D. Ojala and G. Attardi, *Nature* **290**, 465 (1981).
22. A. M. Myers, M. D. Crivellone and A. Tzagoloff, *JBC* **262**, 3388 (1987).
23. J. A. Partaledis and T. L. Mason, *MCBiol* **9**, 3647 (1988).
24. C. J. Leaver and M. W. Gray, *Annu. Rev. Plant Physiol.* **33**, 373 (1982).
25. D. A. Clayton, *ARB* **53**, 573 (1984).
26. E. Schwob, A. Sanni, F. Faiolo and R. P. Martin, *EJB* **178**, 235 (1988).
27. H.-J. Gabius and F. Cramer, *BBRC* **106**, 325 (1982).
28. M. Diatewa and A. J. C. Stahl, *BBRC* **94**, 189 (1980).
29. D. C. H. Yang, J. V. Garcia, Y. D. Johnson and S. Wahab, *Curr. Top. Cell. Regul.* **26**, 324 (1985).
30. H.-J. Gabius, R. Engelhardt, F. R. Schroder and F. Cramer, *Bchem* **22**, 5306 (1983).
31. J. M. Schneller, C. Schneller, R. Martin and A. J. C. Stahl, NARes **3**, 1151 (1976).
32. Y. Kumazawa, T. Yokogawa, E. Hasegawa, K. Miura and K. Watanabe, *JBC* **264**, 13005 (1989).
33. A. M. Myers and A. Tzagoloff, *JBC* **260**, 15371 (1985).
34. L. K. Pape, T. J. Koerner and A. Tzagoloff, *JBC* **260**, 15362 (1985).
35. T. J. Koerner, A. M. Myers, S. Lee and A. Tzagoloff, *JBC* **262**, 3690 (1987).
36. A. Tzagoloff, A. Akai, M. Kurkulos and B. Repetto, *JBC* **263**, 850 (1988).
37. A. Tzagoloff, A. Vambutas and A. Akai, *EJB* **179**, 365 (1989).
38. A. Gampel and A. Tzagoloff, *PNAS* **16**, 6023 (1989).
39. D. Gatti and A. Tzagoloff, *JMB* in press.
40. R. Hay, P. Bohni and S. Gasser, *BBA* **779**, 65 (1984).
41. G. Natsoulis, F. Hilger and G. Fink, *Cell* **46**, 235 (1986).
42. B. Chatton, P. Walker, J.-P. Ebel, F. Lacroute and F. Fasiolo, *JBC* **263**, 48 (1988).
43. X. Jordona, B. Chatton, M. Paz-Weisshaar, J.-M. Buhler, F. Cramer, J. P. Ebel and F. Fasiolo, *JBC* **262**, 7189 (1987).
44. R. W. Davis, R. B. Waring, J. A. Ray, T. A. Brown and C. Scazzocchio, *Nature* **300**, 719 (1982).
45. F. Michel and B. Dujon, *EMBO J.* **2**, 33 (1983).
46. T. R. Cech, A. J. Zaug and P. Grabowski, *Cell* **27**, 487 (1981).
47. P. McGraw and A. Tzagoloff, *JBC* **258**, 9459 (1983).
48. B. Seraphin, A. Boulet, M. Simon and G. Faye, *PNAS* **84**, 6810 (1987).
49. H. De La Salle, C. Jacq and P. P. Slonimski, *Cell* **28**, 721 (1982).
50. R. A. Collins and A. M. Lambowitz, *JMB* **184**, 413 (1985).
51. P. Q. Anziano, D. K. Hanson, H. R. Mahler and P. S. Perlman, *Cell* **30**, 925 (1982).
52. J. Lazowska, C. Jacq and P. P. Slonimski, *Cell* **22**, 333 (1980).
53. J. Krieke, M. Schulze, T. Pillar, A. Korte and G. Rodel, *Curr. Genet.* **1**, 185 (1986).
54. J. M. Burke, *Gene* **73**, 273 (1989).
55. R. S. Akins and A. M. Lambowitz, *Cell* **50**, 331 (1987).
56. J. Labouesse, C. J. Herbert, G. Dujardin and P. P. Slonimski, *EMBO J.* **6**, 713 (1987).
57. H. Bertrand, P. Bridge, R. S. Collins, G. Garriga and A. M. Lambowitz, *Cell* **29**, 517 (1982).
58. G. Garriga and A. M. Lambowitz, *Cell* **46**, 669 (1986).

59. A. L. Majumder, R. A. Akins, J. G. Wilkinson, R. L. Kelley, A. J. Snook and A. M. Lambowitz, *MCBiol* **9**, 2089 (1989).
60. F. G. Nobrega and A. Tzagoloff, *JBC* **255**, 9828 (1980).
61. S. Bonitz, G. Coruzzi, B. E. Thalenfeld, A. Tzagoloff and G. Macino, *JBC* **255**, 11927 (1980).
62. L. A. M. Hensgens, L. Bonen, M. De Haan, G. van der Horst and L. A. Grivell, *Cell* **32**, 379 (1983).
63. S. Dhawale, D. L. Hanson, N. J. Alexander, P. S. Perlman and H. R. Mahler, *PNAS* **78**, 1778 (1981).
64. G. Dujardin, C. Jacq and P. P. Slonimski, *Nature* **298**, 628 (1982).
65. G. Dujardin, P. Pajot, O. Groudinsky and P. P. Slonimski, *MGG* **179**, 469 (1980).
66. O. Groudinski, G. Dujardin and P. P. Slonimski, *MGG* **184**, 493 (1981).
67. M. Labouesse, G. Dujardin and P. P. Slonimski, *Cell* **41**, 133 (1985).
68. C. J. Herbert, M. Labouesse, G. Dujardin and P. P. Slonimski, *EMBO J.* **7**, 473 (1988).
69. A. Tzagoloff, A. Akai and R. Needleman, *JBC* **250**, 8228 (1975).
70. A. Myers, L. K. Pape and A. Tzagoloff, *EMBO J.* **4**, 2087 (1985).
71. A. P. Sibler, G. Dirheimer and R. P. Martin, *FEBS Lett.* **132**, 344 (1981).
72. L. K. Pape and A. Tzagoloff, *NARes*, **13**, 6171 (1985).
73. J.-F. Mayaux, G. Fayat, M. Fromant, M. Springer, M. Grumberg-Manago and S. Blanquet, *PNAS* **80**, 6152 (1983).
74. D. G. Barker, C. J. Bruton and G. Winter, *FEBS Lett.* **150**, 419 (1982).
75. J. D. Heck and G. W. Hatfield, *JBC* **263**, 868 (1988).
76. M. Hartlein and D. Madern, *NARes* **15**, 10199 (1987).
77. P. Walter, J. Gangloff, J. Bonnet, Y. Boulanger, J.-P. Ebel and F. Fasiolo, *PNAS* **80**, 2437 (1983).
78. F. Dardel, G. Fayat and S. Blanquet, *J. Bact.* **160**, 1115 (1984).
79. C. V. Hall, M. van Cleemput, K. H. Muench and C. Yanofsky, *JBC* **257**, 6132 (1982).
80. G. Fayat, J.-F. Mayaux, C. Sacerdot, M. Fromant, M. Springer, M. Grunberg-Manago and S. Blanquet, *JMB* **171**, 239 (1983).
81. M. Sellami, G. Prevost, J. Bonnet, G. Dirkheimer, J.-P. Ebel and J. Gangloff, *NARes* **14**, 1657 (1986).
82. M. Mirande and J. Waller, *JBC* **263**, 18443 (1988).
83. K. Kawakami, Y. H. Joensson, G. R. Bjoerk, H. Ikeda and Y. Nakamura, *PNAS* **85**, 5620 (1988).
84. R. Freedman, B. Gibson, D. Donovan, K. Biemann, S. Eisenbeis, J. Parker and P. Schimmel, *JBC* **260**, 10063 (1985).
85. N. W. Woodbury and R. F. Doolittle, *J. Mol. Evol.* **15**, 129 (1980).
86. T. Webster, H. Tsai, M. Kula, G. A. Mackie and P. Schimmel, *Science* **226**, 1315 (1984).
87. C. Houtondji, P. Dessen and S. Blanquet, *Biochimie* **68**, 1071 (1986).
88. C. Houtondji, S. Blanquet and F. Lederer, *Bchem* **24**, 1175 (1986).
89. R. M. Starzyk, T. A. Webster and P. Schimmel, *Science* **237**, 1614 (1987).
90. P. Brick, T. N. Bhat and D. M. Blow, *JMB* **208**, 83 (1989).
91. D. M. Blow, T. N. Bhat, A. Metcalfe, J. L. Risler, S. Brunie and C. Zelwer, *JMB* **171**, 571 (1983).
92. P. Hoben, N. Royal, A. Chung, F. Yamao, K. Biemann and D. J. Söll, *JBC* **257**, 11644 (1982).

93. R. Breton, G. Sanfacon, I. Papyannopoulous, K. Biemann and J. Lapointe, *JBC* **261**, 10610 (1986).
94. G. Eriani, G. Dirheimer and J. Gangloff, *NARes* **17**, 5725 (1989).
95. D. J. Lipman, S. F. Altschul and J. D. Kececioglu, *PNAS* **86**, 4412 (1989).
96. D. J. Lipman and W. R. Pearson, *Science* **227**, 1435 (1985).
97. W. R. Pearson and D. J. Lipman, *PNAS* **85**, 2444 (1988).
98. P. Thommes, R. Fett, B. Schray, N. Kunze and R. Knippers, *NARes* **16**, 5391 (1988).
99. S. W. Ludmerer and P. Schimmel, *JBC* **262**, 10801 (1987).
100. I. Weygand-Durasevic, D. Johnson-Burke and D. Söll, *NARes* **15**, 1887 (1987).
101. M. Hartlein, D. Madern and R. Leberman, *NARes* **15**, 10005 (1987).
102. C. Zelwer, J. L. Risler and S. Brunie, *JMB* **155**, 63 (1982).
103. T. N. Bhat, D. M. Blow, P. Brick and J. Nyborg, *JMB* **158**, 699 (1982).
104. T. Yokota, H. Sugisaki, H. Takanami and Y. Kaziro, *Gene* **12**, 25 (1980).
105. J. E. Walker, M. Saraste and N. J. Gay, *BBA* **768**, 164 (1984).
106. H. Aquila, D. Misra, M. Eulitz, and M. Klingenberg, *ZpChem* **363**, 345 (1982).
107. R. Serrano, M. C. Kielland-Brandt and G. Fink, *Nature* **319**, 689 (1985).
108. E. Kolb, P. J. Hudson and J. I. Harris, *EJB* **108**, 587 (1980).
109. A. Heil, G. Muller, L. H. Noda, T. Pinder, H. Schirmer, I. Schirmer and I. von Zabern, *EJB* **43**, 131 (1974).
110. D. J. Capon, E. Y. Chen, A. D. Levinson, P. H. Seeburg and D. V. Goedel, *Nature* **302**, 33 (1983).
111. H. Jornvall, *EJB* **16**, 25 (1970).
112. S. S. Taylor, *JBC* **252**, 1799 (1977).
113. J. E. Walker, M. Saraste, M. J. Runswick and N. J. Gray, *EMBO J*.**1**, 945 (1982).
114. D. C. Fry, S. A. Kuby and A. S. Mildvan, *PNAS* **83**, 907 (1986).
115. R. K. Wierenga, P. Terpstra and W. G. J. Hol, *JMB* **102**, 759 (1986).
116. E. F. Pai, W. Kabsch, U. Krengel, K. C. Holmes, J. John and A. Wittinghofer, *Nature* **341**, 209 (1989).
117. F. Jurnak, *Science* **230**, 32 (1985).
118. P. Y. Chou and G. D. Fasman, *Adv. Enzymol.* **47**, 45 (1978).
119. J. Garnier, D. J. Osguthorpe and B. Robson, *JMB* **120**, 97 (1978).
120. P. A. Karplus and G. E. Schulz, *Naturwissenschaften* **72**, 212 (1985).
121. W. Kabsch and C. Sander, *FEBS Lett.* **155**, 179 (1983).

Ribosomal Frameshifting from −2 to +50 Nucleotides

Robert B. Weiss,
Diane M. Dunn,
John F. Atkins and
Raymond F. Gesteland

*The Howard Hughes Medical
Institute and Department of
Human Genetics
The University of Utah School of
Medicine
Salt Lake City, Utah 84132*

I. Perspectives

A. The Reading Frame after Thirty Years

Evidence from diverse lines of inquiry now supports the notion that some segments of mRNA contain sequences that alter the reading frame of the translating ribosome at incredibly high levels. In some cases, these sites of "programmed" ribosomal frameshifting serve to control dynamically the level of a gene product, while in others the purpose is to provide a fixed ratio of two overlapping proteins. In some others, the purpose is not readily apparent. A common thread connecting these various frameshifts is that the alteration in the protein synthetic apparatus that causes such anomalous behavior is, so far, not in

159

ribosomes, tRNAs or factors, but is instead coded in the mRNA. What can frameshifting at these sites tell us about how ribosomes really work? and what can we glean from low-level frameshifting that occurs normally, to help in understanding the origins and mechanisms of high-level frameshifting? These, and other semirhetorical questions, are the focus here as we consider ribosomal frameshifting from the mRNA's point of the view.

It has been almost thirty years since the rIIB experiments of Crick and Brenner and co-workers (1) demonstrated that the genetic units for translating RNA into protein are trinucleotide units. Based on an assumption that certain mutagenic dyes cause small insertions and deletions in DNA, their simple phage crosses allowed them to play a genetic summation game in which all active combinations are divisible by three. The success of these experiments was, of course, contingent on the assumption that there was no inherent definition of the reading frame; that is, the zero frame of translation is chosen solely by where the ribosome starts, not by some inherent pattern in the mRNA. Here was the birthplace of our notion of what the reading frame is, and formal considerations of overlapping codes, doublet or quadruplet code words, and other exotic coding schemes were excused from further serious consideration. It is a simple and conservative design for translating RNA: start at the beginning, move lock-step down the message, and stop at the end. All that was left to do was to figure out the biochemical details and gain some evolutionary perspective on the process and its origins.

The details, of course, are fascinating. Here we concern ourselves with one aspect of one method that examines one particular detail of the vast assortment of macromolecular interactions that occur during protein synthesis. The detail is how ribosomes maintain the alignment of their reading frames, and inferentially, how ribosomes control their movement. The method is the analysis of nontriplet ribosomal translocation, and the particular aspect examined here is the residual level of activity seen in sets of synthetically derived frameshift mutations in the nonessential 5' end of the *lacZ* coding sequence from *Escherichia coli*. These insertions and deletions of nucleotides in a coding sequence move the ribosome out of the zero frame; thus the residual gene activity, in this case β-galactosidase activity, is a monitor of compensating ribosomal frameshifts nearby (given the elimination of the myriad of possible explanations such as reinitiation, reversion, activity of truncated fragments, transcriptional stuttering, RNA editing, etc.). With proper experimental design, the ribosomal frameshifts can be culled away from these other events and examined in isolation. The remarkable aspect of frameshift "leakiness" that has emerged in the past few years is the enormous variation in ribosomal frameshifting in a sequence-context-dependent manner, and it is the nature of some of these context effects that are further explored here.

In the initial enthusiasm accompanying the concept of the ribosome as a complex that propagates itself along mRNA during polypeptide synthesis, many mechanisms were considered. Their essence is perhaps best commented on by Crick's response to a proposal for a multisite merry-go-round ribosome model: that reading-frame enthusiasts could be classified as "sliders, rollers or wigglers" (2). By 1966, the code was complete, codons were matched with anti-codons, and by 1969, the molecular biologist's view of protein synthesis had congealed into two massive ribosomal subunits filled with RNA, factors, synthetases, tRNAs, mRNA, and lots of energy. The ribosome was a massive workbench upon which peptide bonds were hammered out, and concealed within were the sites through which the ribosomes gated the tRNA and mRNA, which was now tethered via codon : anti-codon pairing.

Historically, genetic analysis of reading-frame alignment has inextricably linked the three major players: tRNA, ribosomes (including factors) and mRNA, and classically this involved isolation of internal or external suppressors of frameshift mutations. Physical and biochemical analysis of ribosomal translocation has also proceeded successfully along separate lines and has served as a solid foundation for interpreting various pathways of ribosomal frameshifting (reviewed in 3). The early strong internal suppressors restored gene activity to near wild-type levels and were compensating frameshift mutations within the coding sequence (1, 4, 5). There were also weak internal suppressors, which were inferred to be base substitutions (4), and these were, along with rIIB mutants classified as minutes, initially thought to be reinitiation sites, although increased levels of spontaneous ribosomal frameshifting caused by these weak internal suppressors remained a possibility.

With the isolation of 31 lacZ frameshifts (6) and the analysis of the variation in their residual activities, a strong case was made for ribosomal frameshifting on arbitrary sequences at frequencies approaching 10^{-3} missteps per translocation (7). The early external suppressors, also fairly weak and site-specific, were thought to be altered tRNAs (5, 8). With the sequencing of the frameshift suppressor tRNA, sufD from Salmonella typhimurium (9), it was deduced that the frameshift suppressor mutation was a single nucleotide insertion in the *glyU* gene, creating an altered glycine tRNA with an 8-nucleotide anticodon loop due to the insertion of a cytidine residue into the anticodon sequence.

Since the *sufD* mutation causes increased levels of quadruplet translocation, presumably at GGG-G sequences, a direct link was established between the structure of codon : anticodon interaction and triplet movement; the problem of reading-frame alignment was essentially solved. The tRNA was not only the adaptor molecule between RNA and protein, but by virtue of its very structure, it was the watchman of the reading frame. All that really remained at that point were the details.

B. Inherent Variability of Reading-frame Alignment

The fine details of ribosome movement were continually tracked down through the ensuing years by those dogged few who sought to catalogue the various and sundry deviations from normal triplet movement. Two distinct routes were followed during this period: analysis of external frameshift suppressor mutations, and analysis of the effects of tRNA pool bias on spontaneous ribosomal frameshifting. These two routes share a common experimental rationale in attempting to gain experimental power by perturbing the leakiness of frameshift mutations by genetic alterations (reviewed in *10–14*) or by physiological alterations in tRNA levels (*15–21*). The latter approach grew out of consideration for the various parameters defining translational fidelity (reviewed in *22–24*). Both these approaches yielded intriguing observations on both the kinds of genetic alterations in tRNAs, rRNA, ribosomal proteins, and the factors that affected reading-frame alignment and the types of tRNA imbalances having similar effects.

One curious and complicated observation in common between these two lines was that all these effects on reading-frame alignment were severely context-dependent. The implication was that the playing field is not at all level, that different sequences cause ribosomes to frameshift at different rates, and that the rules of the game are in the sequence of the mRNA at the site of the frameshift. Cases of ribosomal frameshifting at levels approaching 10^{-2} began to accumulate and, not surprisingly, strings of repetitive nucleotides were implicated as the frameshift sites (*25, 26*).

As the number of these cases increased along with the levels of their leakiness, there was speculation regarding the regulatory uses of ribosomal frameshift events. After an initial false start in the phage

MS2 lysis gene (27, 28), there was an explosion of cases of naturally occuring medium-level ($>10^{-2}$) and high-level ($>10^{-1}$) ribosomal frameshifts (29–49). The occurrence of so many examples of "programmed" ribosomal frameshifting revitalized interest in reading-frame alignment. That such enormous levels of ribosomal frame-shifting observed at the high-level sites could be gained by context effects in the mRNA was not clearly anticipated and came as a surprise. Notably, in all of these examples except one, the frameshift site appears to be a −1 or +1 shift on a string of repetitive nucleotides, and the high levels of shifting are attained mainly through context effects of flanking sequence on these sites.

The one exception is the case of a + 50 nucleotide ribosomal jump found in gene 60 of bacteriophage T4 (42). This case is unusual in the distance the ribosome traverses, and also in the high level of frameshif-ting observed (~75% efficient). Its one connection to previously observed phenomena is a facile similarity to tRNA "hopping" (14, 40, 50–52), a phenomenon most simply explained by a decoded tRNA detaching from its zero-frame codon and reattaching on a synonymous codon elsewhere on the mRNA (40). Perhaps the most unsettling aspect of the gene 60 ribosome jump is its location: a scant 1500 nucleotides on the T4 genome from the rIIb region, where the analysis of the reading frame begins.

II. Exploration of the Effects of Simple Sequence Context on Reading-frame Alignment

A. Synthetic Frameshift Windows

Nontriplet ribosome translocations can be isolated and studied by synthetically constructing a region near the start codon of a lacZ gene that delimits a sequence where frameshifting will lead to productive synthesis of β-galactosidase. A typical frameshift lacZ construct is dia-grammed in Fig. 1. Synthetic oligonucleotides are cloned into unique restriction sites near the start codon where insertions are known to be tolerated without altering β-galactosidase activity. The levels of β-galactosidase produced in vivo from these constructs are, to a first approximation, a measure of the degree of ribosomal frameshifting within the test sequence. Boundaries are contained within the test sequence in the form of nonsense codons that limit detectable frame-

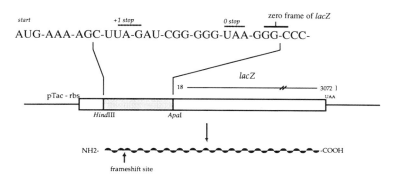

FIG. 1. Schematic illustration of synthetic reading-frame window 4p101. The diagram shows the AUG start codon of the plasmid-borne *lacZ* gene and the unique *Hind*III and *Apa*I sites used for cloning synthetic oligonucleotides. The actual frameshift window is defined by the +1 frame and zero-frame nonsense barriers. Window 4p101 produces β-galactosidase at a level of 1.7% relative to a related in-frame window (4p901, Table I). Two related windows and their activities are shown: 4p102 changes a G to A, reducing activity fourfold, and 4p201 changes the zero-frame stop to a sense codon, resulting in a decrease in β-galactosidase production to a tenth of its former value. Stationary phase cultures were diluted 1/40 into LB + 2 mM isopropyl-β-D-thiogalactopyranoside (iPrSGal) grown at 37°C with rapid shaking, and chilled to 0°C at an OD_{600} of 0.7–0.8. Whole cell assays were done in a final volume of 1.0 ml Z-buffer (40). The assays were started by the addition of 0.2 ml of 4 mg/ml *o*-nitrophenyl-β-D-galactopyranoside and stopped by the addition of 0.5 ml of 1 M Na_2CO_3, pH 11. All reactions were run at 28°C. The assay tubes were centrifuged before reading the A_{420}. The whole cell unit definition = $[1000(A_{420})]/[OD_{600} \times time(min) \times vol (ml)]$. Cell extracts were prepared by freeze-thawing; the cell extract unit definition = $[1000 (A_{420})]/[time(min) \times vol (ml) \times mg/ml protein]$. All assays were measured in duplicate or triplicate.

shifting to within their borders; this region is called the "frameshift window." Reinitiation of translation in this region will also contribute to the activity, and this component can be assessed by amino-terminal sequencing. It is important to keep in mind that, although the results are presented in terms of ribosomal frameshifting, the basic experiment is incapable of distinguishing whether rephasing occurred during transcription or translation (replication is ruled out as genetic variation at the requisite level is not observed).

The analyis of reading-frame alignment presented here is based on this simple experimental design, which has allowed rapid variation of sequence in a dispensible region of a plasmid-borne *lacZ* gene. The technical details (40) consist of expressing these *lacZ* genes in E. coli, quantitating the level of ribosomal frameshifting by measuring β-galactosidase activity, and confirming the frameshift by purification and amino-terminal sequencing of the frameshifted protein. Localization of the ribosomal frameshift site junction by amino-terminal sequencing combined with the sets of sequence combinations quickly accessible through synthetic DNA manipulation aids in defining the components of a frameshift. All the constructs described below were constructed from synthetic DNA inserts into *Hind*III-*Apa*I sites in the pBR-*lacZ* plasmid described in Fig. 1. Series nomenclature designates the orientation of the incoming to outgoing frame: the 4p series requires a shift of $3n + 1$ bases to rephase productively, and the 2p series requires a shift of $3n - 1$ bases, where n is an integer. The p series are in-frame.

B. "Shifty" Stop Codons Revisited

Ribosomal frameshifting at short stretches of repetitive nucleotides ("strings") has been examined, due in part to the technical ease of analyzing shifts displaying this medium level of β-galactosidase activity (10^{-1}–10^{-3}), and in part to the observed variation in the levels of shifting shown by different constructs. That strings are sites of ribosomal frameshifting is not surprising; they present a dilemma to a reading-frame mechanism for which correct codon : anticodon interaction is the paramount rule. However, the base-pairing rules and the sequence contexts that enhance frameshifting at strings illustrate an unexpected level of complexity and detail. String decoding tRNAs are used here as "Trojan-horse" probes into the ribosome, easily carried past the elaborate proofreading mechanism of the A site. Cloaked as a well-decoded tRNA, it serves as a sensitive vane for monitoring components of the ribosome or mRNA that tug on the translocation complex.

Earlier experiments in *E. coli* led to the hypothesis that "stop" codons can increase the level of ribosomal frameshifting at adjacent repeats of identical bases (strings) (*40*). Examples of such "shifty stops" are shown in Table I. The frameshifted construct 4p101 (CGG-GGG-UAA) produces activity at a level of ~1.7% to an in-frame construct. Replacement of the in-frame stop codon in 4p101 by a "sense" codon (UAU tyr, 4p201 CGG GGG UAU) decreases β-galactosidase activity from 170 units to 15 units, indicating a role for the stop in promoting the 1.7% level of frameshifting. The ribosome's path through the 4p101 window is shown in Fig. 2(a), where a −2 shift ($n = -1$ in the $3n + 3$ 1 formulation) is seen to occur on the G string adjacent to the stop codon.

TABLE I

FRAMESHIFT LEAKINESS OF REPETITIVE STRINGS OF NUCLEOTIDES: SHIFTY STOPS[a]

Series			β-Galactosidase activity	
			Whole cells	Extracts
4p100 AGC-UUA-GAU-CNG-GGG-UAA-GGG-C				
101- *		G	170	170
102-		A	40	15
103-		C	12	12
4p200 AGC-UUA-GAU-CNG-GGG-UAU-UCA-UAA-G				
201-*		G	15	15
202-		U	16	12
2p300 AGC-UUU-AAU-CNG-GGG-UAA-AGG-GC				
301-*		C	450	460
302-		U	140	130
303-		A	120	90
304-		G	30	40
2p400 AGC-UUU-AAU-CUN-GGG-UAA-AGG-GC				
401-		A	7	6
402-		C	5	6
403-		U	5	5
2p500 AGC-UUU-AAU-CUG-GGG-UAN-UCA-AG				
501-		A	110	110
502-		G	60	55
503-		C	50	40
4p600 AGC-UUA-ANU-UUN-UGA-CAA-GGG-C				
601-	C	U	170	120
602-	A	U	150	150
603- *	U	U	130	100
604- *	G	U	100	160
605-	A	C	8	7
606-	C	C	8	5
607-	A	G	7	4
608-	U	A	6	5
609-	U	G	5	4
4p700 AGC-UUA-AUU-UUU-UAN-CAA-GGG-C				
701-		G	45	45
702-		A	45	40
703-		C	20	20
4p800 AGC-UUA-GAU-CGC-GCG-UNA-GGG-C				
801		G	1	2
802		C	1	1
p900 AGC-UUA-GAU-UGG-NNU-AAG-GGC-				
901		AA	10100	7900
902		UC	10000	6600
903		GG	4600	4800

[a] The host is SU1675 F'I^Q, 37°C in LB. Asterisks indicate shiftsite confirmed by NH$_2$-terminal sequencing (see text).

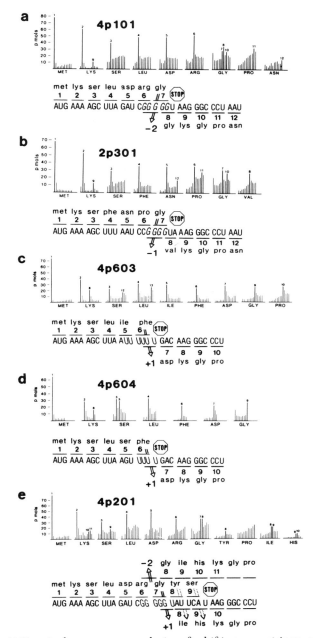

FIG. 2. N-Terminal sequence analysis of shifting on strings of repetitive nucleotides. Each panel shows the yield in picomoles of phenylthiohydantoin (PTH) amino acids analyzed during each sequencing cycle. A number over a vertical line represents the major PTH amino acid recovered from that cycle. Underneath the panels are interpretations of the shifts seen by superimposing the protein sequence and the mRNA sequence.

A simple interpretation of this path is that frame is maintained through codon 7 and then shifts by -2 bases on the string of G residues. This shift may be facilitated by the alternative base-pairing possibilities between the glycine tRNA decoded at codon 7 and the string of Gs. Disruption of this alternative base-pairing potential by substituting A or C for the first G in the string decreases the level of frameshifting from 170 units to 40 and 12 units, respectively (4p101 series, Table I). The pattern displayed by this simple set of mutations suggests that the basic recipe for a shifty stop is alternative base-pairing potential formed by a string of identical bases adjacent to a stop codon.

Shifting promoted by stop codons on adjacent strings, and the use of alternative base-pairing to facilitate the shift are examined further in Table I. Decreases in shifting accompanying stop-to-sense substitutions can be observed with the following comparisons: CGG-GGG-UAA, 170 units (4p101) with CGG-GGG-UAU, 15 units (4p201); CUG-GGG-UAA, 140 units (2p302) with CUG-GGG-UAC, 50 units (2p503); and AUU-UUU-UGA, 130 units (4p603) with AUU-UUU-UAC, 20 units (4p703). The requirement for unbroken strings of identical bases is explored by breaking the string in the incoming frame (4p605-609, Table I) which decreases activity from 170 units to 5–8 units, and breaking the string in the outgoing frame (constructs 4p101/103 and 2p302/402, Table I) which decrease activity from 170 to 12 units and 140 to 5 units, respectively.

The paths the ribosomes follow in constructs 2p301, 4p603, and 4p604 are shown in Figs. 2(b)–(d). The sequence derived from 2p301 CCG GGG UAA shows that a glycine tRNA can shift -1 onto the 5′ overlapping GGG codon in the string of Gs. Construct 4p603 AGU-UUU-UGA shifts the frame by $+1$ ($n = 0$) at codon 7; the decoding phenylalanine tRNA has an alternative pairing possibility with the 3′ overlapping UUU codon. The decoding phe–tRNA in construct 4p604 AUU-UUU-UGA is faced with a dilemma, since alternative pairing exists both -2 and $+1$; Fig. 2(d) shows the major shift at codon 7 is $+1$. Further definition is given to -2 shifting by comparing 4p101 CGG-GGG-UAA with 4p801 CGC-GCG-UGA (170 units versus 1 unit, Table I), suggesting stops can increase efficient -2 shifting of a GGG decoding glycine tRNA onto an overlapping GGG, but cannot increase -2 shifting of a GCG decoding alanine tRNA onto an overlapping GCG. It is surprising that the mixed analog (4p801 GC-GCG-UAA) cannot utilize the alternate, suggesting that sliding between tRNA and mRNA may be tightly constrained; perhaps purines on opposite strands cannot pass each other.

The precise requirements for repeated nucleotides within strings are examined in Table IIA, where the codon adjacent to a UAA stop is varied while monitoring the $-2/+1$ frame. 4p1001 UGG-UUU-UAA and 4p1002 UGG-GGG-UAA have perfect alternative pairing, either $+1$ or -2, respectively, and have the highest activities of the set. As the

TABLE II

REQUIREMENTS OF STRINGS AND STOPS FOR $-2/+1$ FRAMESHIFTING[a]

β-Galactosidase activity			β-Galactosidase activity		
Series		Whole cells	Series		Whole cells
A.			B.		
4p1000	-GAU-UGG-NNN-UAA-GGG-C		4p1100	-CGG-GGG-URR-NNG-UAA-G	
1001-*	UUU	150	1101-	UGG-GGG	430
1002-*	GGG	110	1102-	UAA-CCG	305
1003-	CCU	75	1103-	UGA-CUG	230
1004-	GAG	45	1104-	UGA-AUG	230
1005-	GGA	40	1105-	UGA-UCG	195
1006-*	GAA	20	1106-	UGA-CCG	155
1007-	CUU	20	1107-	UAA-ACG	140
1008-	AAG	20	1108-	UAA-CUG	135
1009-	GGU	15	1109-	UAA-AUG	135
1010-	AAU	10	1110-	UAA-AGG	135
1011-	GGC	10	1111-	UGA-AAG	130
1012-	CCG	8	1112-	UAA-AAG	130
1013-	AGA	7	1113-	UAA-UGG	125
1014-	AUU	7	1114-	UGA-UGG	120
1015-	CAA	7	1115-	UAA-CGG	120
1016-	ACC	7	1116-	UAA-UCG	120
1017-	UCU	6	1117-	UAA-GGG	110
1018-	UAU	6	1118-	UGA-UUG	95
1019-	CGA	6	1119-	UAA-GUG	95
1020-	GAC	6	1120-	UAA-UAG	85
1021-	GCG	5	1121-	UGA-UAG	50
1022-	CUA	5	1122-	UAG-GUG	40
1023-	AUG	5	1123-	UAG-UCG	35
1024-	UAG	5	1124-	UAG-UGG	30
1025-	CUC	4	1125-	UAG-UUG	25
1026-	GCA	4	1126-	UAG-GAG	25
1027-	UAC	4	1127-	UAG-GGG	25
1028-	ACA	4	1128-	UGG-ACG	25
1029-	UCA	3	1129-	UGG-GAG	20
1030-	ACG	4	1130-	UGG-AUG	15
1031-	CGU	4	1131-	UGG-UUG	15
1032-	AGU	2	1132-	UGG-CUG	10

[a] The host is SU1675 F'I^Q, 37°C in LB; assay conditions are described in Experimental Procedures. Asterisks indicate constructs that were N-terminal sequenced: 4p1001 shifts $+1$ at the UUU Phe codon, 4p1002 shifts -2 at the GGG Gly codon, and 4p1006 shifts -2 at the GAA Glu codon.

quality of the match between the codon adjacent to the stop and the triplets overlapping either +1 or −2 decreases, so does the amount of shifting. The gradient of activity is consistent with the degree of slippage at a shifty stop being proportional to the potential for the string decoding tRNA to pair in an alternative frame, allowing for G · U pairing. Amino-terminal sequencing shows that 4p1001 UGG UUU UAA, like 4p603 and 604, shifts +1 on the U string, while 4p1006 UGG-GAA-UAA, like 4p101, shifts −2 on a GGGAA string. This −2 shift may require G · U pairing between the decoding glutamate tRNA and the alternative GGG codon in the −2 frame.

The rules for potential codon : anticodon interactions found in string shifts are noteworthy. In the case of −2 shift of 4p1002 UGG-GGG-UAA and 4p1006 UGG-GAA-UAA, the decrease in shifting from 4p1002 to 4p1006 is between five- and sixfold, which is a rough measure of the strength of interaction between glycine tRNA and GGG versus glutamate tRNA and GAA somewhere in the translation cycle after each tRNA has correctly decoded the zero-frame. It may be surmised that the frequency of GAA-reading glutamate tRNA decoding of GGG codons in the A site is at least 1000-fold below glycine tRNA decoding of GGG (24). Therefore the rules of acceptable codon : anticodon interaction must be relaxed in the sector of the translation cycle where string shifting occurs, and such shifts must not encounter severe proof-reading mechanisms that check the exactness of codon : anticodon pairing. Even though the rules are relaxed, the level of shifting is still determined by the number and quality of potential base-pairs. Shrinking a G-string from five to four residues heavily favors −1 shifts at the expense of −2 shifts, and from four to three G residues decreases the amount of shifting overall.

The efficacy of each of the three stops at promoting shifting of the reading frame −2 on a G string is examined with the 4p1100 series (Table IIB). The three stops are compared with a UGG tryptophan codon, while also varying the 3′ context of the stop position. In this series, the order of shiftiness is UGA=UAA > UAG > UGG; this order is paralleled in earlier series (Table I). The 4p1001 GGG-UGG-GGG-UAA is shifty due to the creation of a string of Gs next to the UAA. It might have been expected that multiple stop codons should not affect shiftiness; however, triple stops (4p1120 and 4p1121) are less prone to shifting than their single-stop counterparts.

The amino-terminal sequence of 4p101 CGG-GGG-UAA versus 4p201 CGG-GGG-UAU [Figs. 2(a) and (e)] shows that the stop-to-sense substitution leads to a qualitatively, as well as quantitatively, different frameshift. Ribosomes follow a complicated set of paths through the

4p201 window, in contrast to the unique −2 shift of 4p101. The decoded glycine tRNA at codon 7 of 4p201 appears to shift both +1 and −2, and a substantial fraction of the ribosomes shift +1 in the latter half of the window (codons 8 and 9). The stop codon in 4p101 promotes only one part of an initially multicomponent shift.

C. How Stops Promote Shifting

Replacement of the stop codon in a shifty stop by a sense codon results in a sharp decrease in the level of shifting. One explanation of this effect is that a component in the termination pathway catalyzes shifting on the adjacent string. An alternative to active triggering of shifting by some component of the termination pathway is that string slippage occurs predominantly while the string-decoding tRNA is situated in the P-site awaiting the decoding of the A-site codon; therefore, stops would simply be slow to decode, by a factor of 20 in some cases. A predominant P-site string shift should be reflected in a distribution of activities for string-sense constructs that parallels the speed of decoding at the adjacent codon (53a). There is evidence to suggest that rare codons are decoded more slowly because of a correspondingly lower level of cognate tRNA (54, 55); if slippage occurs predominantly in the P-site then strings bordered by rare codons should be more slippery than strings bordered by abundant codons.

Alternatively, string slippage of the peptidyl tRNA : mRNA complex may occur predominantly before the next codon is in the A site and available for decoding. Thus the speed of decoding at this next codon may not grossly affect the level of shifting. Such is the case at the retroviral frameshift sites, where the slippage appears to occur during translocation as two tRNAs achieve alternate pairing in the −1 frame on a string (45, 56).

Alternatively shifty stops could be abortive terminations caused by the rephasing of peptidyl-tRNA after release factor binding and subsequent resumption of elongation. If this were the case, then increased levels of release factor should not affect the amount of frameshifting, while if the shift occurs prior to release-factor binding, increased amounts of release factor should lead to decreased amounts of frameshifting. In analogy to the competition between release factors and suppressor tRNAs for stop codons, the frameshift should be antisuppressed (57).

The results of such an experiment are shown in Table III. When the concentration of RF1 is raised by overexpression of the cloned gene (57), the shifty stops containing UAG codons are indeed anti-suppressed. Also anti-suppression of a UAG stop, as well as the high-

TABLE III
ANTI-SUPPRESSION OF SHIFTY STOPS BY RELEASE FACTOR 1[a]

lacZ Plasmid-frame		Key feature	β-Galactosidase activity (whole cell assays)		
			−pBR-RF1	+pBR-RF1	Ratio
p163UCG	0		14,000	12200	0.87
p163UAG	0	UAG stop	720	170	0.24
4p2101	+1,	RF2-UGA shifty stop	6200	4500	0.73
4p2201	+1,	RF2-UAG shifty stop	4750	790	0.17
2p2621	−1,	GGG-AGA sense shift	40	35	0.88
2p2602	−1,	GGG-UAG shifty stop	230	65	0.28

[a] The host is CP79-813Z supE, 37°C in LB. pBR-RF1 consists of an AvaI fragment containing the release-factor-1 gene from pRF1 (55) cloned into the AvaI site of pBR322. p163UAG is an in-frame stop codon for monitoring amber suppression by supE, and p163UCG is the isogenic in-frame construct. 4p2101 and 4p2201 constitute the high-level RF2 frameshift site with a UGA or UAG codon, respectively, and have been described previously (39).

level RF2-UAG frameshift, which consists of a shifty stop (CUU-UAG) enhanced by 5′ flanking mRNA : rRNA interaction (40, 42), can be observed in Table III. Thus frameshifting at shifty stops is inferred to occur prior to release-factor binding.

If frameshifting at stop codons is not due to release factor binding, is it that stop codons are simply slow to decode by release factor compared to the speed of sense decoding by normal tRNAs?—that is, are shifty stops P-site slips? Table IV lists a series of sense changes bordering strings; also listed is the rank order of usage for the sense codon. The 2p2600 series scans 22 different sense changes adjacent to a −1 G-GGG string, and reveals no correlation between slippage and codon usage. The activity of the sense derivatives in the 2p2600 series is caused by slipping on the string of Gs as shown by the decreased activity of the broken string construct (2p2700) and amino-terminal sequencing of 202621-AGA. The activity of 2p2601-UGA is slightly elevated due to a composite signal of frameshifting at the string-stop and reinitiation at the GUG overlapping the UGA; this component is seen in isolation by breaking the string in the shifty stop (2p2800, Table IV) and amino-terminal sequencing (70 : 30 ratio of frameshifted : reinitiated β-galactosidase). The lack of correlation within these sense constructs with 3′ codon usage suggests that −1 shifting on G strings bordered by sense codons does not occur predominantly in the P site; shifting on the string in the P site may be only a minor com-

TABLE IV
Context Variants of −1 Shifting on Sense Strings[a]

Series	β-Galactosidase activity — Whole cells	β-Galactosidase activity — Cell extracts		RCU1	Series	β-Galactosidase activity — Whole cells	β-Galactosidase activity — Cell extracts	
2p2600	−CUG−GGG−NNN−CAC−UAA−				2p3100	−GAC−NNG−GGG−GCC−		
2601−*	120	UGA	100		3101−	80	GG	40
2602−	60	UAG	40		3102−	35	CC	40
2603−	30	UUG	30	39	3103−	25	GA	25
2604−	25	GGC	15	8	3104−	25	UG	20
2605−	20	UUC	25	21	3105−	20	GU	20
2606−	20	GGG	15	44	3106−	7	AA	7
2607−	20	UCU	15	34	3107−	7	UU	7
2608−	15	AGC	10	25	3108−	6	AU	7
2609−	10	CCC	7	54	3109−	6	CG	6
2610−	10	AAG	6	32	3110−	5	CA	6
2611−	10	AUG	6	11	3111−	5	CU	5
2612−	9	AGU	5	48				
2613−	8	CUU	10	43				
2614−	7	AAC	5	10				
2615−	7	CCG	5	12				
2616−	7	CUG	5	1				
2617−	7	GCC	4	18				
2618−	6	CCU	6	49				
2619−	6	ACU	6	36				
2620−	6	GCU	5	22				
2621−*	6	AGA	5	60				
2622−	6	ACA	5	51				
2623−	6	AUC	5	6				
2624−	6	CAA	3	31				
2p2700	−CCG−GNG−AGA−CAC−							
2701	1	C	1					
2p2800	−CCG−NGG−UGA−CAC−							
2801−	180	G	170					
2802−	50	A	45					

[a] The host is SU1675 F′I^Q, 37°C in LB; assays are performed both in whole cells and cell extracts (39). RCU is the Rank of Codon Usage, with 1 the most frequent and 61 the least frequent codon in *E. coli* (52). 2p2601 and 2p2621 shift −1 at the GGG glycine codon.

ponent of their overall activity. One possible explanation for the variation observed with these "sense" substitutions is the slight concordance with the tandem slippery codon rule observed at retroviral ribosomal frameshift sites, but now known to be operative in *E. coli* (56).

The mechanism of enhancement at shifty stops is left unresolved.

An aggravated P site slippage model is the simplest explanation for shifty stops, but the failure to ascribe the low level of activity in the 2p2600 sense series to P site shifting implies either that stops are very slow (and if so, why is nonsense suppression generally inefficient?) or that the elevated level of frameshifting is caused by some component of the release pathway that affects the codon : anticodon complex prior to release-factor binding. Perhaps this component is the hypothetical rRNA : mRNA pairing postulated to be the recognition complex in the termination pathway (58).

D. A Look at the Natural and Unnatural Variation of Slipping on Strings

The context changes in the 2p2600 series do not change the quality of the base-pairing alternatives for the slipping glycine tRNA, although the major variation in this series may have the same *de facto* explanation since some tandem slippery codon pairs were inadvertently created. Here, we examine context changes that affect alternative base-pairing a little more closely. The 4p2900 series (Table V) tests 3′ contexts for +1 slippage on isolated GGG codons and shows little 3′ effect on shifting even when overlapping base-pairing is restored (4p2903). Thus the ability to form three proper base-pairs in the +1 frame seems irrelevant to the frequency of this type of slip. This is not to say, in general, that alternative base-pairing is not a factor; rather, for the GGG +1 case, two alternative G · C pairs seem to be as good as three.

The +1 frameshifting at GGG codons is reminiscent of the frameshifting by *sufD* of *S. typhimurium*, a +1 frameshift suppressor tRNA containing an 8-nucleotide anticodon loop (9). The analogous suppressor from *Saccharomyces cerevisiae*, *suf16*, shows little or no preference for base-pairing between the extra nucleotide in the anticodon loop and the 3′ nucleotide flanking the zero-frame codon (59). Some observations suggest that 8-nucleotide anticodon loops promote frameshifting predominantly by steric hindrance of the next tRNA (59, 60 and not necessarily by quadruplet codon : anticodon pairing (61). It has been assumed that *sufD* belongs to the class that requires pairing with the 3′ flanking nucleotide (61, 62), but this has not been tested. Since it provides a relevant comparison to string slippage by normal tRNAs, we tested the requirement for a 3′ flanking nucleotide for efficient +1 frameshifting at GGG codons (Table VI).

Since the slight variation seen in the suppressibility of GGG-G versus GGG-A and GGG-C does not correlate with the base-pair potential in the fourth position between the codon : anticodon pair, it can be inferred that *sufD* does not require quadruplet interaction to

TABLE V
CONTEXT VARIANTS OF +1 SHIFTING ON SENSE STRINGS

	β-Galactosidase activity				β-Galactosidase activity		
Series	Whole cells	Cell extracts		Series	Whole cells	Cell extracts	
4p2900	-AUC-GGG-NNA-UUA-			4p2700	-GAU-AAA-NCG-		
2901-	25	UC	10	2701-*	120	A	
2902-	20	AC	15	2702-	10	U	
2903-	20	GA	10	2703-	2	G	
2904-	20	UU	10	4p2800	-GAU-CCC-NCG-		
2905-	15	GC	15	2801-	160	A	
4p3200	-GAC-NNG-GGG-GCC-			2802-	65	U	
3201-	15	GG	8	2803-	25	G	
3202-	10	GA	10	2804-	15	C	
3203-	9	UG	9	4p3300	-GAU-AAA-ANG		
3204-	9	CC	7	3301-	170	G	
3205-	7	CG	4	3302-	160	A	
3206-	6	GU	4				
3207-	6	CA	3	4p3500	-GAU-NNA-AAA-AUA-		
3208-	5	AU	4	3501-	390	CC	420
3209-	5	UU	2	3502-	300	AA	220
3210-	4	CU	3	3503-	160	CG	180
3211-	4	AA	3	3504-	140	AU	60
				3505-*	130	CA	100
				3506-	80	CU	55
				3507-	55	AG	50
				3508-	30	AC	20
				3509-	10	UA	

[a] The host is SU1675 F'I^Q, 37°C in LB; assays were performed both in whole cells and extracts (39). 4p2701 and 4p3505 shift +1 at the AAA lysine codon.

shift +1. Surprisingly, *sufD* is as efficient at shifting −1 at G-GGG as it is at shifting +1 (Table VI), although in this case there is a strong preference for a 5′ overlapping G. The glycine tRNA altered by the *sufD* mutation may therefore be viewed simply as a "de-tuned" slippery tRNA, and thus may be qualitatively distinct from 8-nucleotide loops that promote +1 shifting at nonstring codons (60–63).

The level of shifting on AAA lysine codons in Table V (series 4p2700, 3300, and 3500) is markedly elevated over GGG glycine codons (series 4p2900). Amino-terminal sequencing demonstrates a +1 shift on the AAA-A string (4p2701 and 4p3505). The 3′-nucleotide context in this case is remarkable: an AAA-A context displays an activity 60-fold higher than AAA-G, even though a single isoaccepting lysine tRNA is used to decode AAA and AAG (64). Why should the

TABLE VI

SPECIFICITY OF *sufD* SUPPRESSION IN *Salmonella typhimurium*[a]

| | | β-Galactosidase activity | |
lacZ plasmid		*sufD41*	sufD[wt]
A.			
4p2903	–AUC-GGG-GAA–	660	130
4p2906	–AUC-GGG-AAA–	920	225
4p2907	–AUC-GGG-CCA–	900	290
4p2908	–AUC-GGG-CGA–	410	210
B.			
2p2621	–CUG-GGG-AGA–	1240	75
2p2618	–CUG-GGG-CCU–	230	70
2p2616	–CUG-GGG-CUG–	160	55
2p401	–CUA-GGG-UAA–	135	105

[a] The hosts are *S. typhimurium* TR1441 *hisO1242 hisC3736 sufD41* or its isogenic parent *S. typhimurium* TR968 *hisO1242 hisC3736* (obtained from J. R. Roth). The cultures were grown in liquid minimal media supplemented with His and Trp. The β-galactosidase activity is given in whole-cell units.

same lysyl-tRNA or peptidyl-tRNA[Lys] display such a preference to shift and stick on an overlapping AAA versus AAG codon? A discriminating preference of lysyl-tRNA for AAA versus AAG codons was observed previously in another context. When tandem slippery codons are monitored in *E. coli*, it is observed that A-AAA-AAG is 30-fold more adept at slipping −1 than A-AAA-AAA (56). In this case, it was inferred that the lysine tRNA decoding AAG has a much greater propensity for slipping onto the overlapping AAA than it does when decoding AAA initially.

Both this observation and the context effect seen in the 4p2700 series can be interpreted as the consequence of weak codon : anticodon pairing of lysine tRNA at AAG codons compared with strong pairing at AAA codons. Thus, contrasting with the +1 context effects at GGG codons, the ability for strong alternative pairing for +1 shifting at AAA is paramount, perhaps reflecting the relative stabilities of A · U versus G · C base-pairs.

The level of frameshifting observed with certain simple contexts for an AAA lysine codon approaches 1–2% of an analogous in-frame construct. Such levels of frameshifting might be quite burdensome to the cell's synthetic capacities if they occurred frequently. One way of obtaining a comparative value of the actual burden is to monitor a lengthy segment of a natural open reading frame for frameshifting, to ascertain whether there has been a circumspect purging of shifty contexts from lengthy open reading frames. To this end, the longest segments free of stop codons in the out-of-frame sequences from one of the largest genes in *E. coli*, *rpoC*, which codes for the B' subunit of RNA polymerase (65), were cloned into the pBR-*lacZ* plasmid. The aggregate values of frameshifting within these segments, 123 codons in the $+1$ and 95 in the -1 configuration as shown in Table VII, are quite low ($+1 = 110$ units and $-1 = 10$ units). Apparently, shifty contexts do not occur in these two segments. Even when the frames are reversed, such that the ribosomes enter what was previously an out-of-frame sequence, the region is still nonshifty (Table VII: 4p4001 $= 115$ units, and monitors shifting from the overlapping noncoding frame into the coding frame). Such an observation also emphasizes the arbitrary definition of the zero frame (it only matters where the ribosome starts) and argues against any intrinsic framing mechanism within the coding sequence, as has recently been proposed (66).

III. Further Observations on the Context of High-level Frameshifts

A. RF2 versus Retroviral Context: The Immovable Object Meets the Irresistible Force

Both the $+1$ shift seen in the *E. coli* RF2 gene and the -1 shifts seen in a number of retroviral gene overlaps use slippery tRNAs in a special context to effectively attain high levels of ribosomal frameshifting. Figure 3 summarizes the view of these two distinct frameshift mechanisms as observed in *E. coli* (40, 43, 56). The RF2 shift utilizes a shifty stop, and elevates the level of shifting by a precisely positioned inter-

TABLE VII
AGGREGATE LEVEL OF SHIFTING IN LENGTHY OVERLAPS FROM *rpoC*[a]

Series	No. of overlapping codons	β-Galactosidase activity
4p4000	123	110
2p4000	125	115
2p4100	95	10

[a] The host is SU1675 F'I^Q, 37°C in LB; assays were performed in whole cells. 4p4000 contains codons 1209 to 1332 from *rpoC*, and 2p4100 contains codons 1281 to 1376 from *rpoC*. Both these segments were isolated from *E. coli* SU1675 chromosomal DNA by polymerase chain reaction, and cloned into HIII/*Apa*I cut pBR-*lacZ* vector. 2p4000 monitors -1 frameshifting from the noncoding to the coding frame in the 1281 to 1376 segment of *rpoC*.

action between the 16-S rRNA and mRNA 5' from the frameshift site
(43). The retroviral-like sequence shown in Fig. 3 obeys the tandem
slippery codon rule at the A-AAA-AAG shift site (45, 56) and enhances
the −1 shifting at this site by downstream mRNA structure (45, 47, 56).

The analysis of the interaction 5' of the RF2 shift site, essentially a
"Shine–Dalgarno" (S–D) interaction occurs during the elongation
phase, inferred that this base-pairing between the mRNA and rRNA
could occur throughout the coding sequence (43). Two questions are
raised by this observation: how long is the hybrid maintained before
melting out?, and what is the function of the implied continuous hybridization and melting of the 3' end of 16-S rRNA with the mRNA as
the ribosome translocates along the message? A maximum estimate for
the length of the loop between the 16-S rRNA : mRNA hybrid and the P

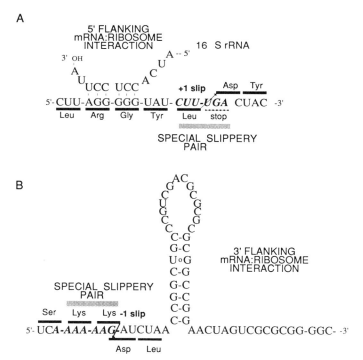

FIG. 3. Two distinct mRNA contexts that promote high-level frameshifting in *E.
coli*. (A) 4p2101, a synthetic version of the high-level frameshift site from the *E. coli*
release-factor-2 gene (35) necessary for efficient +1 shifting. The required components,
an mRNA : rRNA duplex and a special slippery codon pair (40, 43), are highlighted.
(B) 2p4301, a synthetic sequence that causes ribosomes to slip −1 on the special slippery
pair A-AAA-AAG (56), under the influence of a 3' flanking potential stem-loop structure.

site was inferred to be 34 nucleotides, based on the distance between the initiating Shine–Dalgarno (S–D) sequence and where the frameshift site occurs in a synthetic RF2-*lacZ* construct (*40*). Table VIII shows that an S–D sequence, when positioned 15 nucleotides before the frameshift site, can interfere with frameshifting.

The simple interpretation of this interference is that the 3' end of 16-S rRNA is still hybridized with S-D #1 in constructs 4p4201 and 4202, but not in 4203 or 4204 where the interaction is partially disrupted, when the decoding sites reach the shifty stop. This implies that there may exist a loop of the intervening 15 nucleotides within the ribosome if the positions of these two sites are fixed. An alternate view of this process would imagine a cyclical expansion and contraction of the distance between the 3' end of 16-S rRNA and the decoding sites as the ribosome elongates, determined by the relative strengths of the sequential hybrids formed with S–D sequences in the mRNA.

Since the RF2 context and retroviral context can be viewed as forcing the mRNA in opposite directions, it would be interesting to place these two opposing agents against each other and see if one dominates. Such an experiment is described in Fig. 4. An S–D sequence is positioned 5' of a high-level retroviral-like −1 frameshift. It is evident that the S–D sequence does indeed interfere with the −1 slipping at the tandem slippery codons. This effect is most pronounced when the distance between the S–D interaction and the first slippery codon is precisely the same as that seen between the S–D interaction and the CUU-decoding leucine tRNA at the RF2 shift site. The observed interference implies that the S–D interaction constrains the positioning of mRNA and tRNAs in the decoding sites. In this case, even weak base-pairing interactions (AGCGGG versus AGGGGG) near the decoding sites are effective, although only if close. It may be worth noting that this interaction may tug the mRNA in the same direction as ribosome movement, and this could conceivably facilitate

TABLE VIII

INTERFERENCE BETWEEN SHINE-DALGARNO SEQUENCES IN RF2 FRAMESHIFTING[a]

Series	S-D#1	S-D#2	β-Galactosidase activity
4p4201	AGG–GGG–CUU–AGG–GGG–UAU–CUU–UGA		165
4p4202	AGG–AGG–CUU–AGG–GGG–UAU–CUU–UGA		140
4p4203	AGG–CGG–CUU–AGG–GGG–UAU–CUU–UGA		4170
4p4204	AGG–UGG–CUU–AGG–GGG–UAU–CUU–UGA		5400

[a] The host is SU1675 F'I^Q, 37°C in LB; assays were performed in whole cells.

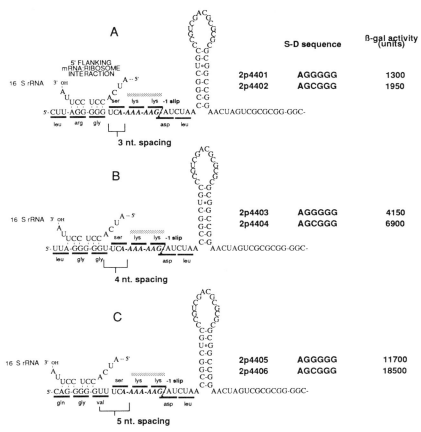

FIG. 4. Inhibition of a tandem slippery codon −1 shift by mRNA:rRNA base-pairing. (A) 2p4401, (B) 4403, and (C) 4405 are synthetic *lacZ* frameshift windows that place a potential S–D sequence upstream from the efficient −1 slippery pair from 2p4301 (Fig. 3). Each set has the S–D sequence AGGGGG or AGCGGG located 3, 4, or 5 nucleotides upstream from the A-AAA-AAG frameshift site. The β-galactosidase activity (whole cell units) of each construct is indicated.

translocation, although the actuality of this interaction during elongation is unresolved.

B. Future High-level Possibilities

While the reading-frame antics displayed by these unusual mRNA sequences serve to amuse and inform us as to what goes on between ribosomes, tRNA, and mRNA, the quiet, nonshifty sequence observed in *rpoC* is reassuring. Ribosomes can obviously progress in a stately and efficient manner through coding sequences without being unduly worried about losing their way. Since slippery strings in certain contexts seem to be responsible for most of the leaky frameshifts, careful pruning of these sequences from open reading frames would serve to minimize loss of elongating ribosomes, although given the various patterns observed and the combinational possibilities left untried, accurate prediction of shifty sites is still, at the moment, not possible.

The paramount precept observed so far that dominates most types of ribosomal frameshifting is the potential for stable anticodon pairing with a codon outside the zero frame. Frameshifting on strings of repetitive nucleotides obey this rule, as the many examples explored here confirm. There is another combination of sequence that conforms to this rule, which is the passage of tRNA from a nonrepetitive zero-frame codon to an overlapping or nonoverlapping synonymous codon. This rare type of event, termed a tRNA hop (*40*), has been observed with normal tRNAs and suppressor tRNAs in only a few instances (*14, 40, 51*). The frequency of occurrence of nonoverlapping synonymous or partially synonymous codons within coding sequences is enormous, and the occurrence of tRNA hopping between these sites would be catastrophic, implying that ribosomes are somehow designed to keep such "hops" in check. But the unexplained existence of the +50 nucleotide jump that occurs in gene *60* with an efficiency greater than 70% (*42, 52*) suggests we have not yet exhausted this particular line of inquiry.

References

1. F. H. C. Crick, L. Barnett, S. Brenner and R. J. Watts-Tobin, *Nature* **192**, 1227 (1961).

2. F. H. C. Crick, *CSHSOB* **28**, 296 (1962).

3. A. S. Spirin, *This Series* **32**, 75 (1985).

4. E. Terzaghi, Y. Okada, G. Streisinger, J. Emrich, M. Inouye and A. Tsugita, *PNAS* **56**, 500 (1966).

5. S. Riyasty and J. F. Atkins, *JMB* **34**, 541 (1968).

6. A. Newton, *JMB* **49**, 589 (1970).

7. J. F. Atkins, D. Elseviers and L. Gorini, *PNAS* **69**, 1192 (1972).

8. D. L. Riddle and J. R. Roth, *JMB* **54**, 131 (1970).

9. D. L. Riddle and J. Carbon, *Nature NB* **242**, 230 (1973).

10. E. J. Murgola, *ARGen* **19**, 57 (1985).

11. M. D. Mendelhall, P. Leeds, H. Fen, L. Mathison, M. Zwick, C. Sleiziz and M. R. Culbertson, *JMB* **194**, 41 (1987).

12. J. F. Curran and M. Yarus, *Science* **238**, 1545 (1987).

13. B. Weiss-Brummer, H. Sakai and F. Kaudewitz, *Curr. Genet.* **11**, 295 (1987).

14. M. B. Falahee, R. B. Weiss, M. O'Connor, S. Doonan, R. F. Gesteland and J. F. Atkins, *JBC* **263**, 18099 (1988).

15. J. Gallant and D. Foley, *in* "Ribosomes: Structure, Function and Genetics" (G. Chambliss, G. R. Craven, J. Davies, K. Davis, L. Kahan and M. Nomura, eds.), pp. 615–638. Univ. Park Press, Baltimore, Maryland, 1980.
16. J. F. Atkins, R. F. Gesteland, B. R. Reid and C. W. Anderson, *Cell* **18**, 1119 (1979).
17. R. Weiss and J. Gallant, *Nature* **302**, 389 (1983).
18. T. Dayhuff, J. F. Atkins and R. F. Gesteland, *JBC* **261**, 7491 (1986).
19. R. B. Weiss and J. A. Gallant, *Genetics* **112**, 727 (1986).
20. R. Weiss, D. Lindsley, B. Falahee and J. Gallant, *JMB* **203**, 403 (1988).
21. R. A. Spanjaard and J. van Duin, *PNAS* **85,**7967 **(1988).**
22. C. G. Kurland and J. A. Gallant, *in* "Accuracy in Molecular Processes" (T. B. L. Kirkwood, R. F. Rosenberger and D. J. Galas, eds.), pp. 127–157. Chapman & Hall, New York, 1986.
23. M. Yarus and R. F. Thompson, in "Gene Function in Prokaryotes" (J. Beckwith, J. Davies and J. Gallant, eds.), pp. 23–63. CSHLab, Cold Spring Harbor, New York, 1983.
24. J. Parker, *Microbiol. Rev.* **53**, 273 (1989).
25. T. D. Fox and B. Weiss-Brummer, *Nature* **288**, 60 (1988).
26. J. F. Atkins, B. P. Nichols and S. Thompson, *EMBO J.* **2**, 1345 (1988).
27. R. A. Kastelein, E. Remaut, W. Fiers and J. van Duin, *Nature* **295**, 35 (1982).
28. B. Berkhout, B. F. Schmidt, A. van Strien, J. van Boom, J. van Westrenen and J. van Duin, *JMB* **195**, 517 (1987).
29. M. Beremand and T. Blumenthal, *Cell* **18**, 257 (1979).
30. J. J. Dunn and F. W. Studier, *JMB* **166**, 477 (1983).
31. T. Jacks and H. E. Varmus, *Science* **230**, 1237 (1985).
32. W. J. Craigen, R. G. Cook, W. P. Tate and C. T. Caskey, *PNAS* **82**, 3616 (1985).
33. J. Clare and P. Farabaugh, *PNAS* **82**, 2829 (1985).
34. J. Mellor, S. M. Fulton, M. J. Dobson, W. Wilson, S. M. Kingsman and A. J. Kingsman, *Nature* **313**, 243 (1985).
35. W. J. Craigen and C. T. Caskey, *Nature* **322**, 273 (1986).
36. R. Moore, M. Dixon, R. Smith, G. Peters and C. Dickson, *J. Virol.* **61**, 480 (1987).
37. T. Jacks, K. Townley, H. E. Varmus and J. Majors, *PNAS* **84**, 4298 (1987).
38. A. Hizi, L. E. Henderson, T. D. Copeland, R. C. Sowden, C. V. Hixson and S. Oroszlan, *PNAS* **84**, 7041 (1987).
39. I. Brierly, M. E. G. Boursnell, M. M. Binns, B. Bilimoria, V. C. Block, T. D. K. Brown and S. C. Inglis, *EMBO J.* **6**, 3779 (1987).
40. R. B. Weiss, D. M. Dunn, J. F. Atkins and R. F. Gesteland, *CSHSQB* **52**, 687 (1987).
41. T. Jacks, M. D. Power, F. R. Masiarz, P. A. Luciw, P. J. Barr and H. E. Varmus, *Nature* **331**, 280 (1988).
42. W. M. Huang, S. Z. Ao, S. Casjens, R. Orlandi, R. Zeikus, R. Weiss, D. Winge and M. Fang, *Science* **239**, 1005 (1988).
43. R. B. Weiss, D. M. Dunn, A. E. Dahlberg, J. F. Atkins and R. F. Gesteland, *EMBO J.* **7**, 1503 (1988).
44. J. J. Clare, M. Belcourt and P. J. Farabaugh, *PNAS* **85**, 6816 (1988).
45. T. Jacks, H. D. Madhani, F. R. Masiarz and H. E. Varmus, *Cell* **55**, 447 (1988).
46. W. Wilson, M. Braddock, S. E. Adams, P. D. Rathjen, S. M. Kingsman and A. J. Kingsman, *Cell* **55**, 1159 (1988).
47. I. Brierly, P. Digard and S. C. Inglis, *Cell* **57**, 537 (1989).
48. Y. Sekine and E. Ohtsubo, *PNAS* **86**, 4609 (1989).
49. T. Icho and R. B. Wickner, *JBC* **264**, 6716 (1989).
50. R. B. Weiss, D. M. Dunn, J. F. Atkins and R. F. Gesteland, *in* "Ribosomes: Structure

and Function" (W. Hill, P. Moore, R. Garrett, J. Warner, A. Dahlberg and D. Schlessinger, eds.). Am. Soc. Microbiol., Washington, D.C., in press.

51. M. O'Connor, R. F. Gesteland and J. F. Atkins, *EMBO J.* **13**, 4315 (1989).
52. R. B. Weiss, W. M. Huang and D. M. Dunn, *Cell* in press (1990).
53. T. Maruyama, T. Gojobori, S. Aota and T. Ikemura, *NARes* **14** (Suppl.), 151 (1986).
53a. J. F. Curran and M. Yarus, *JMB* **209**, 65 (1989).
54. S. Pedersen, *Alfred Benzon Symp.* **19**, (1984).
55. S. Varenne, J. Buc, R. Lloubes and C. Lazdunski, *JMB* **180**, 549 (1984).
56. R. B. Weiss, D. M. Dunn, M. Shuh, J. F. Atkins and R. F. Gesteland, *New Biologist* **1**, 159 (1989).
57. R. Weiss, J. Murphy and J. Gallant, *J. Bact.* **158**, 362 (1984).
58. E. J. Murgola, K. A. Hijazi, H. U. Goringer and A. E. Dahlberg, *PNAS* **85**, 4162 (1988).
59. R. Gaber and M. Culbertson, *MCBiol* **4**, 2052 (1984).
60. L. Bossi and D. Smith, *PNAS* **81**, 6105 (1984).
61. J. Curran and M. Yarus, *Science* **238**, 1545 (1987).
62. J. R. Roth, *Cell* **24**, 601 (1981).
63. S. D. Tucker, E. J. Murgola and F. T. Pagel, *Biochimie* **71**, 729 (1989).
64. T. Ikemura, *JMB* **146**, 1 (1981).
65. Y. A. Ovchinnikov, G. S. Monastyrskaya, W. Gubanov, S. O. Guryev, O. Y. Chertov, N. N. Modyanov, V. A. Grinkevich, I. A. Makova, T. V. Marchenko, I. N. Polovnikova, V. M. Lipkin and E. D. Sverdlov, *EJB* **116**, 621 (1981).
66. E. N. Trifonov, *JMB* **194**, 643 (1987).

Inaccuracy and the Recognition of tRNA

M. JOHN ROGERS AND
DIETER SÖLL

*Department of Molecular Biophysics
and Biochemistry
Yale University
New Haven, Connecticut 06511*

The faithful transmission of genetic information relies on the accuracy of protein biosynthesis in matching the codon of the messenger RNA (mRNA) with the correct amino acid. Crucial in this scheme is the correct attachment of each amino acid to its corresponding (cognate) transfer RNA (tRNA). This aminoacylation reaction is catalyzed by a

Progress in Nucleic Acid Research
and Molecular Biology, Vol. 39

family of enzymes, aminoacyl-tRNA synthetases, that recognize specifically each amino acid and its cognate tRNA. For instance, the glutaminyl-tRNA synthetase (GlnRS)[1] of *Escherichia coli* esterifies glutamine onto the 3'-terminal adenosine of tRNA^{Gln}.

Aminoacyl-tRNA synthetases (amino-acid—tRNA ligases, EC 6.1.1.1–.22) are a diverse class of enzymes (*1, 2*). Although they all carry out the esterification of tRNA [albeit with differences in the detailed reaction mechanism (*3*)], they are all of varied tertiary structure, their expressions are regulated by different methods (*4*), and some assume other roles as well. For example, some fungal mitochondrial synthetases are also required for splicing introns out of mitochondrial RNA (*5, 6*). Synthetases also catalyze the disproportionation of ATP to diadenosine tetraphosphate (*7*), which may function as a pleotropic activator of cellular proliferation (*8*).

The high specificity of these enzymes toward their substrates (amino acid, ATP, and tRNA) has attracted much experimental attention. The most detailed studies regarding the binding of ATP and amino acid were based on the crystal structure (*9*) of *Bacillus stearothermophilus* TyrRS. Protein-engineering experiments involving those critical residues indicated by the structure gave some information on the binding of ATP and tyrosine (summarized in *10*), although there is some doubt on the interpretation of these results based on a refined crystal structure (*11*). However, the studies so far revealed no detailed information on the binding of tRNA (*12*), the macromolecular substrate for these enzymes.

For the past decade, our interest has focused on the *E. coli* GlnRS and its interaction with tRNA. There are a number of reasons why this system is appealing to experimental studies. Compared with other synthetases, this enzyme is relatively small; it is active as a monomer of 63.4 kDa comprised of 553 amino acids (*13–15*). There are a number of mutants available in which tRNA binding to the enzyme is affected. They include an allele giving rise to a thermolabile enzyme (*16*) and, most interestingly, a number of mischarging mutants (see Section I) in which the enzyme's tRNA specificity is relaxed. To complement *in vitro* studies, this system allows *in vivo* experiments, as the suppressor tRNA^{Gln}(*supE*)-mediated suppression of amber mutations provides an easy *in vivo* assay for tRNA charging by GlnRS. In addition, there are

---

[1] Throughout the review, the following abbreviations are used: (a) In the notation of charged or mischarged tRNA (for example Gln-tRNA^{Tyr}), the prefix refers to the amino acid charged, the superscript refers to the tRNA specificity as determined by the anticodon. (b) Aminoacyl-tRNA synthetases are denoted by the three-letter abbreviation of the amino acid followed by RS, e.g., GlnRS is glutaminyl-tRNA synthetase.

two *E. coli* tRNA^{Gln} isoacceptors that have been sequenced and cloned (*17, 18*). The small size of the enzyme and the ability to produce a large amount of enzyme and tRNA from cloned genes (*19*) has allowed biophysical studies of the GlnRS : tRNA^{Gln} complex by NMR (*20*) and X-ray crystallographic analysis to near-atomic resolution (*21*). The *E. coli* GlnRS–tRNA^{Gln} system is one of the best studied tRNA/synthetase systems to date, and has yielded significant information on the question of tRNA recognition.

Transfer RNA recognition by aminoacyl-tRNA synthetases has been the subject of several recent reviews (e.g., *22–24*). In this paper we review the central role of GlnRS in misaminoacylation (or mischarging) and the implication of these results for the recognition of tRNA by GlnRS.

What is meant by "mischarging?" Briefly, it can be termed the coupling of the "incorrect" amino acid onto a tRNA. With relevance to GlnRS, this is the esterification of glutamine onto, for example, the suppressor derived from tRNA^{Tyr}(*supF*) giving rise to Gln–tRNA^{Tyr}.

How can mischarging occur? One can imagine as possible mechanisms mutations in either the tRNA or in the tRNA-recognition domain of the synthetase. These are the focus of this review. It may also be possible to obtain mutants in the amino-acid-recognition domain of the synthetase, although to date these have not been found; possible reasons for this are discussed in Section VI.

How is mischarging detected? Classically, experiments have relied on a genetic selection utilizing amber suppressor tRNAs. Experiments in the early 1970s (*25–29*) detected the mischarging of a mutated *supF* with glutamine by the suppression of a specific amber mutation in the gene for β-galactosidase, *lacZ*$_{1000}$. This amber mutation is unusual in that it can be suppressed (i.e., confer a Lac$^+$ phenotype on an *E. coli* strain with this mutation) by the glutamine-inserting amber suppressor *supE*, but not by suppressors carrying tyrosine, leucine, or serine (*30*). This suppression is presumably because the insertion of glutamine, but not other amino acids, into the polypeptide is compatible with the function of the gene product. Therefore, this spectrum of suppression can be used as an assay for the mischarging by GlnRS, and is central to the mischarging phenomena discussed in this review.

I. Mischarging Mutants of GlnRS

A. The Genetic Selection for Mischarging Mutants

The availability of a selection for mutants of *supF* mischarged with glutamine prompted the search for mutants of GlnRS that can misacylate *supF*. Using the spectrum of suppression of the *lacZ*$_{1000}$ amber mutation, mischarging of *supF* tRNA by a mutated form of the GlnRS enzyme can be detected. The selection scheme (outlined in Fig. 1) makes use of a mutated *glnS* gene on a prophage in a *lacZ*$_{1000}$, *supF* strain. A Lac$^+$ phenotype will then be detected if a mutated form of *glnS* can mischarge *supF* with glutamine (*30*). Using this selection, three mutant alleles of *glnS* were isolated (*31, 32*). These mutants (*glnS7*, *glnS10*, *glnS15*) were identified as described below.

B. Identification of the Mutations in the *glnS* Gene Responsible for the Mischarging Phenotype

Mapping by genetic complementation and subsequent DNA sequence analysis identified the site of the mutation responsible for the mischarging phenotype in the *glnS7* gene (*15*). The amino-acid sequence of GlnRS7 (the enzyme encoded by the *glnS7* gene) differs from wild-type at position 235, with Asn substituted for Asp. The alteration in the *glnS7* gene is a G → A transition; this mutation interrupts a *Bst*N1 restriction site found in the wild-type gene. This feature can then be used to screen for additional mischarging mutants that are

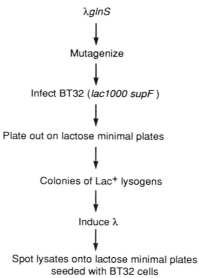

FIG. 1. The use of an *E. coli* strain (BT32) that is Lac$^-$ to select for mutants of *glnS* that mischarge *supF* (the tyrosine-inserting amber suppressor tRNA) with glutamine. This then confers a Lac$^+$ phenotype on the strain.

not of the *glnS7*-type. One allele, *glnS10*, was found that was not interrupted at the *Bst*N1 site. However, by genetic mapping and DNA sequence analysis, the site of the *glnS10* mutation was found to contain an A → G transition immediately adjacent to the base-pair altered in the *glnS7* allele (*32*). This changes the same codon at position 235 as the GlnRS7 mutation, but the change is Asp to Gly for GlnRS10.

To search for additional alleles not of the *glnS7/glnS10* type, DNA sequence analysis of isolates was performed to search for alleles containing the wild-type sequence at amino acid 235; the site of the mutation responsible for the mischarging phenotype must then be elsewhere in the gene. This was simplified, as both the *glnS7* and *glnS10* mutations involve G residues, so single-track sequencing was performed of several mutant phages. One isolate, *glnS15*, contained the wild-type sequence at amino acid 235. By genetic complementation and DNA sequencing, the mutation in the *glnS15* gene was found to differ from the wild-type *glnS* gene by a single T → C transition, resulting in the substitution of Thr for Ile at amino acid 129 in GlnRS15 (*32*). This mutation also interrupts a *Xho*II site found in the wild-type *glnS* gene, and this feature was used to confirm the results from DNA sequencing. The positions of the mutations in the *glnS* structural gene that confer mischarging are summarized in Fig. 2.

Although these mutant *glnS* genes were isolated originally by mischarging of *supF*, two additional questions can be addressed by the availability of the mutant enzymes: (i) are they affected in recognition of the cognate tRNA^{Gln}; and (ii) do they mischarge other amber suppressor tRNAs? It can be deduced by successful complementation of a temperature-sensitive *glnS* strain (*16*) that all three mischarging mutants can still recognize and aminoacylate the usual substrate, tRNA^{Gln}. To determine if additional amber suppressor tRNAs were mischarged in the *glnS7*, *glnS10*, and *glnS15* strains, suppression of

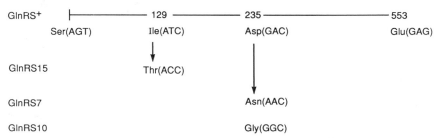

FIG. 2. The *glnS* gene and the location of the mutations and corresponding amino-acid changes of the *in vivo*-derived mischarging mutants of GlnRS.

$lacZ_{1000}$ was determined in the presence of the serine-inserting $supD$ and leucine-inserting $supP$ suppressors, and the synthetic Phe, Cys, and Ala amber suppressor tRNAs (22), as shown in Table I (R. N. Swanson, unpublished). No suppression by tRNAs other than $supE$ or $supF$ was detected. Thus, it appears that all three mischarging enzymes retain some discrimination for tRNA.

C. In Vitro Mischarging by GlnRS7

Although the mischarging mutants retain specificity for tRNA *in vivo*, the availability of the purified GlnRS7 allows examination of the mischarging of other tRNA species *in vitro*, as mischarging *in vivo* can more readily be detected with amber suppressor tRNAs (30). Therefore, the aminoacylation of Gln–tRNAs charged by wild-type GlnRS and GlnRS7 was compared (15). For aminoacylation, tRNA prepared from a strain overproducing $supF$ was aminoacylated under standard reaction conditions with [^{14}C]glutamine (for GlnRS), and [^{3}H]glutamine (for GlnRS7). When complete, the reactions were mixed and the glutaminyl–tRNAs separated by reversed-phase chromatography. The separation is shown in Fig. 3.

As the figure shows, both enzymes aminoacylate tRNA^{Gln} present in the first peak. In addition, GlnRS7 mischarges other species of tRNA, of which $supF$ is probably the major one. Therefore, it is clear that other tRNAs can be mischarged *in vitro* by GlnRS7. However, it is interesting to note the minor peaks of [^{14}C]glutamine-accepting tRNAs, which are caused by the wild-type enzyme mischarging non-

TABLE I

MISCHARGING OF AMBER SUPPRESSORS IN $lacZ_{1000}$ STRAINS CARRYING WILD-TYPE AND MISCHARGING MUTANTS OF GlnRS

Suppressor	glnS Allele			
	$glnS^+$	$glnS7$	$glnS10$	$glnS15$
$supD$ (Ser)	$-^a$	$-$	$-$	$-$
$supE$ (Gln)	$+^b$	$+$	$(+)^c$	$(+)$
$supF$ (Tyr)	$-$	$+$	$+$	$+$
$supP$ (Leu)	$-$	$-$	$-$	$-$
pGFIB:Cys	$-$	$-$	$-$	$-$
pGFIB:Phe	$-$	$-$	$-$	$-$
pGFIB:Ala2	$-$	$-$	$-$	$-$

^{a} $-$, No growth.
^{b} $+$, Growth on lactose minimal medium.
^{c} $(+)$, Slower growth on lactose minimal medium.

cognate tRNAs with glutamine to a low level. As discussed in Section II, even wild-type GlnRS can mischarge *supF* when overproduced in the cell and hence the mischarging of the same tRNAs shown in Fig. 3 is also likely to occur *in vivo*. This is the first example of critical *in vitro* and *in vivo* tests to examine the specificity of aminoacyl-tRNA synthe-

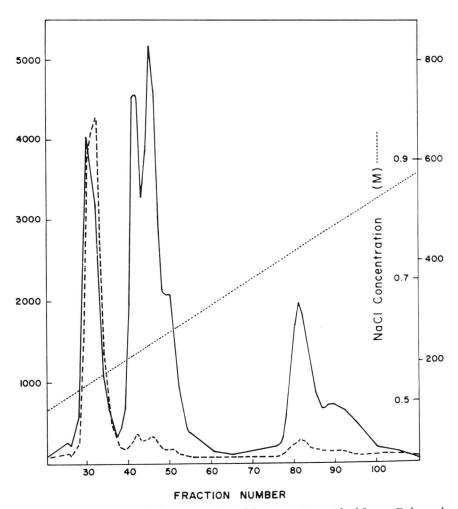

FRACTION NUMBER

FIG. 3. Comparison of Gln-tRNAs isolated from a strain enriched for *supF* charged by wild-type GlnRS and GlnRS7. Reversed-phase chromatography (RPC-5) of unfractionated [^{14}C]Gln–tRNA charged by wild-type GlnRS (---) and [^{3}H]Gln-tRNA charged by GlnRS7 (—). [Reprinted with permission from 15 by Springer-Verlag.]

tases. It remains to be seen if other synthetases show low levels of mischarging.

D. Additional Mutants of GlnRS Made by *in Vitro* Site-Directed Mutagenesis

Additional amino acid substitutions were made at amino acid 235 in GlnRS to probe the nature of the mischarging effected by the mutation. Position 235 was systematically altered by *in vitro* site-directed mutagenesis (33). The effect of these changes, and thus on the interaction with *supF*, can then be assayed for mischarging by β-galactosidase assays of a $lacZ_{1000}$, *supF* strain carrying the mutant *glnS* genes. The results of the substitutions on mischarging of GlnRS are shown in Table II.

Interestingly, the original genetic selection (31) described above led to the isolation of mutations with the strongest phenotypes, *glnS7* and *glnS10* (Table II). All the mutations at position 235 retain the ability to complement a strain that is temperature-sensitive for *glnS* (16), indicating that they retain charging of tRNA^{Gln}. However, there is a correlation between mischarging and the steric effect of the amino-acid substitution at 235. Thus the enzymes GlnRS13 and GlnRS14 (Lys and Glu substitutions, respectively) do not mischarge *supF*, presumably because of the steric hindrance introduced compared to Asp at position 235. The other substitutions are equal in size or smaller than Asp235.

TABLE II

THE LEVEL OF MISCHARGING AS MEASURED BY β-GALACTOSIDASE LEVELS OF GLNRS MUTANTS ALTERED AT AMINO ACID 235[a]

Strain	Amino acid 235	β-Galactosidase activity (units)
RS109(λglnS+)	Asp	2
RS109(λglnS7)	Asn	29
RS109(λglnS10)	Gly	16
RS109(λglnS11)	Val	16
RS109(λglnS12)	Ala	13
RS109(λglnS13)	Lys	3
RS109(λglnS14)	Glu	2
RS109(λsupE)	—	39

[a] The suppression of $lacZ_{1000}$ by *supF* in strain RS109 is measured in β-galactosidase units (Miller units). Reprinted with permission from 33 by Oxford University Press.

E. Structural Basis for Mischarging by the Mutant GlnRS Enzymes

The isolation of mutant forms of GlnRS that can mischarge *supF* implies that the amino acids in the positions of these mutations in the polypeptide chain are important for interaction with tRNA. When mutated, these positions reduce discrimination between the suppressor tRNA^{Tyr} (*supF*) and tRNA^{Gln} (*supE*). The possible molecular basis for reduced selectivity of the mischarging mutants could be a more favorable interaction with *supF* or a less favorable interaction with *supE*, or both. The availability of the X-ray structure of the complex of tRNA^{Gln} with GlnRS allows a more detailed view of the nature of the interaction of tRNA with the mischarging mutant enzymes (34).

Most aminoacyl-tRNA synthetases share a region of weak amino-acid similarity in the amino-terminal portion of the protein, in which the amino-acid sequence His–Ile–Gly–His is most conserved. This region of the synthetase is involved in formation of the aminoacyl–adenylate intermediate (35). In *E. coli* and *B. stearothermophilus* TyrRS and *E. coli* MetRS, this structural homology extends over some 200 amino acids and contains a dinucleotide fold motif (11, 36), As the structure of the tRNA^{Gln} : GlnRS complex is known (21), the location of the amino acids altered in the mischarging mutants can be examined (34). The site of the GlnRS15 mutation, amino acid 129, is in a domain of the enzyme that binds the acceptor stem of tRNA, placing the 3′ end near the active site of the adenylate-forming region of the enzyme. This domain interrupts the dinucleotide binding domain in GlnRS responsible for glutaminyl–adenylate formation. The region that binds the acceptor stem of tRNA is composed of amino acids 25–100 and 210–260; it is therefore interesting if similar disruption of the dinucleotide binding domain occurs in other synthetases. The interactions with tRNA of amino acids 129 and 235, which are altered in the mischarging mutants, are discussed in Section IV.

II. Mischarging by Overproduction of Wild-type GlnRS

A. Characterization of Overproduction Mischarging

In the course of studies on the characterization of mischarging by mutant *glnS* alleles, it was discovered that the same phenotype could be caused by overproduction of the wild-type *glnS* gene on a multi-copy plasmid. Therefore, when the *glnS* gene is on a multicopy plasmid in a $lacZ_{1000}$, $supF$ strain the cells are phenotypically Lac$^+$ (37). This indicates that when wild-type GlnRS is overproduced in the cell, it can apparently misacylate $supF$. This phenomenon has not been observed to date in other aminoacyl–tRNA synthetase systems.

B. The Mechanism of Overproduction Mischarging

We assumed that competition between tRNAs for GlnRS molecules in $vivo$ was probably resulting in the mischarging observed. In the normal situation in $vivo$, most of the GlnRS and tRNA^{Gln} molecules are complexed with each other. Elevation of the GlnRS levels in the cell by $glnS$ on a multicopy plasmid results in uncomplexed GlnRS molecules free to interact with noncognate tRNAs. If so, a test should be the abolition of mischarging, as reflected in a Lac$^-$ phenotype, by concomitant overproduction of tRNA^{Gln}. This would restore the ratio of complexed GlnRS with cognate tRNA. Similarly, overproduction of TyrRS simultaneously with GlnRS would complex more completely $supF$ tRNA, which would then no longer be available for mischarging by GlnRS. The results from such experiments are described below.

In order to overexpress the genes for GlnRS and tRNA^{Gln} in the same cell from separate, compatible plasmids, the genes for tRNA$_2^{Gln}$ were placed behind an inducible λ p_L promoter (19). Transcription from this promoter is activated by raising the temperature to 42°C. The $glnS$ gene is placed on a compatible plasmid derived from pACYC184 to form pRS11. For the experiment, cultures of double transformants of a $lacZ_{1000}$, $supF$ strain that can induce expression from the λ p_L promoter were grown at 30°C and shifted to 42°C. The assay of β-galactosidase levels (38) at time points was monitored as a reflection of mischarging in the cell. As shown in Fig. 4(A), in the control culture with no tRNA$_2^{Gln}$ overproduction, the β-galactosidase activity increases in parallel with cell density after a small initial drop. However,

---

Fig. 4. Overproduction of tRNA$_2^{Gln}$ abolishes mischarging caused by overproduction of GlnRS, as assayed by β-galactosidase levels (○) at time points following induction of the expression of tRNA$_2^{Gln}$ at 42°C. Cell densities are indicated by (●). The tandem tRNA$_2^{Gln}$ genes were cloned into the λ p_L expression-vector pLC28 to form pRS3. A derivative of BT32 (RS108) that can produce a temperature-labile λ repressor was then constructed. The $glnS$ gene was also cloned into pACYC184, a plasmid that is compatible with pLC28, to make pRS11 (37). (A) Cell density and β-galactosidase activity of RS108/pRS11/pLC28 after temperature induction at time 0. This construct overproduces GlnRS, but not tRNA^{Gln}. (B) Cell density and β-galactosidase levels of a culture of RS108/pRS3/pRS11. This construct overproduces both GlnRS and, upon induction, tRNA^{Gln}. [Reprinted with permission from 37 by the A.A.A.S.]

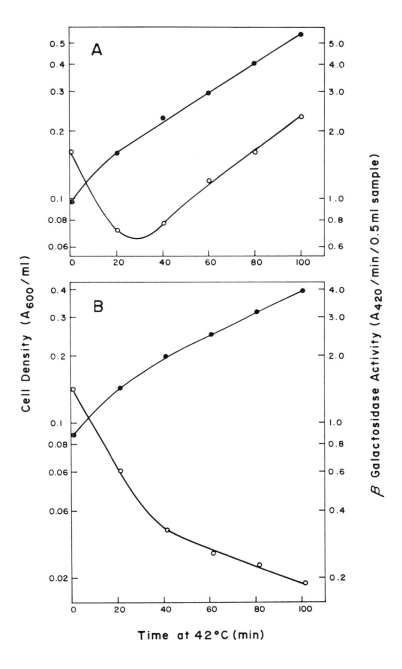

in a strain where $tRNA_2^{Gln}$ production can be induced at the same time as GlnRS overproduction [Fig. 4 (B)], the activity of β-galactosidase decreases. This was expected if the hypothesis was correct. To ensure that elevated $tRNA^{Gln}$ levels do not repress the expression of the *glnS* gene, both GlnRS and $tRNA^{Gln}$ assays were performed on parallel cultures to those for β-galactosidase assays. Both GlnRS and $tRNA^{Gln}$ levels were more than 20-fold elevated after 60-minutes induction, at a time when β-galactosidase levels are clearly reduced (37) (Fig. 4).

An analogous situation to that described above was found when both TyrRS and GlnRS were overproduced on compatible plasmids in a *lacZ*$_{1000}$, *supF* strain (M. J. Rogers and R. N. Swanson, unpublished). In a control containing pBR322 with no TyrRS overproduction, β-galactosidase activity increased in parallel with cell density. This is similar to the overproduction mischarging in Fig. 4 above. However, in a strain containing the TyrRS gene on a multicopy plasmid [pBRYTS (39)], β-galactosidase activity is almost completely abolished. The results are exactly what one would expect if the hypothesis were correct, that an important factor in maintaining accuracy of aminoacylation *in vivo* is the ratio of free aminoacyl-tRNA synthetase to synthetase complexed with cognate tRNA.

The results of these experiments indicate competition *in vivo* between tRNAs for a limited number of GlnRS molecules, as overproduction of GlnRS leads to mischarging of *supF*. It was shown some time ago by experiments *in vitro* that mischarging reactions are inhibited by the presence of the cognate tRNA, and thus the existence of cognate synthetase : tRNA complexes might contribute to specificity by making the enzyme unavailable for mischarging reactions (40). The results shown above indicate that this is also the case *in vivo*, and that the contribution of this effect to accuracy of aminoacylation is significant. Because most tRNAs exist in the cell in excess of their respective synthetases, overproduction of *supF* has little effect on misacylation with glutamine (37).

To maintain accuracy of aminoacylation, the level of each aminoacyl-tRNA synthetase must be regulated within certain limits, as the presence of excess enzyme can act on uncomplexed noncognate tRNA. The regulation may be more important for GlnRS than for other synthetases, as GlnRS is unusual in that the ratio of GlnRS : $tRNA^{Gln}$ is only about 1 : 1, which is much lower than the synthetase : tRNA ratios of parallel synthetase systems studied to date in *E. coli* (41). Therefore, the unusually low ratio of synthetase : tRNA for the glutamine system may account for the observed mischarging by overproduction of GlnRS, and explain why so many mutant tRNAs are aminoacylated by

GlnRS *in vivo* (summarized in 22). It is apparent that GlnRS may not take full advantage of the importance of cognate complex formation to maintain accuracy of *in vivo* aminoacylation.

III. Mischarging of Mutant tRNAs by GlnRS

A. Mischarging of Mutant *E. coli* tRNA Species by Wild-Type GlnRS

As mentioned above, the first studies on *E. coli* tRNA mutants that can be mischarged by wild-type aminoacyl-tRNA synthetases were performed in the early 1970s (25–29). The genetic selection of mutations depended on the mutant *supF* tRNA^{Tyr} molecules to be charged with glutamine and thus restore functional β-galactosidase (i.e., a Lac$^+$ phenotype) to a strain carrying the *lacZ*$_{1000}$ gene. The positions of these mutations were found in the acceptor stem of the tRNA molecule. The single mutations at $G_1 \rightarrow A$, $G_2 \rightarrow A$, $C_{72} \rightarrow U$ and $A_{73} \rightarrow G$ and the double mutations to $A_1 \cdot G_{72}$ and $A_1 \cdot G_{73}$ of *supF* were mischarged with glutamine (summarized in 42); the mutations A_2, U_{72}, and $A_1 \cdot U_{72}$ retain aminoacylation with tyrosine as well as mischarging with glutamine. In addition, the molecular analysis of the amber suppressor *supU*, derived from tRNA^{Trp} by a single mutation in the anticodon (43) showed that mischarging is the basis for suppression. This suppressor tRNA is mischarged by glutamine both *in vivo* and *in vitro* (44, 45). Taken together, these early experiments pinpointed areas in the acceptor stem and in the anticodon of tRNA as important recognition elements for GlnRS. Below we describe in more detail the use of mischarging and how the results define more accurately the recognition by GlnRS.

The collection of mutant tRNAs shown to be mischarged with glutamine has been expanded by work in recent years (22). While the mischarging of mutants of *supF* (tRNA^{Tyr}) and *supU* (tRNA^{Trp}) was shown by genetic experiments, more recent techniques have been used to construct mutant tRNAs. By enzymatic replacement *in vitro* of the CAU anticodon of *E. coli* tRNA$_f^{Met}$ to CUA, corresponding to the amber codon, a large increase in the rate of aminoacylation with GlnRS was seen (46). The kinetic parameters for aminoacylation by MetRS and GlnRS show that the altered tRNA is a better substrate for the noncognate synthetase. A similar situation is seen *in vivo* for tRNA$_f^{Met}$, although repair of the terminal $C_1 \cdot A_{72}$ base-pair as well as the anticodon mutation is necessary for glutaminylation *in vivo* (47). Therefore, these results, although showing the importance of the terminal base pair $(1 \cdot 72)$ for recognition by GlnRS, indicate that recognition is not sequence dependent.

More recent experiments in tRNA identity have shown a number of mutant amber suppressor tRNAs to be mischarged *in vivo*. Some of these tRNAs are mischarged with glutamine (reviewed in 22). Thus, the amber suppressors derived from tRNA^{Gly}, tRNA^{Phe}, tRNA^{Ile}, and tRNA^{Glu} by synthetic gene construction and analyzed for suppression *in vivo* show mischarging by GlnRS. Experiments described in Section III,B also resulted in a tRNA derived from tRNA$_1^{Ser}$ mischarged by glutamine. The level of incorporation of glutamine by these mutant tRNAs, as detected by the dihydrofolate reductase assay described below ranges from 6% (tRNA^{Phe}) to 95% (tRNA$_1^{Ser}$(CUA)). These data are summarized in Fig. 5. Therefore, in addition to the anticodon nucleotides, in particular U$_{35}$, these data reinforce the importance of the acceptor stem to recognition by GlnRS. The conversion of glutamine acceptance, in most cases, is not complete and shows that competition *in vivo* by other aminoacyl-tRNA synthetases may determine the aminoacylation of tRNA. It is of interest that many of the collection of mutant amber suppressors are mischarged by LysRS (22), which may also be less discriminatory than most other synthetases (discussed in Section VI,B).

B. Mischarging of tRNA^{Ser} and the Discrimination between SerRS and GlnRS

Based on the observation that the purified, mischarging GlnRS7 enzyme could misacylate noncognate *E. coli* tRNAs *in vitro* with glutamine (15) (Fig. 3) a search was started to determine the nature of these tRNA species. It turned out that two different purified *E. coli* serine tRNAs are aminoacylated *in vitro* at a low level by GlnRS7 (48). In order to confirm these results *in vivo*, two changes in the anticodon of tRNA$_1^{Ser}$ were made in order to convert it to an amber suppressor tRNA (Fig. 6). Glutaminylation of this tRNA by wild-type GlnRS *in vivo* would lead to suppression of the *lac*Z$_{1000}$ mutation. The mutant amber suppressor tRNA$_1^{Ser}$(CUA), although a very efficient suppressor tRNA (in suppressing amber codons that show no preference for a particular amino acid inserted) is not mischarged with glutamine *in vivo* (49), as determined by both genetic selection and amino-terminal protein sequencing of mutated *E. coli* dihydrofolate reductase (DHFR). The gene for the mutant protein was engineered with an amber codon at position 10 in the *fol* gene (50). Suppression of the amber codon will then give DHFR with the amino acid at position 10 corresponding to the amino acids inserted by the mutant tRNA$_1^{Ser}$(CUA).

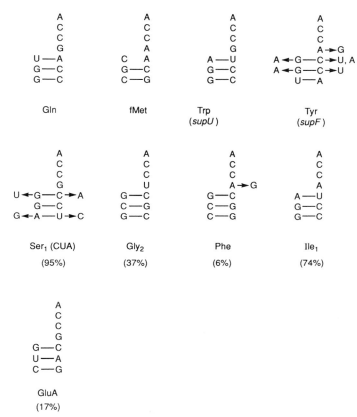

FIG. 5. The sequences of the acceptor stem in tRNAs shown to be aminoacylated with glutamine. The positions of mutations that effect aminoacylation by GlnRS are indicated by arrows. Unless otherwise indicated, the mischarging is detected by conversion to an amber suppressor. Figures in brackets indicate the level of mischarging detected by the dihydrofolate reductase (DHFR) assay (50). References for these data are: tRNA^{fMet} (46), supU (45), supF (42), tRNA$_1^{Ser}$ (49), tRNA^{Gly} (52), tRNA^{Phe} (53), tRNA^{Ile} (22), and tRNA^{Glu} (22).

In *in vivo* experiments, there are at least 19 other aminoacyl-tRNA synthetases present in the cell. This situation is clearly different from the usual *in vitro* experiment where only a single purified aminoacyl-tRNA synthetase is allowed to react with the tRNA present. Thus, competition in the cell between SerRS and GlnRS may prevent the tRNA$_1^{Ser}$(CUA) from being aminoacylated with glutamine *in vivo*.

To confirm this hypothesis, further changes in the tRNA$_1^{Ser}$(CUA) were made to convert it toward glutamine acceptance and away from

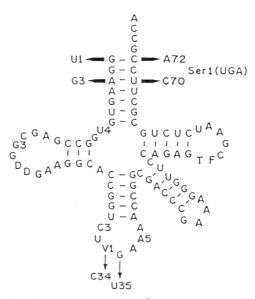

FIG. 6. The nucleotide sequence of tRNA$_1^{Ser}$ shown in cloverleaf form. Narrow arrows indicate changes to an amber suppressor tRNA. Thick arrows indicate changes subsequently made to effect mischarging by GlnRS (50).

serine acceptance. A number of different studies have implicated the terminal base-pairs of the acceptor stem of tRNA^{Ser} as being important for its identity (22, 50, 51). Changes in the acceptor stem of tRNA$_1^{Ser}$(CUA) were made to mimic those of tRNA^{Gln} (Fig. 6). By the criteria of both genetic selection (suppression of $lacZ_{1000}$) and amino-terminal sequencing of mutant DHFR, this tRNA is mischarged with glutamine (49). However, conversion from serine acceptance is not complete; the mutant tRNA$_1^{Ser}$(CUA) with base changes in base-pairs 1 · 72 and 3 · 70 is mischarged 95% with glutamine but retains a residual 5% serine acceptance, from the incorporation at amino acid 10 in mutant DHFR. Therefore, the two aminoacyl-tRNA synthetases share discriminants in the acceptor helix of tRNA, and the results show that an important contribution to tRNA identity is competition by aminoacyl-tRNA synthetases *in vivo*. A set of nucleotides that determine the specificity of tRNA can be interpreted both in terms of the recognition of the cognate aminoacyl-tRNA synthetase and blocking recognition of noncognate synthetases. Thus, the interpretation of results from *in vivo* and *in vitro* experiments may differ.

IV. The Structure of the GlnRS : tRNA^{Gln}
Complex as It Relates to tRNA^{Gln} Identity

We would like to use biophysical approaches to support the data from genetic and biochemical experiments on the recognition of GlnRS. These approaches using NMR and X-ray crystallography, may reveal in detail the molecular basis for discrimination between tRNA^{Gln} and noncognate tRNAs. In the past, such studies have been hampered by limited quantities of reasonably pure tRNA and, to a lesser extent, of aminoacyl-tRNA synthetase.

Our studies began with the cognate GlnRS : tRNA^{Gln} complex (19). We then sought to construct a strain that would overproduce tRNA^{Gln} to a high level by cloning the dimeric tRNA$_2^{Gln}$ genes behind the inducible λ p_L promoter (37), to give the plasmid pRS3 described in Section II. The plasmid was constructed with the dimeric tRNA$_2^{Gln}$ tRNA genes subcloned from an operon containing seven tRNA genes (18). When tRNA is isolated from a strain carrying this plasmid, about 60–70% of the total tRNA following induction is aminoacylated by GlnRS. The tRNA^{Gln} is approximately 90–95% pure after chromatographic fractionation (19), and is suitable for NMR (20) and X-ray crystallographic studies (19). The synthetase was also overproduced by cloning the glnS gene behind the inducible λ p_L promoter (M. Nichols, unpublished); the availability of large amounts of cognate tRNA and synthetase made it possible to determine the structure of the cocrystal of tRNA^{Gln} : GlnRS (21).

The results provide a molecular basis for understanding the mischarging of GlnRS (34). The mischarging mutants, when mutated at positions 235 and 129 (Fig. 2), have the ability to interact with the the acceptor stem region of cognate and noncognate tRNAs. This supports the results from genetic experiments described above that this part of tRNA^{Gln} is important for identity. However, the discrimination between cognate and noncognate tRNA requires structural information from GlnRS complexed with the mischarged tRNA, work currently in progress.

The structural studies of the tRNA^{Gln} : GlnRS complex show that base-pair U$_1$ · A$_{72}$ is disrupted in the complex, with a conformational change hairpinning back the 3' end of the molecule toward the anticodon (21). The nucleotide G$_{73}$ helps maintain the stability of the conformation via a specific intramolecular hydrogen bond. There are additional extensive interactions with the anticodon region, as well as sequence-specific interactions with nucleotides at G$_{10}$ and C$_{16}$. It is gratifying that the structural data support other experiments on the recognition of GlnRS, and provide information for further mutagenesis on both tRNA and GlnRS for understanding recognition in this system.

V. The Identity Elements of tRNA^{Gln}

The available genetic (42–45, 49), biochemical (46), and biophysical studies (20, 21) provide a view of the nucleotides of tRNA^{Gln} important for recognition by GlnRS (summarized in Fig. 7). As discussed above, the acceptor stem and the anticodon are the two major regions shown thus far to be involved in specific interaction with the enzyme. Data for the acceptor stem region of tRNA are summarized in Fig. 5. Interestingly, the nucleotide modification at position 34 in tRNA$_1^{Gln}$ was shown by chemical modification (54) to be in close proximity to GlnRS. The importance of the discriminator nucleotide G$_{73}$ (55) was first recognized in genetic experiments (42); in the structure of the tRNA : synthetase complex, this nucleotide participates in a sequence-specific intramolecular interaction with the acceptor stem of tRNA (21).

Refinement of the structure from X-ray crystallography will provide a basis for further experiments to distinguish nucleotides in tRNA^{Gln}

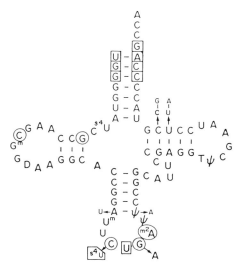

FIG. 7. The identity of tRNA^{Gln} as shown by genetic, biochemical, and structural data. The sequence shown is of tRNA$_2^{Gln}$ in cloverleaf form, with the sequence of tRNA$_1^{Gln}$ shown in lightface. Boxed residues were shown by genetic and biochemical data from *supF* (42), *supU* (45), tRNA^{fMet} (46), tRNA$_1^{Ser}$(CUA) (49), and tRNA$_1^{Gln}$ (54). Circled residues are additional interactions indicated by structural data (20).

that provide specific contacts with GlnRS and those common to other tRNA/protein or tRNA/synthetase interactions.

VI. Mischarging by Other Aminoacyl-tRNA Synthetases

A. Mischarging of tRNA^{Gln} by Other Aminoacyl-tRNA Synthetases

The number of tRNAs mischarged by GlnRS (Section III,B) raises the question of the conversion of tRNA^{Gln} to recognition by other aminoacyl-tRNA synthetases. Mutations have been found in the amber suppressor derived from tRNA$_2^{Gln}$ that increase the efficiency of amber suppression (56), and it has also been proposed that these mutations cause mischarging with tryptophan (57, 58), although the effect on suppressor efficiency of these mutations is not clear. In initial experiments, we were interested in the mutagenesis of the acceptor stem nucleotides to examine the effect of these mutations on competition with other synthetases. These changes were carried out on the amber suppressor derived from tRNA$_2^{Gln}$ (*supE*) so that the effect of these mutations could be analyzed *in vivo*. Selection can again be carried out by suppression of amber mutations showing a different spectrum of suppression. In these experiments, it is crucial that glutamine insertion at the amber site should not lead to an active gene product. We found that the *supE* $G_1 \cdot C_{72}$ mutant gene is able to suppress the *met*$_3$ allele (30), although the suppression is temperature-sensitive. Given the spectrum of suppression data for this allele it is possible that the *supE* mutant may be misacylated with tyrosine. This seems to be confirmed by a very low tyrosine insertion in the DHFR assay (58a). These studies are encouraging, as it is possible that additional mutations in the *supE* $G_1 \cdot C_{72}$ gene may lead to complete conversion to tyrosine identity. The parameters for *in vitro* aminoacylation of the *supE* $G_1 \cdot C_{72}$ mutant with purified TyrRS also allows comparison of the effects of competition *in vivo* to be evaluated, as it is interesting that the terminal $(1 \cdot 72)$ base-pair may provide a site of discrimination between GlnRS and TyrRS as tRNA^{Tyr} contains a $G \cdot C$ base-pair at this position.

B. Mischarging Mutants of Other Aminoacyl-tRNA Synthetases

It is interesting that GlnRS is so far the only synthetase for which mutations in the gene effect mischarging (Section I). This raises the question of whether mutations that cause mischarging can be found in other synthetases. With the availability of defined amber mutations in *E. coli* where the spectrum of suppression is known (*30, 59*), a wide number of genetic selections for mischarging amber suppressor tRNAs can be performed. Clearly, for the GlnRS system, the *lacZ*$_{1000}$ selection enabled the search for mischarging mutants (*31*). Also, the genes for a number of *E. coli* synthetases have now been cloned (*4*), making genetic manipulations easier. Advances in the ability to synthesize and express mutant tRNA genes have resulted in expanding the original set of amber suppressor tRNAs to a total of 11 amino acids (*22*). These amber suppressors, and mutants of them, may be used in a selection for mischarging mutants, as they may contain identity elements closer to those of the cognate tRNA to allow a mutation in the synthetase to confer mischarging.

The large number of mutant amber suppressor tRNAs mischarged by LysRS (*22*) prompts the question that mischarging mutants may be found for this enzyme, as it may be less discriminating than other synthetases. The availability of amber mutations in the *trpA* and *lacI* genes that may show some specificity for insertion by lysine (*59, 60*) provides a genetic selection for mischarging mutants of LysRS. The gene for the constitutive LysRS has also been cloned and sequenced (*61*), so there may be more than one form of LysRS (*62*).

Finally, it should be noted that mischarging *in vivo* is a stringent selection; the misacylation of GlnRS occurs only with *supF* among the suppressors tested (Table I), as mischarging of a large number of tRNAs would presumably be lethal for the cell. In contrast, it is apparent that because of the degeneracy of the genetic code, misreading of mRNA codons may occur *in vivo* at a low level (*63*).

VII. Outlook

How common is mischarging in nature *in vivo?* Mischarging of tRNA (at least to a large extent) is lethal to the cell if it interferes with the correct production of proteins. However, there may be vestiges of older, less precise synthetase systems present today. One way of ensuring correct charging is to build mechanisms for error correction into aminoacyl-tRNA synthetases. Thus, in an ATP-dependent step, noncognate aminoacyl-tRNAs are hydrolyzed before dissociation of the incorrectly aminoacylated product from the enzyme (*3, 64*), or an editing mechanism with the noncognate aminoacyl-adenylate is hydrolyzed prior to acylation onto tRNA (*65*). Conformational changes upon amino-acid binding and aminoacyl-adenylate formation may also contribute to accuracy of aminoacylation (66). The operation of these mechanisms of amino-acid discrimination may explain the failure of obtaining mutants in amino-acid binding.

A. The Naturally Occurring Mischarging System in Gram-positive Eubacteria and the Chloroplasts of Higher Plants

The precedent for mischarging in the glutamine system is, in fact, well established and widespread in nature. It was known some time ago that Gram-positive organisms lack GlnRS activity (67). The involvement of a tRNA^{Glu} species in the synthesis of δ-aminolevulinic acid (68), the precursor to porphyrins in the chloroplasts of higher plants, prompted the search for other glutamate-accepting tRNAs that are not active in δ-aminolevulinic acid synthesis. Two glutamate-acceptors were found (69). Surprisingly, upon purification and sequencing, both tRNAs are very different from tRNA^{Glu} and are in fact misacylated chloroplast tRNA^{Gln} species. There is no GlnRS activity detectable in chloroplasts (69). Therefore, there is apparently widespread occurrence of misacylation of tRNA^{Gln} with glutamate, as subsequent charging experiments with mitochondrial extracts and cyanobacterial extracts showed no detectable GlnRS activity present (reviewed in 70). Clearly, in a variety of organisms (Gram-positive eubacteria, archaebacteria) and in organelles, the GluRS is a naturally occurring mischarging enzyme. The mischarged Glu–tRNA^{Gln} species is then converted to Gln–tRNA^{Gln} by a tRNA-specific amidotransferase in the presence of a suitable amide donor (69). Thus, in organisms where Gln–tRNA^{Gln} is formed via mischarging and transamidation, the tRNA-specific amidotransferase possesses a role similar to GlnRS.

It then seems likely that the mischarging and transamidation pathway preceded the pathway of direct formation of Gln–tRNA^{Gln}, as the presence of GlnRS activity is limited to Gram-negative eubacteria and the cytoplasm of eukaryotic cells (70). It will then be interesting to compare the recognition of the tRNA-dependent amidotransferase with what we have learned about the recognition of *E. coli* GlnRS.

B. The Contrast between *in Vivo* and *in Vitro* Studies

At this point, the use of genetic, biochemical, and biophysical studies has led to a model of the recognition of *E. coli* GlnRS that involves a number of factors as being important (Fig. 7). Clearly the advantage of genetic selection allows the competition *in vivo* to be examined. However, an *in vitro* approach allows the synthesis of large amounts of a tRNA by *in vitro* transcription (71). One can then quantitate the kinetic parameters for the effects of individual nucleotide changes on the recognition of the synthetase, as the specificity constant (k_{cat}/K_M) may be orders of magnitude lower for a poorly acylated or misacylated substrate (23). Such biochemical studies are necessary to determine the individual contribution of each identity element to the overall process of recognition. Coupled with the results presented above, this will lead to a more complete understanding of the recognition of GlnRS.

C. General Considerations

The errors rate of, for example, incorporation of valine instead of isoleucine in protein biosynthesis has been estimated at 1 : 3000 (72). One must then marvel at the overall accuracy of the intricate process of protein biosynthesis, with many potential sources of inaccuracy (e.g., 73). Therefore, the consideration of accuracy in protein biosynthesis has important implications when considering the overproduction of mutant proteins (74), when even low levels of misincorporation of amino acids can affect the interpretations of results. This effect could become significant when the expression conditions change the ratio of synthetases to tRNA in the cell.

The ability to detect mischarging and its implication for recognition of tRNA in the glutamine system will be relevant to other tRNA systems. Of particular importance is the widespread mischarging with lysine of a number of mutant tRNAs (22). The homology of yeast AspRS with *E. coli* and yeast LysRS (75) may reflect the sharing of recognition elements in the respective tRNAs. Perhaps the glutamine and lysine enzymes represent "default" pathways for the mischarging of mutant tRNAs.

ACKNOWLEDGMENTS

We are indebted to the members of the D. Söll laboratory, especially John Perona, for many stimulating discussions. The work in the authors' laboratory described in this article was supported by grants from the National Science Foundation and the National Institutes of Health.

REFERENCES

1. P. R. Schimmel and D. Söll, *ARB* **48**, 601 (1979).
2. P. Schimmel, *ARB* **56**, 125 (1987).
3. W. Friest, *Bchem* **28**, 6787 (1989).
4. M. Grunberg-Manago, in "*Escherichia coli* and *Salmonella typhimurium*," (F. C. Neidhardt, J. L. Ingraham, K. B. Low, B. Magasanik, M. Schaechler, and H. E. Umbarger, eds.), Vol. 2, p. 1386. Am. Soc. Micobiol., Washington, D. C., 1987.
5. A. Akins and A. Lambowitz, *Cell* **50**, 331 (1987).

6. C. Herbert, M. Labouesse, G. Dujardin and P. Slonimski, *EMBO J.* **7**, 473 (1988).
7. P. Plateau, J.-F. Mayaux and S. Blanquet, *Bchem* **20**, 4654 (1981).
8. A. Varshavsky, *Cell* **34**, 711 (1983).
9. C. Monteilhet and D. M. Blow, *JMB* **122**, 407 (1978).
10. R. J. Leatherbarrow and A. R. Fersht, *Protein Eng.* **1**, 7 (1986).
11. P. Brick, T. N. Bhat and D. M. Blow, *JMB* **208**, 83 (1989).
12. H. Bedouelle and G. Winter, *Nature* **320**, 371 (1986).
13. F. Yamao, H. Inokuchi, A. Cheung, H. Ozeki and D. Söll, *JBC* **257**, 11639 (1982).
14. P. Hoben, N. Royal, A. Cheung, F. Yamao, K. Biemann and D. Söll, *JBC* **257**, 11644 (1982).
15. H. Uemura, J. Conley, F. Yamao, J. Rogers and D. Söll, *Protein Sequences Data Anal.* **1**, 479 (1988).
16. A. Körner, B. B. Magee, B. Liska, K. B. Low, E. A. Adelberg and D. Söll, *J. Bact.* **120**, 154 (1974).
17. M. Sprinzl, T. Hartmann, F. Meissner, J. Moll and T. Vorderwülbecke, *NARes* **15**, r53 (1987).
18. H. Inokuchi, M. Kodaira, F. Yamao and H. Ozeki, *JMB* **132**, 663 (1979).
19. J. J. Perona, R. Swanson, T. A. Steitz and D. Söll, *JMB* **202**, 121 (1988).
20. A. G. Redfield, B.-S. Choi, R. H. Griffey, M. Jarema, P. Rosevear, P.Hoben, R. Swanson and D. Söll, *in* "Structure and Dynamics of RNA" (P.H. van Knippenberg and C. W. Hilbers, eds.), p. 99. Plenum New York, 1986.
21. M. A. Rould, J. J. Perona, D. Söll and T. A. Steitz, *Science* **246**, 1135 (1989).
22. J. Normanly and J. Abelson, *ARB* **58**, 1029 (1989).
23. P. Schimmel, *Bchem* **28**, 2747 (1989).
24. M. Yarus, *Cell* **55**, 739 (1988).
25. Y. Shimura, H. Aono, H. Ozeki, A. Sarabhai, H. Lamfrom and J. Abelson, *FEBS Lett.* **22**, 144 (1972).
26. M. L. Hooper, R. L. Russell and J. D. Smith, *FEBS Lett.* **22**, 149 (1972).
27. J. D. Smith and J. E. Celis, *Nature NB* **243**, 66 (1973).
28. H. Inokuchi, J. E. Celis and J. D. Smith, *JMB* **85**, 187 (1974).
29. A. Ghysen and J. E. Celis, *JMB* **83**, 333 (1974).
30. H. Ozeki, H. Inokuchi, F. Yamao, M. Kodaira, H. Sakano, T. Ikemura and Y. Shimura, *in* "Transfer RNA: Biological Aspects" (D. Söll, J. N. Abelson, and P. R. Schimmel, eds.), p. 341. CSHLab, Cold Spring Harbor, New York, 1980.
31. H. Inokuchi, P. Hoben, F. Yamao, H. Ozeki and D. Söll, *PNAS* **81**, 5076 (1984).
32. R. N. Swanson and D. Söll, manuscript in preparation (1990).
33. H. Uemura, M. J. Rogers, R. Swanson, L. Watson and D. Söll, *Protein Eng.* **2**, 293 (1988).
34. J. J. Perona, R. N. Swanson, M. A. Rould, T. A. Steitz and D. Söll, *Science* **246**, 1152 (1989).
35. T. Webster, H. Tsai, M. Kula, G. A. Mackie and P. Schimmel, *Science* **226**, 1315 (1984).
36. C. Zelwer, J. L. Risler and S. Brunie, *JMB* **155**, 63 (1982).
37. R. Swanson, P. Hoben, M. Sumner-Smith, H. Uemura, L. Watson and D. Söll, *Science* **242**, 1548 (1988).
38. J. H. Miller, "Experiments in Molecular Genetics." CSHLab, Cold Spring Harbor, New York, 1972.
39. D. G. Barker, C. J. Bruton and G. Winter, *FEBS Lett.* **150**, 419 (1982).
40. M. Yarus, *Nature NB* **239**, 106 (1972).
41. H. Jakubowski and E. Goldman, *J. Bact.* **158**, 769 (1984).

42. J. E. Celis and P. W. Piper, *NARes* **10**, r83 (1982)
43. M. Yaniv, W. R. Folk, P. Berg and L. Soll, *JMB* **86**, 245 (1974).
44. J. E. Celis, C. Coulondre and J. H. Miller, *JMB* **104**, 729 (1976).
45. M. Yarus, R. Knowlton and L. Soll, *in* "Nucleic Acid–Protein Recognition" (H. J. Vogel, ed.), p. 391. Academic Press, New York, 1977.
46. L. H. Schulman and H. Pelka, *Bchem* **24**, 7309 (1985).
47. B. L. Seong, C.-P. Lee and U. L. RajBhandary, *JBC* **246**, 6504 (1989).
48. P. Hoben, Ph.D. thesis. Yale Univ., New Haven, Connecticut, 1984.
49. M. J. Rogers and D. Söll, *PNAS* **85**, 6627 (1988).
50. J. Normanly, R. C. Ogden, S. J. Horvath and J. Abelson, *Nature* **321**, 213 (1986).
51. H. Grosjean, K. Nicoghoshian, E. Haumont, D. Söll and R. Cedergren, *NARes* **13**, 5697 (1985).
52. W. H. McClain and K. Foss, *Science* **240**, 793 (1988).
53. W. H. McClain and K. Foss, *JMB* **202**, 697 (1988).
54. T. Seno, P. F. Agris and D. Söll, *BBA* **349**, 328 (1974).
55. D. M. Crothers, T. Seno and D. Söll, *PNAS* **69**, 3063 (1972).
56. D. Bradley, J. V. Park and L. Soll, *J. Bact.* **145**, 704 (1981).
57. F. Yamao, H. Inokuchi and H. Ozeki, *Jpn. J. Genet.* **63**, 237 (1988).
58. F. Yamao, H. Inokuchi, J. Normanly, J. Abelson and H. Ozeki, *Jpn. J. Genet.* **63**, 251 (1988).
58a. M. J. Rogers, M. Jahn, U. Burkhard and D. Söll, unpublished.
59. E. J. Murgola, *ARGen* **19**, 57(1985).
60. J. H. Miller, C. Coulondre and P. J. Farabaugh, *Nature* **274**, 770 (1978).
61. K. Kawakami, Y. H. Jonsson, G. R. Bjork, H. Ikeda and Y. Nakamura, *PNAS* **85**, 5620 (1988).
62. I. N. Hirshfield, P. L. Bloch, R. A. vanBogelen and F. C. Neidhardt, *J. Bact.* **146**, 345 (1981).
63. M. J. Toth, E. J. Murgola and P. Schimmel, *JMB* **201**, 451 (1988).
64. F. von der Haar and F. Cramer, *Bchem* **15**, 4131 (1976).
65. A. N. Baldwin and P. Berg, *JBC* **241**, 831 (1966).
66. J. Rubin and D. M. Blow, *JMB* **145**, 489 (1981).
67. M. Wilcox, *EJB* **11**, 405 (1969).
68. A. Schön, G. Krupp, S. P. Gough, S. Berry-Lowe, C. G. Kannangara and D. Söll, *Nature* **322**, 281 (1986).
69. A. Schön, C. G. Kannangara, S. Gough and D. Söll, *Nature* **331**, 187 (1988).
70. A. Schön, G. O'Neill, D. Peterson and D. Söll, *in* "Molecular Biology of RNA" (T. R. Cech, ed.), p. 271. Liss, New York, 1989.
71. J. R. Sampson and O. C. Uhlenbeck, *PNAS* **85**, 1033 (1988).
72. R. B. Lotfield and M. A. Vanderjagt, *BJ* **128**, 1353 (1972).
73. R. Weiss, D. Lidsley, B. Falahee and J. Gallant, *JMB* **203**, 403 (1988).
74. P. Schimmel, *Acc. Chem. Res.* **22**, 232 (1989).
75. A. Gampel and A. Tzagoloff, *PNAS* **86**, 6023 (1989).

Ribonucleases, tRNA Nucleotidyltransferase, and the 3' Processing of tRNA

Murray P. Deutscher

Department of Biochemistry
University of Connecticut Health
Center
Farmington, Connecticut 06032

I. Overview: 3' Terminus of tRNA

All tRNA molecules contain at their 3' termini the identical trinucleotide sequence, C-C-A, that plays an important role in various steps of the protein biosynthetic process (*1*). The terminal adenosine residue serves as the site of attachment for the amino acid, although the specific recognition of an amino acid for its cognate tRNA does not involve the 3'-terminal residues (*2*). The -C-C-A sequence also participates in the aminoacyl transfer reaction on the ribosome, and recent work has shown a direct interaction between these residues and various sites on 23-S rRNA (*3*). Numerous alterations of the -C-C-A sequence have been made over the years to study the function of these residues in detail. These alterations have included changes in the length of the sequence, base modifications, and base substitutions made both enzymatically and chemically. Much of this work has been presented earlier in this series by Sprinzl and Cramer (*4*). In summary, some small

209

Progress in Nucleic Acid Research
and Molecular Biology, Vol. 39

changes in the terminal sequence can be tolerated, but most lead to inactivation of the tRNA.

The -C-C-A residues are unpaired in the two-dimensional clover-leaf structure of tRNA, but a variety of physicochemical studies indicate that the sequence is stabilized by stacking interactions with the aminoacyl stem (4–6). X-ray diffraction analysis of several tRNAs has confirmed that the -C-C-A terminus is not involved in tertiary interactions within the molecule, although its exact conformation varies from one tRNA to another (7). It is to be expected that the unpaired, accessible nature of the 3′ terminus of tRNA is a prerequisite to its many interactions with various macromolecules during the course of its functioning in protein synthesis. On the other hand, its high degree of accessibility raises the possibility of unwanted interactions, including those with degradative ribonucleases (RNases).

All tRNA molecules are synthesized initially as tRNA precursors containing additional residues at their 5′ and 3′ termini that must be removed to generate active tRNAs. The strict requirement for an intact -C-C-A sequence for the proper functioning of tRNA necessitates a specific and accurate processing machinery for 3′ maturation and also a mechanism to repair tRNA molecules with faulty 3′ termini. Such enzymes are known. In addition, there are differences in 3′-terminal structure between most prokaryotic and eukaryotic tRNA precursors that introduce an additional level of complexity to this process. The details of tRNA processing have been discussed in earlier reviews (8, 9). In this review, the focus is on 3′ maturation and repair, with particular emphasis on the ribonucleases and tRNA nucleotidyltransferase, the enzymes that participate in these processes.

II. Encoding of the -C-C-A Sequence

A major question relevant to processing of the 3′ terminus of tRNA precursors is whether or not the -C-C-A sequence is encoded in the tRNA gene and, as a consequence, whether or not it is present in the precursor transcript. For precursors in which -C-C-A residues are already present (type-I precursors), 3′ maturation would only require removal of residues following the mature terminus, either by exonucleolytic trimming or by a specific endonucleolytic cut following the 3′ terminal adenosine. In contrast, for precursors that lack the -C-C-A sequence (type-II precursors), extra residues would have to be removed to a point in the aminoacyl stem that would allow -C-C-A addition, presumably by tRNA nucleotidyltransferase. These two modes of 3′ processing would most likely use different types of processing nucleases because of the disparate specificity requirements of each pathway. As is discussed in Section IV, RNases with specificity for either type-I or type-II precursors have been identified.

Since tRNA precursors are difficult to isolate and to sequence, the most direct means for determining whether the -C-C-A sequence is present in the precursor transcript is to sequence the tRNA gene. Fortunately, due to the ease of cloning and sequencing tRNA genes, there has been an explosion of information about their structure in recent years. At present, the sequences of over a thousand tRNA genes are known, with examples available from eubacteria, archaebacteria, higher and lower eukaryotes, organelles, and viruses (*10*).

Based on the compilation of tRNA genes by Sprinzl and co-workers (*10*), as well as other recent data (*11, 12*), it is clear that certain patterns exist with regard to whether or not the -C-C-A sequence is encoded. The overall patterns can be summarized as follows: (i) eukaryotic tRNA genes do not encode the terminal -C-C-A sequence; (ii) pro-karyotic tRNA genes present a mixed picture with some organisms encoding, some not, and some containing genes of each type.

Specifically, of close to 800 tRNA genes sequenced from eukaryotic cells, including those from single-cell organisms, plants, animals, and organelles (chloroplasts and mitochondria), only four organellar genes have been found to encode the -C-C-A sequence. In prokaryotes, the large majority of eubacteria encode the sequence, whereas archae-bacteria generally do not. It has been shown recently that all 77 tRNA genes in *E. coli* (*11*) and the 27 tRNA genes sequenced in *Mycoplasma capricolum* (*12*) encode the -C-C-A sequence. In the former case, the sequence information is consistent with data indicating that tRNA nucleotidyltransferase is not essential for *E. coli* viability (see Section V). In contrast to *E. coli* and *Mycoplasma*, about one-quarter of the approximately 50 tRNA genes sequenced from *Bacillus subtilis* lack the -C-C-A sequence (*13*). Of the remaining tRNA genes sequenced from other eubacteria, most, but not all, encode the -C-C-A residues. However, the number of examples known are too limited for any generalizations. Of the archaebacterial tRNA genes sequenced (~50), over 80% lack -C-C-A. An interesting situation was found in the cyanelles, the photosynthetic organelles of *Cyanophora*. These organ-elles are thought to be evolutionary precursors of chloroplasts, and like chloroplasts, the six tRNA genes sequenced until now lack -C-C-A sequences.

Bacteriophages represent an additional example of mixed tRNA genes. All tRNA genes of bacteriophage T5 encode -C-C-A. However, only four of the eight genes of phage T4 encode the sequence, and of the four that lack it, two lack the entire sequence and two lack only the last two residues (14, 15). Even more confusing is that tRNA^{Ser} of phages T2 and T4 have identical mature sequences, but the T2 gene encodes the -C-C-A sequence and the T4 gene lacks it (16).

The physiological significance of the differences in 3′-terminal structure among tRNA genes is not known. Of particular interest is the difference between the eukaryotes and many of the prokaryotic systems. At present, it is not at all clear whether eukaryotic tRNA genes have lost the -C-C-A sequence, or whether many prokaryotic tRNA genes have acquired it. It is known that the presence of the -C-C-A residues in a phage tRNA precursor results in a more rapid rate of precursor processing compared to a precursor lacking this sequence (16). Likewise, the specific cleavage of tRNA precursors by the 5′ tRNA processing enzyme, RNase P, is greatly affected by the presence of the 3′ -C-C-A sequence (17–22). Perhaps details of the specificity of RNase P in different organisms influence whether there would be a selective advantage to particular tRNA precursors carrying or lacking a -C-C-A sequence. Alternatively, the presence of the -C-C-A sequence might stabilize certain tRNA precursors, and thereby confer a selective advantage in some organisms leading to fixation of these residues in the genome. Although verification of these possibilities requires further work, it is clear that examination of mutant tRNA genes in which -C-C-A sequences have been added, removed, or modified would be helpful to unravel this puzzle.

III. Outline of tRNA Processing

The primary products of transcription of tRNA genes are precursor molecules that must undergo several processing steps to generate mature, functional tRNAs. These processing reactions include removal of extra 5′ and 3′ sequences, modification of nucleotide residues, and in some systems, excision of introns or addition of the -C-C-A sequence.

Considerable progress has been made in recent years in our understanding of tRNA processing, especially with the advent of recombinant DNA techniques. The sequencing of many tRNA genes (Section II) has provided information on the expected primary structure of many tRNA precursors; likewise, the availability of specific tRNA gene clones has made possible the synthesis of large amounts of normal and mutant precursors for pathway studies in vivo and enzymatic analyses in vitro. These investigations, over the past 15 years, have helped to define processing pathways for tRNA precursors (8, 9) and have led to the identification of many new RNases that carry out these reactions

(23, 24). However, although much has been learned during this period, I think it is fair to say that we are still a long way from a complete understanding of a processing pathway for any tRNA precursor molecule.

As with any biosynthetic pathway, a complete understanding of tRNA processing requires the identification and characterization of all the intermediates between the primary transcript and the mature tRNA, and information on whether the order of processing steps is obligatory. Second, one needs to isolate and define the enzymes that participate in the various processing steps. Third, the possible involvement of additional factors, such as carrier proteins or higher order structures to protect the naked processing intermediates, needs to be elucidated. Finally, and perhaps most importantly, is the question of whether the pathway is regulated and how the availability of specific tRNA molecules might affect protein synthesis or other cellular processes. Obviously, much more work is needed before we can even approach this level of understanding of tRNA processing.

Because of the difficulties associated with the isolation of processing intermediates, most of our current knowledge of tRNA maturation pathways comes from the study of mutants blocked at a particular processing step. Such mutants could affect either a specific processing enzyme or the tRNA itself leading to the accumulation (or degradation) of a particular intermediate. Since the availability of tRNA processing mutants is largely confined to *E. coli* (8, 9), more is known about the details of prokaryotic tRNA maturation, including that of phage-T4 tRNAs. Information about eukaryotic tRNA processing has come mainly from the use of cloned tRNA genes, either by injection into *Xenopus laevis* oocytes or by introduction of plasmids into various cells (8). The high number of tRNA gene copies in these types of experiments frequently leads to the accumulation of processing intermediates, presumably because the processing machinery becomes overloaded, and makes their identification possible. However, this is not a normal physiological situation and some molecules could accumulate that do not ordinarily exist in the cell.

In addition, our understanding of tRNA processing in eukaryotic systems lags behind that in prokaryotes because the lack of mutants has made it difficult to obtain information about eukaryotic processing RNases. Thus, in the absence of mutants it is not possible to ascertain whether a newly identified eukaryotic enzyme actually participates in tRNA processing *in vivo* or merely displays activity *in vitro* against a particular precursor substrate. This is an important consideration since examples of this type have been observed in prokaryotes (i.e., an enzyme is active against a precursor *in vitro,* but mutants lacking the enzyme show normal viability) (see Section IV). Also, an RNase that can act on a certain RNA *in vitro* may not even be accessible to that molecule in the cell (24). For these reasons, a combined biochemical–genetic approach will prove most useful to unravel the complexities of RNA processing.

tRNA genes can be found in a variety of different contexts, i.e., as single genes, in clusters of several or many tRNA genes, in spacer and distal regions of rRNA operons, and near protein genes (8). As a consequence, a variety of gene transcripts have been observed in different systems in which a tRNA is embedded among a number of what will become other mature RNAs. Extraction of the individual tRNAs from such a diversity of transcripts involves different types of maturation events, and consequently, different processing enzymes. In general, tRNA processing pathways appear to follow a pattern in which the tRNA transcripts are first cleaved from each other or from other RNAs by endonucleases, and these monomers are then processed further to make the precise 5′ and/or 3′ termini of the mature molecule. In cases in which introns must be removed or -C-C-A sequences added, other reactions are also required.

A. Prokaryotic tRNA Processing

1. BACTERIA

Studies of tRNA processing in prokaryotes have dealt almost exclusively with *E. coli* and bacteriophage-infected *E. coli* (8, 9), although interest in *B. subtilis* is increasing (25, 26). Surprisingly, even with *E. coli,* information about the processing of tRNA precursors is extremely limited. Much of our knowledge about this system has come from work with a single precursor, su_3^+ tRNA^{Tyr} (27). This tRNA precursor was the first specific one to be identified and sequenced (27, 28); it has been used for a variety of studies to delineate processing pathways (29–34) and to identify processing enzymes (35–37).

The currently accepted scheme for processing of this precursor is shown in Fig. 1. Initially, an endonucleolytic cleavage is made in a potential hairpin structure downstream from the mature 3′ terminus (30). This is followed by further removal of 3′ nucleotides, most likely by the action of an exonuclease (30, 33, 37). It is thought that the 3′ trimming reaction proceeds in two stages, since in mutants defective in RNase P, the 5′ processing enzyme, an intermediate accumulates that contains two or three residual nucleotides following the -C-C-A terminus (30), as well as a 43-nucleotide 5′ tail. Normally, after the first

exonucleolytic trimming reaction, RNase P would make a precise endonucleolytic cleavage at the 5′ terminus of the mature tRNA (34). This
would then be followed by exonucleolytic removal of the remaining
extra 3′ residues to generate the mature tRNA species.

Very little of the evidence to support this scheme is solid. There is
no doubt that RNase P is responsible for processing at the 5′ terminus,
as mutants lacking this enzyme accumulate intermediates containing
extra 5′ residues, but processing at the 3′ terminus is still uncertain. It
is also likely that the endonucleolytic cleavage shown in step 1 (Fig. 1)
occurs, as this has been observed with long precursors both *in vitro*
(*36, 37*) and *in vivo* (*33*). The exonucleolytic nature of the remaining
steps (2 and 4) has been inferred from the finding of frayed 3′ ends in
various experiments (*33, 37*), but this has not been established conclusively. Likewise, it is not known which enzyme (or enzymes) may be
responsible for the 3′ processing reactions, although several candidates are available (Section IV). The major difficulty in elucidating the
processing pathway for this, and other, precursors is that intermediates
are processed so rapidly that they do not accumulate and thus cannot
be identified. Intermediates have been observed with a mutant su_3^+
tRNA^{Tyr} precursor that does not make mature tRNA (*33*), but one
cannot be certain that they are true intermediates. tRNA, as well as
other RNA, processing reactions appear to require a delicate balance
between the precursor and the processing enzymes. Alterations in
precursor structure or elimination of processing enzymes can lead to
abnormal side pathways or to nonspecific degradations that can cloud
evaluation of the real processing pathway.

The mode of processing of the precursor to su_3^+ tRNA^{Tyr} appears to
be representative of the processing of other monomeric *E. coli* tRNA
precursors as well (*32, 38–40*). RNase P apparently participates in the
5′ processing of most, if not all, tRNA precursors, as mutants defective

Fig. 1. Postulated processing pathway for an *E. coli* tRNA precursor. Information
based largely on su_3^+ tRNA^{Tyr} is shown. An initial endonucleolytic cleavage (step 1)
removes most of the 3′ "trailer" sequence. This is followed by an exonucleolytic
trimming reaction (step 2) that removes some, but not all, of the remaining 3′ extra
residues. An endonucleolytic cleavage by RNase P generates the mature 5′ terminus
(step 3). Final 3′ trimming by an exonuclease generates the mature 3′ terminus without
entering the -C-C-A sequence. 1: endonuclease; 2,4: exonuclease; 3: endonuclease-
RNase P.

in this enzyme do not make mature tRNAs (*29, 41*). In most cases, the removal of the extra 5' sequence by RNase P precedes final processing of the 3' terminus (*32, 38–40*), but this is not a universal finding with all tRNA precursors (*32*). Since the processing of so few precursors has been studied in detail, it remains to be seen whether our initial insights gleaned from just a few examples will turn out to be of general applicability.

In addition to monomeric tRNA precursors, many tRNA gene transcripts in *E. coli* are polycistronic or multimeric and include sequences for other tRNAs, or even rRNA and mRNA. Maturation of these transcripts is thought to proceed in a manner similar to that of the monomeric precursors (*32, 38*) except that additional endonucleolytic cleavages are required to separate the tRNAs from the rest of the molecule. Since the majority of molecules that accumulate in RNase P-mutant cells are monomeric and dimeric precursors lacking 5' triphosphate termini, they have most likely been derived by cleavage of larger molecules by enzymes other than RNase P. A variety of other endonucleases have been implicated in these intercistronic processing events, but at present there is still considerable confusion about how many enzymes actually are involved, and whether all the named activities are really distinct entities (*8, 9;* and Section IV,B).

2. BACTERIOPHAGE

Of the eight tRNAs specified by bacteriophage T4, precursors to six of them can be isolated as three dimeric molecules from *E. coli* strains lacking RNase P or as unstable intermediates from normal cells (*16, 42, 43*). These include pre-tRNA$^{Pro+Ser}$, pre-tRNA$^{Gln+Leu}$, and pre-tRNA$^{Thr+Ile}$. Maturation of these precursors has been studied in some detail *in vivo* and *in vitro* using mutant strains or extracts lacking particular processing enzymes. As an example of the processing of these dimeric phage precursors, the pathway of maturation of pre-tRNA$^{Pro+Ser}$ is shown in Fig. 2 (*44*). Processing is initiated by exonucleolytic removal of the 3'-terminal -U-A-A residues of the precursor (step 1) followed by addition of the -C-C-A residues found in mature tRNA (step 2). These reactions are blocked *in vivo* in mutant strains lacking, respectively, RNase BN (*45–47*) and tRNA nucleotidyltransferase (*17, 48, 49*), and can be carried out *in vitro* by preparations containing the respective enzymes. Interestingly, addition of the 3' -C-C-A residues is a prerequisite to cleavage of the dimeric precursor by RNase P (step 3) *in vivo*. The RNase P cleavage generates tRNA^{Ser} and an immature form of tRNA^{Pro} in which the 5' end has been cleaved by RNase P, but the 3' end still contains precursor-specific

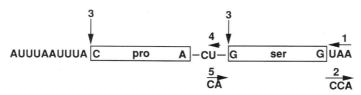

FIG. 2. Processing pathway for phage T4 pre-tRNA$^{Pro+Ser}$. 1: 3' trimming-RNase BN; 2: CCA addition-tRNA nucleotidyltransferase; 3: cleavage-RNase P; 4: 3' trimming-RNase BN; 5: CCA addition-tRNA nucleotidyltransferase. [Adapted from McClain (44).]

residues. Although addition of the -C-C-A sequence is absolutely required for RNase P cleavage *in vivo*, the enzyme can act on the dimeric precursor *in vitro*, although at a reduced rate (18). Final processing of the immature tRNA^{Pro} involves removal of the 3' terminal U residue (step 4) and -C-A addition (step 5).

The maturation of T4 pre-tRNA$^{Pro+Ser}$ is probably the most completely understood example of a tRNA-processing pathway. The ordered sequence of events leading to mature tRNA^{Pro} and tRNA^{Ser} shows that each step in the pathway changes the precursor in such a way as to facilitate the subsequent processing step and to avoid aberrant cleavages. The validity of this statement has been demonstrated in several systems. For example, mature tRNA^{Thr} and tRNA^{Ile} can be produced in equal or unequal amounts from pre-tRNA$^{Thr+Ile}$ depending on whether the 3'-end has been matured first (42). If 3' maturation has not taken place, an unstable tRNA^{Ile} intermediate is generated that is subsequently degraded, leading to lower production of this tRNA (42). In a second example from the phage system, the endonuclease, RNase III, is required for cleavage of pre-tRNA$^{Gln+Leu}$ prior to RNase-P action (50). In mutant strains lacking RNase III, the level of mature tRNA^{Gln} is greatly decreased because an alternate cleavage occurs leading to a product that is a poorer substrate for RNase P, and consequently, is often degraded rather than converted to the mature product (51). From these findings, it is clear that disruption of the normal sequence of events in a tRNA-processing pathway, even to an apparently minor degree, can greatly affect the speed and accuracy of tRNA processing, leading to degradation rather than maturation.

B. Eukaryotic tRNA Processing

Although the broad outlines of tRNA maturation in eukaryotic cells are similar to those in prokaryotes, there are also significant differences. For example, in addition to removal of the extra 5' and 3' sequences, some tRNA precursors contain introns, which must be spliced out, and in all cases, the 3' terminal -C-C-A sequence must be added post-transcriptionally. Furthermore, eukaryotic cells contain multiple subcellular compartments (nuclei, mitochondria, chloroplasts), each of which can serve as a separate site for tRNA biosynthesis and maturation, and not necessarily by identical processing pathways. Thus, tRNA genes in the nuclear compartment of eukaryotic cells are almost always transcribed as monomeric precursors (52).

In contrast, tRNA genes in mitochondria and chloroplasts are often part of larger transcription units containing other tRNAs, rRNAs, or protein-coding genes (53–58). At a minimum, these differences in tRNA gene organization suggest that additional endonucleolytic cleavages, and presumably additional processing nucleases, would be needed in the organellar systems.

Another difference in eukaryotes is that tRNAs made in the nuclear compartment must be transported to the cytoplasm. How this is accomplished, and how it is related to processing, has received little attention (59, 60), although it is an issue of considerable importance.

The maturation of a relatively large number of tRNA precursors has been examined in several different eukaryotic systems. Most of these studies have been carried out *in vitro*, using crude extracts from yeast (61), *Drosophila* (62), *Bombyx* (63), *Xenopus* (64, 65), mammalian cells (57, 66–69), mitochondria (70), or chloroplasts (71) for analysis of transcription and processing, or of processing alone. These studies have been complemented by others in which cloned tRNA genes are microinjected into *Xenopus* oocytes (72, 73), transformed into mammalian cells (68), or in which tRNA processing intermediates are analyzed by Northern blots (58). What emerges from all these studies is that there is no single mode of eukaryotic tRNA processing that applies to all precursors in all cells. Rather, although any individual precursor may have a preferred pathway for maturation in a particular system, both the nature of the precursor and of the cell influence the actual pathway used. In fact, as extreme examples, two tRNA^{Tyr} precursors follow different pathways of processing in the same HeLa cell extracts (67), and a tRNA^{Leu} precursor that can be processed by extracts of CV1 cells is not matured in these cells *in vivo* (68). The explanations for these surprising results are not clear, but these findings support the idea that the precursor structure and processing enzyme levels are critical.

Maturation of the 5' terminus of tRNA precursors by a precise endonucleolytic cleavage is carried out by the eukaryotic equivalent of RNase P, although the exact nature of the enzyme is in dispute. The enzymes from a number of eukaryotic sources, including mitochondria and chloroplasts, have been studied (71, 74–78). In some cases, an RNA moiety has been suggested to be associated and required for enzyme activity (75–77), and in others not (71, 78, 79). Also, one report (78) indicates that the enzyme is a large, multisubunit complex, but this has not been confirmed. Whatever the structure of RNase P turns out to be, it is clear that this aspect of tRNA maturation is similar to that in prokaryotes.

Maturation at the 3' terminus also has led to some disagreement. In most of the situations studied, the 3' "trailer" sequence is removed by an endonucleolytic cleavage at a position that would allow -C-C-A addition (62, 64, 65, 69–72), but the possibility of exonucleolytic 3' processing, as in prokaryotes, has also been suggested (61, 63, 80). Addition of the -C-C-A residues is then carried out by tRNA nucleotidyltransferase, present in all the compartments in which tRNA is matured (81–83). Further discussion of 3' processing nucleases and tRNA nucleotidyltransferase is deferred to Sections IV and V.

The order of processing events also shows some variability in different systems. For example, removal of introns from intron-containing precursors in HeLa cell extracts precedes maturation of the 5' and 3' termini (67, 84), whereas in yeast and *Xenopus* oocytes *in vivo*, the order is reversed; removal of the intron occurs last (72, 84, 85). A similar disparity is found in the relative order of maturation of the 5' and 3' termini of eukaryotic precursors. In many cases, 5' cleavage precedes 3' processing (62, 63, 69–71), but in others, the order is reversed (57, 61, 66).

One explanation for all of these results is that there is not a single obligatory order for processing tRNA precursors. However, a major concern when carrying out these types of studies in cell extracts is that there is no assurance that the yields and stabilities of all processing activities are the same. Since the order of processing events may simply reflect the relative levels of different enzymes, incorrect conclusions may be drawn if a particular enzyme is easily inactivated or poorly extracted, thereby slowing down the maturation event catalyzed by that enzyme. For this reason, I would have more confidence in processing pathways determined from *in vivo* studies, although they also suffer from the pitfalls of generally using cloned tRNA genes expressing abnormally high levels of precursors, and the possibility that mutants may lead to the use of aberrant pathways. From a theoretical standpoint, the best approach would appear to be Northern blot analysis of normal tRNA maturation events *in vivo*. Unfortunately, the low level of processing intermediates usually makes this method impractical as well. We are thus confronted with a situation in which no single approach is completely satisfactory, pointing out the inherent difficulties in studies of macromolecular processing.

IV. RNases Active at the 3' Terminus of tRNA and tRNA Precursors

Elucidation of a biochemical pathway involves first the identification of the intermediates in the process. Once that has been accomplished, which is roughly the stage of our understanding of tRNA processing, the problem becomes an enzymological one, i.e., identifying the enzymes that catalyze each of the processing steps, exploring their specificity and mechanism of action, and determining whether they are subject to any sort of regulation. At present, much of our information about tRNA processing enzymes, other than those involved in splicing, comes from work with *E. coli*, since in this system certain defects in processing have been correlated with the absence of a particular RNase in a mutant strain.

In addition, a large number of potential tRNA processing nucleases have been isolated from *E. coli* and studied for their possible role in tRNA maturation (*24*). From this work, it is already clear that RNase P participates in the 5' maturation of many, if not all *E. coli* tRNA precursors (*29, 32, 38, 41*). It is also possible that the endonuclease, RNase E (*86*), is involved in the processing of some *E. coli* precursors. RNase III has been implicated in the maturation of at least one T4 tRNA precursor (*50, 51*), but its role, if any, in host tRNA processing is not clear. Information about 3' processing enzymes is less advanced, although quite a few candidates have been identified (see below).

There are several problems associated with the identification and characterization of RNA processing enzymes, in general, and with tRNA processing enzymes, in particular. First of all, there is the problem of obtaining sufficient amounts of substrate to use for enzyme assays because the natural precursors are so difficult to isolate. To overcome this problem, investigators have resorted to the use of artificial precursors, or to precursors transcribed from cloned tRNA genes, or to natural precursors that have been made to accumulate under certain conditions. Nevertheless, in many studies the amount of precursor substrate is extremely limited, and assays are often carried out under conditions in which substrate is at a lower level than enzyme. This can lead to misinterpretation of substrate specificity and to confusion of effects that alter substrate binding versus those that alter catalysis (*8*).

A second problem is the use of impure processing enzyme preparations that result from the difficulty in carrying out extensive purifications. It is now clear that any given cell probably has more than 20 RNases (23, 24), many with overlapping specificities. Given these conditions, the use of impure enzymes can result in incorrect conclusions regarding the specificity and function of an isolated RNase. A high degree of purification is, of course, one solution to this problem. The use of mutant strains devoid of possible contaminating RNases may also help to alleviate this problem.

Finally, a third problem that may be somewhat unique to tRNA processing is a consequence of the highly compact structure of mature tRNA. Due to the relative resistance of mature tRNAs to degradation, a nonspecific RNase might be identified as precursor-specific simply because it can act on the extraneous sequences in a tRNA precursor. Since the mature sequences would be resistant to degradation because of secondary structure, the RNase would appear to carry out a processing reaction, when in fact, it had only removed all the residues to which it had access. As an example, venom phosphodiesterase (EC 3.1.15.1), a nonspecific, 3′→5′ exoribonuclease, will effectively remove only the terminal -C-A residues of tRNA at 20°C (87). If one had identified an unknown activity with such a specificity, a reasonable conclusion might be that this was an enzyme specifically involved in the end-turnover of tRNA (1), when it actually had no such role. Consequently, the only certain way to associate RNase activity *in vitro* with function *in vivo* is, again, through the use of deficient mutants. Our ability to make these associations, especially in eukaryotes, is still quite limited.

Despite all the aforementioned problems, the catalogue of characterized RNases able to act at the 3′ terminus of tRNA and tRNA precursors has been expanding rapidly. In *E. coli*, six exoribonucleases that have the potential to carry out the two presumed exoribonucleolytic processing reactions of *E. coli* tRNA processing (Fig. 1, steps 2 and 4) are now known. Several endoribonucleases that might be involved in the 3′ endonucleolytic cleavage (Fig. 1, step 1) also are known. Some information dealing with enzymes possibly participating in eukaryotic 3′ processing has been gathered, as well. A summary of our knowledge in each of these areas is presented below.

A. Bacterial Exoribonucleases

All of the exoribonucleases that have been isolated from *E. coli* catalyze RNA hydrolysis in the 3′→5′ direction (23, 24). These include the six discussed below: RNase II, RNase D, RNase BN, RNase T, polynucleotide phosphorylase (PNPase), and RNase PH, as well as one additional enzyme that acts on mRNA and rRNA, termed RNase R (47, 88). Each of these seven enzymes is distinct both biochemically and genetically. Although there is reason to believe that E. coli should also contain a 5′→3′ exoribonuclease, such as for the final 5′ processing of 5-S RNA (89), none has yet been identified.

The large number of exoribonucleases found in a single cell is quite unexpected, especially since many of them have overlapping specificities. Even more surprising is the finding that E. coli strains remain essentially normal even though as many as three of the exoribonucleases are removed by mutation [RNases II, D, BN (90); RNases II, R, D (91)]. As discussed below, the lack of an observable phenotype upon removal of several of these RNases has made it difficult to ascertain a function for them. On the other hand, removal of so many RNases by mutation has made it easier to search for additional enzymes in mutant extracts.

1. RNase II

The catalytic properties of RNase II have been described in detail (92). RNase II was the first hydrolytic exoribonuclease identified in E. coli (93–95), and has subsequently been purified to homogeneity (96, 97). It is a single chain protein with an apparent molecular weight of 70–90,000. It hydrolyzes all types of RNA molecules with the release of 5′ monophosphates. The enzyme requires Mg^{2+} for activity and is stimulated by monovalent cations, preferring K^+ with homopolymer substrates (96). Interestingly, RNase II can initiate hydrolysis at either a 3′-OH or 3′-P group, and its mode of degradation is processive (98), i.e., it completes hydrolysis of one chain before proceeding to another one. The enzyme is sensitive to secondary structure (94, 95), and, in hydrolyzing mRNA, will stop at hairpin structures (99). RNase II is a very active enzyme, accounting for about 98% of all the poly(A) hydrolytic activity in a crude extract (91).

It was originally suggested that RNase II participates in the 3′ processing of tRNA precursors, since preparations of the enzyme can remove extra nucleotides at the 3′ terminus (29, 32). However, the processive nature of RNase II activity results in removal of -C-C-A sequences as well (97), making it unlikely that RNase II has a role in final 3′ tRNA processing in vivo. Inasmuch as studies of tRNA nucleotidyltransferase mutants have shown that this latter enzyme is not required for tRNA biosynthesis (100), whichever nuclease removes the last extra residues must not attack the -C-C-A sequence. Thus, RNase II is an example of a nuclease that can catalyze an apparent processing reaction in vitro, but is unlikely to do so in the cell.

It has not been eliminated, however, that RNase II participates in the initial exonucleolytic trimming of some precursors (Fig. 1, step 2). In fact, an altered pattern of processing of T4 tRNAs has been observed in RNase II-deficient mutants (101). Nevertheless, cells essentially devoid of RNase II are viable and can process tRNA precursors (90); therefore, this enzyme is not required for cellular tRNA processing.

It is now clear that the major role of RNase II is in mRNA degradation. E. coli strains lacking both RNase II and PNPase are inviable (102), and accumulate fragments of mRNA (103). Interestingly, strains with 10-fold higher levels of RNase II still degrade mRNA at normal rates (102). These observations suggest that the rate-limiting steps for mRNA degradation are the endonucleolytic cleavages generating mRNA fragments, and that RNase II (and/or PNPase) acts as a scavenger to clear these fragments from the cell.

RNase II is encoded by the rnb gene mapping at 28 minutes on the E. coli map (102, 104). The gene has now been cloned, subcloned, and overexpressed (102, 105). As a consequence, considerably more information about the structure, function, and regulation of RNase II should appear in the near future.

2. RNase D

Once it became clear that RNase II is not responsible for the final 3' trimming of E. coli tRNA precursors, a search was initiated for another nuclease that might carry out the reaction. To detect such an enzyme, an artificial precursor that contained extra, radioactively-labeled residues following the -C-C-A terminus was synthesized (106). This precursor has essentially the same structure as the final natural precursor intermediate (Fig. 1). Removal of the radioactive residues could be followed by a simple acid-soluble assay. Using this assay, two activities were identified (107). One was RNase II, the other a newly identified enzyme that had been termed RNase D (108). RNase D had been isolated a year earlier as a nuclease specific for tRNAs with altered structures (i.e., denatured tRNA, tRNA lacking its terminal -C-C-A sequence) (108). In this context, then, RNase D was recognizing the artificial tRNA precursor as a tRNA with an altered structure. Both RNase D and RNase II were purified to homogeneity and their properties compared (97). Only RNase D was able to remove extra residues and stop at the -C-C-A sequence, as expected for the 3' processing nuclease. RNase D removed extra residues in a random manner, and slowed down about 40-fold at the mature sequence (97).

RNase D is a single-chain protein of about 42 kDa (97, 109, 110) with an isoelectric point of 6.2 (109). In contrast to RNase II, the enzyme is highly specific for tRNA-like substrates, with no activity against homopolymers (107, 111). RNase D requires a divalent cation for activity, with Mg^{2+} being most effective. It is inhibited by elevated ionic strength (>50 mM); its pH optimum is about 9. RNase D initiates attack on tRNA at a free 3′ hydroxyl group and releases 5′ monophosphates (107, 111). tRNAs with terminal C, U, or A residues work equally well as substrates, but tRNAs terminating with a 3′ phosphate, or a sugar oxidized by periodate, are ineffective. The failure of RNase D to cause hydrolysis at the -C-C-A terminus is not due to this sequence per se, because a second -C-C-A sequence added after the first one is removed rapidly (111).

These properties of RNase D are consistent with a role in tRNA processing. In addition, they are highly instructive because RNase D was the first exoribonuclease to display such a high degree of substrate specificity. Others known at that time, such as RNase II, PNPase, and various diesterases, are nonspecific, being able to act on a variety of nucleic acids. Thus, these observations demonstrate that exoribonucleases, like endoribonucleases, are highly specific enzymes.

Although the substrate specificity of RNase D strongly suggests a role for this enzyme in tRNA processing, such a role has not been confirmed by genetic analysis. Mutant strains containing either a temperature-sensitive RNase D (112) or totally devoid of RNase D activity (113) display no abnormal phenotype. The deletion mutant grows normally at a variety of temperatures in both rich and minimal media, recovers from starvation normally, and shows no defect in plating efficiency of wild-type T4 phage or of a mutant phage requiring a functional tRNA suppressor for growth (113). Even in combination with mutations in RNase II and RNase BN, the RNase-D-deletion mutant displays no obvious altered properties (90). From these findings, it has not been possible to establish whether or not RNase D participates in tRNA maturation.

However, it is now known that tRNA can be degraded by RNase D in vivo (114). Engineered strains that have elevated RNase D activity and lack tRNA nucleotidyltransferase grow extremely poorly because of a 3′ terminal defect in their tRNAs. Despite the fact that RNase D works poorly on intact tRNA (108), when present at a sufficiently high level, it can attack the 3′ terminus of tRNA in vivo leading to defective tRNA if there is no tRNA nucleotidyltransferase to repair the ends. Although this is an abnormal situation, the results suggest that RNase D can participate in tRNA metabolism in vivo. Nevertheless, even if RNase D normally does participate in tRNA precursor processing, it is clear that another enzyme can take over in its absence.

RNase D is encoded by the single rnd gene mapping at about 40 minutes on the *E. coli* genetic map (*112*). The *rnd* gene has been cloned and sequenced (*110, 115*). Its coding region extends for 1128 nucleotides, beginning at a UUG codon and terminating at a UAA codon, which would encode a protein of 375 amino acids (*115*). The UUG initiation codon has been confirmed by N-terminal sequencing of the homogenous protein.

Site-directed mutagenesis that changes this codon to AUG leads to a 10-fold elevation of RNase D expression (*116*). A single promoter for the *rnd* gene is located about 100 nucleotides upstream from the coding region, and the transcription start site is at residue −70 (*116*). Between the promoter region and the translation start site there is a (G+C)-rich hairpin structure followed by eight T residues that looks like a *rho*-independent transcription terminator. Surprisingly, removal of this structure leads to only a small increase in *rnd* mRNA (<twofold), but RNase D expression is decreased >95% (*116*). These data suggest that RNase D expression may be subject to translational regulation. If substantiated, this could have important implications for understanding mechanisms of control of RNA metabolism.

Elevated levels of RNAse D are deleterious to *E. coli* (*115*). It has not been possible to maintain cells with more than a 10- to 20-fold elevation of RNase D activity. Cells with elevated RNase D grow slowly, and there is selection for faster-growing cells that contain lower levels of RNase D. Overexpression of a mutant, inactive form of RNase D indicated that it is elevated RNase D activity that exerts the deleterious effect. At present, it is not known what is the site of action of RNase D that leads to slowed growth. Inasmuch as tRNA nucleotidyltransferase is present at normal levels, and might be expected to repair any defect at the 3′ terminus of tRNA, the possibility of another site of action of RNase D must be considered.

3. RNase BN

Of the eight tRNAs specified by bacteriophage T4, precursors to four are like those of the host in that the -C-C-A sequence is present (type I), whereas precursors to the other four lack all or part of this sequence (type II) (*14, 15*). In view of the differences between these two types of precursors, it was thought likely that different enzymes would be involved in each of their 3′ terminal maturation reactions. This idea was shown to be correct when it was demonstrated that in a mutant *E. coli* strain, termed BN, the 3′ termini of type II precursors are not processed, whereas type I precursors mature normally (*45*). Strain BN, and another strain, CAN, were originally isolated on the basis of their inability to support the growth of a phage T4 strain that requires the suppressor function of a T4 tRNA^{Ser} (*46, 117*). The defect in strain BN was shown to be associated with a decrease in the ability of extracts to hydrolyze the synthetic tRNA precursor, tRNA-C-U, an analog of the type II precursor to T4 tRNA^{Pro} (*106, 118, 119*), suggesting that existence of a distinct "BN ribonuclease." Genetic evidence also indicated that the mutation in strain BN did not affect the known nucleases, RNase II or RNase D (*119*), again suggesting the existence of another enzyme.

Establishing the existence of RNase BN proved difficult because of the large amounts of RNase II and RNase D found in cells. These latter two enzymes also hydrolyze tRNA-C-U to some degree (*107*). The solution to this problem was the removal of these RNases in strain BN and its parent, *E. coli* B, by the introduction of mutations in the *rnb* and *rnd* genes. In the absence of RNases II and D, it was easy to identify an activity that hydrolyzed tRNA-C-U that was present in strain B extracts, but absent from extracts of strain BN (*47*). A similar analysis of strain CAN indicated that it also lacked this ribonuclease as compared to its wild type parent, strain CA265 (*120*). This enzyme was named RNase BN.

RNase BN has been partially purified from a strain lacking RNases II, D, and R (*121*). Based on gel filtration it has a molecular weight of about 60,000. The enzyme releases UMP from tRNA-C-U, with no production of oligonucleotides, indicating an exoribonucleolytic mode of hydrolysis (*47*). The purified enzyme is most active at pH values between 6.0 and 7.0 in the presence of Co^{2+} (*121*). This latter property is quite unusual and requires further examination. RNase BN is most active against substrates with incorrect residues within the -C-C-A sequence, such as tRNA-C-U and tRNA-C-A; in contrast tRNA-C-C with correct residues, but not complete, is only about 10–15% as active as the former substrates. Poly(A) is not hydrolyzed by the enzyme (*47, 121*). Comparison of purified RNase D and RNase BN against artificial type I and type II precursors indicated that while RNase D is about 30 times more active on tRNA-C-C-A-C$_3$ than tRNA-C-U, RNase BN is about twice as active against tRNA-C-U (*121*). Thus, there is about a 60-fold difference in relative specificity of the two enzymes against the two types of substrates. These findings demonstrate again that exoribonucleases can be highly specific enzymes.

Although RNase BN definitely is required for maturation of certain T4 tRNA precursors (*45*), its role in uninfected cells is not known. The BN and CAN mutant strains show no obvious phenotype (*46, 117*), even in combination with *rnb* and *rnd* mutations (*90*). Since RNase BN can act on artificial type-1 precursors *in vitro*, the possibility still must be entertained that it does participate in some way in 3' tRNA processing. On the other hand, total RNase–BN activity in cells is relatively low compared to RNases II and D, and its primary role may not even be in tRNA metabolism. It is also possible that RNase BN is somehow altered or elevated after phage T4 infection resulting in its subsequent participation in tRNA processing. Although two RNase BN mutants are available (116, 117), the map location of the gene encoding it is not known. Attempts to clone the gene for RNase BN have so far been unsuccessful (121).

4. RNase T

tRNA molecules in all cells examined undergo an end-turnover process in which the 3'-terminal AMP residue is removed and then reincorporated by tRNA nucleotidyltransferase (122). The nuclease responsible for removal of the terminal residue is RNase T (123). The existence of RNase T was originally postulated based on assays against various substrates of extracts from a strain deficient in RNases II, D, and BN. It was observed that activity against intact tRNA-C-C-A was essentially the same as in wild-type extracts, whereas activity against other substrates was greatly decreased (90). This observation indicated that another enzyme, distinct from the three missing RNases, was present in the extract and able to hydrolyze mature tRNA.

RNase T has been purified to homogeneity based on this assay (124). The purified enzyme is an $\alpha2$ dimer of 50 kDa. In contrast to the other exoribonucleases, RNase T is extremely sensitive to sulfhydryl oxidation, but can be reactivated by incubation with dithiothreitol. RNase T is most active in the pH range 8–9. It requires a divalent cation for activity, with Mg^{2+} being most effective (123, 124). Purified RNase T exonucleolytically removes the 3' terminal AMP residue from tRNA in a random mode of attack. The rate of removal of the penultimate CMP residue is less than 10% as rapid (123, 124). A free 3' OH group is required. Neither tRNA-C-Cp nor aminoacyl-tRNA is a substrate for this enzyme in vitro (124). The latter observation is consistent with the fact that only uncharged tRNA molecules undergo turnover in vivo (100). RNase T displays a very high degree of substrate specificity. Intact tRNA is the preferred substrate, and all tRNAs in a population are substrates. tRNAs with other 3' termini are much less active. For example, the artificial type I precursor, tRNA-C-C-A-C-C is only about 15% as active, and tRNA-C-C and tRNA-C-U are less than 5% as active. Interestingly, tRNA-C-A is about 15–25% as active (123). Poly(A) is not a substrate.

The involvement of RNase T in the end turnover of tRNA has been conclusively established, based on studies of a mutant strain lacking ~75% of RNase T activity (125). Strains lacking tRNA nucleotidyltransferase grow slowly and accumulate defective tRNA molecules (48). In a cca,rnt double mutant, less defective tRNA is present and cells grow normally (126). Likewise, analysis of 25 fast-growing revertants from cca strains revealed that all had decreased RNase T activity. What is not understood is why cells contain an enzyme whose only function appears to be removal of a 3' terminal residue from a tRNA molecule that will then immediately be repaired. Perhaps, RNase T actually has a different primary function in vivo, but it also happens to attack some tRNA molecules when they are not aminoacylated. This would have no deleterious consequences because of the rapid repair by tRNA nucleotidyltransferase. Alternatively, end-turnover may serve some, as yet, unknown physiological function. Nevertheless, rnt mutant strains display no growth phenotype (126), although the only rnt allele currently available still retains 25% residual activity (125).

Using a combination of physical and genetic mapping, the rnt gene encoding RNase T has recently been located at 36 minutes on the E. coli genetic map (127). The rnt gene has been subcloned to a <2 kb DNA fragment, and sequencing studies are under way (126). Overexpression of RNase T from high-copy number plasmids (pUC) is deleterious to E. coli growth, whereas overexpression from a lower-copy-number plasmid (pHC79) can be tolerated (126). The availability of an rnt clone and knowledge of its map position will make possible a variety of studies of RNase T structure and function.

5. POLYNUCLEOTIDE PHOSPHORYLASE (PNPase)

The properties of PNPase have been reviewed in detail (128), and are discussed here only briefly. The enzyme is not normally considered to be a ribonuclease because it has received so much attention for its synthetic properties. Yet, PNPase can catalyze the phosphorolytic degradation of RNAs with the production of nucleoside diphosphates. PNPase is an exoribonuclease that degrades RNAs in a processive manner. Single-stranded molecules are degraded much more rapidly than those, such as tRNA, that have considerable secondary structure. The degradation of tRNA by PNPase is unusual in that the enzyme seems to be exquisitely sensitive to small changes in the conformation of the RNA chain. PNPase can remove some extra residues from the 3' terminus of tRNA precursors in vitro, but it does not proceed all the way to the -C-C-A terminus (39, 129). Thus, it is possible that PNPase can participate in the first exonucleolytic reaction of 3' maturation (Fig. 1, step 2), but it is unlikely to play a role in the final trimming reaction (Fig. 1, step 4).

PNPases have been purified from a number of microorganisms (128). The enzyme is a large, multisubunit protein consisting of two types of subunits. For degradation of RNA chains the enzyme requires a divalent cation and inorganic phosphate (or arsenate).

A variety of PNPase mutant strains are available, including ones in which the *pnp* gene has been interrupted by transposons, that should be totally devoid of PNPase activity (130, 131). Surprisingly, one of these mutants has increased susceptibility to antibiotics (131). PNPase mutants, by themselves, have small effects on RNA metabolism (e.g, 132), but as noted before, in combination with *rnb* mutations inactivating RNase II, mRNA degradation is inhibited, and cells are inviable (102, 103). Thus, *in vivo*, either RNase II or PNPase can carry out a particular degradative reaction, and at least one of them must be present for the cell to remain viable. PNPase also appears to be the primary enzyme responsible for the degradation of eukaryotic mRNA expressed from genes cloned in *E. coli* (133). Why RNase II does not have a similar effect is unclear. The effect of *pnp* mutants on tRNA metabolism *in vivo* has not been explored.

The *pnp* gene encoding the α subunit of PNPase has been mapped to 69 minutes on the *E. coli* chromosome (134). The gene has been sequenced (135) and studied with regard to control of expression (136, 137). Interestingly, the level of *pnp* mRNA is regulated, and cleavage by the endonuclease, RNase III, keeps its steady-state level low.

6. RNase PH

The absence of any defect in tRNA processing in a cell deficient in RNases II, D, BN, and T (90, 125) suggested that yet another nuclease must still be present in these cells. However, attempts to identify an additional exoribonuclease using the artificial type-I tRNA precursor, tRNA-C-C-A-C_3, were unsuccessful (138). The solution to this problem came with the development of an *in vitro* tRNA processing system that used phage SP6 RNA polymerase-generated transcripts of the gene for su_3^+ tRNA ^{Tyr} as substrates for the processing reactions (37). It was found that precursors with either 5 extra or 25 extra 3' nucleotides, and 49 extra 5' nucleotides, could be accurately processed to mature tRNA in extracts of the multiple RNase-deficient strain. The final 3' trimming reaction was exonucleolytic and generated the correct -C-C-A terminus. A prior endonucleolytic cleavage was also observed for the longer precursor. Maturation of the 3' terminus proceeded optimally at pH 8–9, at 50 mM KCl, and required Mg^{2+}. Of most interest was the observation that the final 3′ processing reaction required the presence of inorganic phosphate, and that nucleoside diphosphates were produced. This work showed that an additional exoribonuclease is present in the mutant extract and that it could process the 3′ terminus of tRNA precursors in a phosphorolytic reaction (37).

The requirement for inorganic phosphate and the production of nucleoside diphosphates initially suggested that PNPase, the only known P_i-requiring nuclease, might be involved. However, further examination revealed that this was not the case, and that the activity was due to a new enzyme, termed RNase PH (129). Thus, neither commercial PNPase nor PNPase purified from an active extract could carry out the processing reaction. Second, extracts from a mutant strain with an interrupted pnp gene (131) retain full activity for phosphorolytic processing. Third, PNPase is a processive nuclease, whereas the exonucleolytic processing in extracts of the RNase-deficient strain proceeds randomly (37). Finally, a new RNase distinct from PNPase could be isolated from the mutant extracts. This new RNase differed in size and specificity from PNPase, and was present at the same level in a wild-type and a pnp-mutant strain. In addition, the enzyme was highly specific for tRNA precursors compared to mature tRNA (129).

RNase PH has been partially purified from a mutant strain deficient in RNases D, BN, T, I, PNPase and carrying a temperature-sensitive RNase II (139). Based on gel filtration the enzyme has a molecular weight of approximately 45,000. The enzyme displays optimal activity at pH 8 and requires Mg^{2+} (129). In addition to the phosphorolytic degradation of tRNA precursors, RNase PH can also catalyze a synthetic reaction in which nucleoside diphosphates are precursors for the addition of nucleotide residues to the 3′ terminus of mature tRNA (139). Several nucleoside diphosphates are substrates, but ATP is inactive. The synthetic reaction is strongly inhibited by inorganic phosphate.

Recently, a temperature-sensitive mutant that displays decreased RNase PH activity was isolated (139). Temperature-insensitive revertants regain normal levels of the enzyme. These findings suggest that RNase PH is an essential enzyme for E. coli viability, at least in the RNase-deficient genetic background used to isolate the mutant. It remains to be seen, however, whether the growth defect in this mutant is due to an effect on tRNA maturation. If so, the availability of this mutant will make possible a test of which of the exoribonucleases identified in E. coli are actually necessary for 3′ tRNA processing.

7. SUMMARY OF EXORIBONUCLEASES

The known *E. coli* exoribonucleases are listed in Table I. The large number already identified, many with overlapping specificities, is a surprising feature of *E. coli* RNA metabolism. It is not clear whether this multiplicity of enzymes is due to a specific requirement for backup systems in these pathways, or whether each enzyme actually has a distinct primary function *in vivo* that can be taken over by another activity in its absence. It is particularly interesting that in two instances, that of RNase II and PNPase and of RNase D and RNase PH, there are two enzymes with almost identical specificities, one acting hydrolytically and one phosphorolytically. Perhaps, depending on the energy state of the cell, there would be a preference for the use of one member of a pair over the other. A considerable saving in energy requirements could be obtained by the use of phosphorolytic nucleases that generate nucleoside diphosphates rather than monophosphates.

B. Bacterial Endoribonucleases

Bacterial tRNA precursors with long 3' extensions require an endonucleolytic cleavage to remove most of this sequence (Fig. 1, step 1). As noted above, in an *in vitro* processing system, a precursor with 25 extra 3' nucleotides was also first cleaved endonucleolytically prior to final 3' trimming (37). The enzyme (or enzymes) responsible for these cleavage reactions has not been conclusively identified. A number of different names have been attached to partially purified preparations that carry out these endonucleolytic cleavages in various systems.

TABLE I
SUMMARY OF *E. coli* EXORIBONUCLEASES

Enzyme	*In vitro* specificity	Suggested function
RNase II	All RNAs	mRNA degradation
RNase D	Type I tRNA precursors, altered tRNAs	tRNA processing, degradation of denatured tRNA
RNase BN	Type II tRNA precursors	T4 tRNA processing, unknown in host
RNase T	Intact tRNA	End-turnover of tRNA
PNPase	All RNAs	mRNA degradation
RNase PH	Type I tRNA precursors	tRNA processing
RNase R	mRNA, rRNA	Unknown

These include ones that have been called RNase PIV (*30*) and RNase F (*140*). In addition, the known endonucleases, RNase E (*86*) and RNase P (*141*) have also been implicated in some 3′ processing events. Other activities, RNases P2 (*32*), RNase O (*38*), and PC (*142*), which have been implicated in the intercistronic cleavage of multimeric precursors, also deserve mention since, in effect, such cleavages may also generate a processing intermediate ready for final 3′ trimming. The specificities of these enzymes have not been explored in detail.

The relationship among all these endonucleolytic activities is not clear. Undoubtedly, some will turn out to be different manifestations of the same enzyme. It is also possible that a number of different endonucleases actually do participate in 3′ tRNA processing depending on the sequence and structure of a particular 3′ trailer region. However, much more work will be needed to sort out this confusing situation.

C. Eukaryotic 3′ Processing Nucleases

In most eukaryotic systems studied, it has been found, based on identification of the appropriate product, that the extra 3′ residues are removed by a single endonucleolytic cleavage at a position that allows -C-C-A addition (see Section III,B). Two endoribonucleases with the appropriate specificity to carry out this reaction were initially identified and partially purified from *X. laevis* oocyte nuclei using an artificial precursor as the assay substrate (*80*). The products of the reaction by each of these enzymes are tRNA-N (lacking the -C-C-A sequence) and an oligonucleotide representing the trailer sequence. These enzymes were not characterized further. Subsequently, an endoribonuclease was purified from *X. laevis* ovaries that could process the precursors to $tRNA_i^{Met}$ and $tRNA^{Ala}$ (*78*). The enzyme appears to be a single chain protein of about 97 kDa. The endonuclease shows optimal activity in the pH range 6.5 to 8.5 and requires Mg^{2+} for activity. The enzyme shows a preference for a precursor that has already been processed at its 5′ terminus, indicating a sequential order of processing.

Processing endonucleases acting at the 3′ termini of tRNA precursors have also been partially purified from rat liver (*143*) and yeast (*70*) mitochondria. As with the *Xenopus* enzyme, both of these endonucleases prefer 5′ processed precursors as substrates. Both enzymes accurately cleave precursors to generate substrates for tRNA nucleotidyltransferase. The rat liver enzyme works optimally at pH 7.2 and requires a low concentration of Mg^{2+}. Additional information about these enzymes awaits further purification.

Exoribonucleases acting at the 3′ termini of tRNA precursors in several eukaryotic systems have been described. However, none have been purified or characterized sufficiently to know whether they are discrete enzymes.

V. tRNA Nucleotidyltransferase

All cells that have been examined, as well as several organelles, contain the enzyme tRNA nucleotidyltransferase that can add all or part of the -C-C-A sequence to tRNA molecules lacking these residues (1, 8). The catalytic properties of this enzyme have been described in detail (144). Earlier information on the biological functions of the enzyme has also been reviewed (122). In this section only a brief summary of earlier work is given, together with the new findings obtained since the previous reviews were written.

tRNA nucleotidyltransferase utilizes CTP and ATP for the synthesis of the -C-C-A terminus. In the presence of both triphosphates, the enzyme will accurately synthesize this sequence despite the fact that no nucleotide template is present in the protein. This is accomplished by the specific arrangement of subsites within the enzyme's active site. Based on studies with fragments of tRNA, with dinucleotide monophosphate acceptor analogs, with affinity reagents, and with mutants, the picture emerges that there is a tandem arrangement of sites for the tRNA, for the two C residues, and for ATP. The tRNA positions itself on the enzyme in the appropriate position to accept the next residue. The two C sites may bind either CTP or a terminal C residue of the tRNA. The presence of the rest of the tRNA in its site stimulates incorporation over 50-fold compared to incorporation of ATP into cytidine or CpC alone, indicating that the tRNA substrate has two functional parts, a stimulating region and an accepting region.

In the presence of only a single triphosphate or in the presence of other nucleoside triphosphates, the enzyme can be induced to make mistakes. Thus, many different tRNA analogs have been made including tRNA-C-A, tRNA-C-U, and tRNA-C-C-A-C_3, which have found use in the tRNA processing studies described above (Section IV). The enzyme has also found wide use as a reagent to further modify or repair the ends of tRNA chains (4).

E. coli mutant strains (*cca* mutants) deficient in tRNA nucleotidyltransferase have been isolated. Using these mutants, it was shown that the enzyme participates in the repair of *E. coli* tRNAs but not in their biosynthesis. On the other hand, the enzyme is required for synthesis of certain T4 tRNAs. *cca* mutants grow slowly because they accumulate defective tRNA and have increased levels of ppGpp. These slow-growing strains frequently revert to faster growing forms that still are deficient in the enzyme, but have less defective tRNA. These strains have decreased amounts of RNase T (Section IV,A). Using a series of mutant strains with different amounts of tRNA nucleotidyltransferase, it was found that the enzyme is normally present at levels about 10 times above its needs in the cell, and that the growth rates of the mutant strains are directly related to the amount of defective tRNA present. Thus, tRNA nucleotidyltransferase is needed for the normal growth of *E. coli*.

tRNA nucleotidyltransferase was originally thought to be a cytoplasmic enzyme, but was later shown to also be present in mitochondria, within the matrix (*81*), and in nuclei (*83*). The enzyme is also a component of plant chloroplasts (*83, 145*). The yeast mitochondrial enzyme has now been purified nearly to homogeneity; from structural and functional properties, it appears to be identical to its cytoplasmic counterpart (*146*). It remains to be seen whether both proteins are products of the same gene.

The finding of tRNA nucleotidyltransferase in every cell compartment in which tRNA is synthesized supports the idea that this enzyme is required for tRNA biosynthesis in eukaryotes. This point has now been demonstrated conclusively with the isolation of a yeast mutant strain deficient in the enzyme (*147*). The strain is temperature-sensitive for growth and accumulates shortened tRNAs at the restrictive temperature that are substrates for AMP incorporation. Direct assays of tRNA nucleotidyltransferase activity indicate that it is low in the mutant cells. The availability of a mutant cell has made it possible to isolate a clone carrying the yeast *cca* gene (see below).

A. *cca* Genes

The *E. coli cca* gene has been cloned, based on its proximity to the known *dnaG* locus at 66 minutes on the genetic map (*148*). The *cca* gene is present as a single copy on the *E. coli* chromosome. Based on Southern blotting, there is no similarity between this gene and its counterparts in *Bacillus subtilis*, *Saccharomyces cerevisiae*, *Petunia hybrida*, or *Homo sapiens*. Only DNA from the closely related species, *Salmonella typhimurium*, hybridizes. The *cca* gene was sequenced and was shown to extend for 412 codons beginning with an initiator GTG codon and encoding a protein of 46.4 kDa. A mutant *cca* gene encoding a tRNA nucleotidyltransferase that had lost AMP-incorporating activity, but retained CMP-incorporating activity, was also sequenced (*149*). This gene contains a single G-to-A point mutation that results in a glycine-to-aspartate substitution in the middle Gly of the sequence Gly-X-Gly-X-X-Gly. Interestingly, this sequence is thought to be near the nucleotide-binding domain of various proteins, but this is the first example of its presence in an enzyme that incorporates nucleotides. Other sequences often associated with ATP-binding sites are not found in *E. coli* tRNA nucleotidyltransferase.

An *E. coli* strain totally devoid of tRNA nucleotidyltransferase was constructed by interruption of the *cca* gene (*150*). This strain grows slowly, but is still viable, as might be expected from the recent finding (*11*) that all *E. coli* tRNA genes encode the -C-C-A sequence. Nevertheless, about 15% of the tRNA population contains defective 3' termini because of the inability to repair the ends of tRNA. Another *cca* mutant (*48*), originally thought to contain 1–2% residual enzyme activity, actually produces an inactive fragment of 40 kDa. The small amount of residual activity was due to another enzyme, perhaps the synthetic activity of PNPase.

The yeast *cca* gene has also been cloned recently based on its ability to complement a temperature-sensitive *cca* mutant (*147*). Sequencing of this gene revealed an open reading frame that would encode a protein of 546 amino acids with a molecular mass of 62 kDa, substantially larger than the *E. coli* enzyme, as was already known from examination of the purified proteins (*144*). Comparison of the amino-acid sequences of the yeast and *E. coli* proteins shows some regions of strong similarity in the amino terminal half of the protein (*147*). Interestingly, the Gly-X-Gly-X-X-Gly sequence is not found in the yeast protein.

Both the *E. coli* (*151*) and yeast (*146*) tRNA nucleotidyltransferases have been overexpressed from the cloned genes, purified to homogeneity or near homogeneity, and characterized. The properties of these purified enzymes are essentially identical to earlier preparations (*144*). Overexpression of the *E. coli* enzyme up to 100 times the wild-type levels has no adverse effects on the cell (*151*).

B. Interactions of tRNA with tRNA Nucleotidyltransferase

Earlier work showed that molecules as small as CpC and cytidine could act as acceptors for rabbit liver tRNA nucleotidyltransferase, albeit with low V_{max} and very high K_m values (*152*). Nevertheless, these observations indicated that the terminal acceptor residue (or residues) was sufficient for the incorporation reaction to occur. With the yeast enzyme, the acceptor requirements for nucleotide incorporation are more stringent (*153*). In this case, single-stranded oligonucleotides from the 3′ terminus of tRNA^{Phe} up to 18 nucleotides long were very poor acceptors for AMP incorporation, but addition of the complementary 5′ oligonucleotide to regenerate the double-stranded aminoacyl stem led to as much as a sevenfold increase in V_{max}. This latter value was still less than a tenth that of tRNA-C-C, however, suggesting that for the yeast enzyme more of the total tRNA structure is required for substrate recognition.

A detailed examination of tRNA recognition by the *E. coli* and yeast enzymes using the technique of damage selection was carried out (*154*). In this procedure, tRNA is chemically modified, in this case with diethyl pyrocarbonate or hydrazine to modify purines or uridines prior to interaction with the enzyme. Molecules able to act as substrates are analyzed for their content of modified bases to see which modifications interfere with enzyme activity. With the *E. coli* enzyme, purine modifications at positions clustered at the corner of the L-shaped tRNA molecule were the most important. In only a few tRNAs did residues near the 3′ end have an effect. The yeast enzyme differs somewhat in that interactions at the corner, though indicated for many tRNAs, are less consistent, and interactions near the 3′ end of tRNA are more evident. This approach to study of tRNA recognition by tRNA nucleotidyltransferase is useful, although at the present level of analysis it does not distinguish between modifications that affect substrate binding and those that affect catalysis. It also does not distinguish between tRNA residues that are direct contact sites with the enzyme, and those modifications that alter the overall three-dimensional structure of the tRNA.

On the other side of the coin, studies have been initiated to identify regions of the protein important for tRNA nucleotidyltransferase activity. Deletions from the carboxy terminus of the *E. coli* enzyme reveal that removal of 11 amino acids has no effect on activity, whereas removal of 10 more abolishes activity (*155*). Within this stretch of 10 residues are three consecutive arginines surrounded by seven uncharged amino acids. Perhaps, this positively charged center is important for interaction with the negatively charged tRNA or nucleoside triphosphate substrates.

In a second approach designed to identify the region of the protein that interacts with the 3′ terminus of tRNA, tRNA was oxidized at its 3′ terminus with periodate, covalently cross-linked to the protein, and stabilized by reduction with cyanoborohydride (*156*). Only a single tRNA molecule was found to cross-link to the protein, and its attachment eliminated enzyme activity. Further studies will attempt to identify the peptide to which the tRNA is linked.

VI. Regulation at the 3′ Terminus of tRNA

Early work on regulatory phenomena that may occur at the -C-C-A terminus of tRNA has been reviewed previously (122). The existence of an enzyme such as RNase T (Section IV,A), whose sole function could be end-turnover of tRNA, focuses attention on the involvement of this process in some regulatory process within the cell. At present, there is no indication of what that process might be. It is interesting that not all tRNA molecules participate in the end-turnover process, but only those specific for certain amino acids (100). Why these tRNAs would spend a greater fraction of the time uncharged, and thereby accessible to RNase T, remains unclear. It has been shown recently that estradiol increases the acceptor activity of uterine tRNAs *in vivo* by increasing the proportion with intact -C-C-A termini (157, 158). This effect is mediated through increases in CTP levels in the uterine cells. The general significance of this type of translational regulation remains to be established.

ACKNOWLEDGMENTS

Work from the author's laboratory was supported by NIH grant GM16317. I thank all my colleagues who provided information prior to publication.

REFERENCES

1. M. P. Deutscher, *This Series* **13**, 51 (1973).
2. J. Normanly and J. Abelson, *ARB* **58**, 1029 (1989).
3. D. Moazed and H. F. Noller, *Cell* **57**, 585 (1989).
4. M. Sprinzl and F. Cramer, *This Series* **22**, 1 (1979).
5. H. Paulsen and W. Wintermeyer, *EJB* **138**, 117 (1984).
6. K. Nagamatsu and Y. Miyazawa, *J. Biochem.* **94**, 1967 (1983).
7. E. Westhof, P. Dumas and D. Moras, *JMB* **184**, 119 (1985).
8. M. P. Deutscher, *CRC Crit. Rev. Biochem.* **17**, 45 (1984).
9. T. C. King, R. Sirdeskmukh and D. Schlessinger, *Microbiol. Rev.* **50**, 428 (1986).
10. M. Sprinzl, T. Hartmann, J. Weber, J. Blank and R. Zeidler, *NARes* **17**, rl (1989).
11. H. Ozeki, personal communication, 1988.
12. A. Muto, personal communication, 1988.
13. B. Vold, *Microbiol. Rev.* **49**, 71 (1985).
14. K.Fukada and J. Abelson, *JMB* **139**, 377 (1980).
15. G. P. Mazzara, G. Plunkett III, and W. H. McClain, *PNAS* **78**, 889 (1981).
16. J. G. Seidman, B. G. Barrell and W. H. McClain, *JMB* **99**, 733 (1975).
17. J. G. Seidman and W. H. McClain, *PNAS* **72**, 1491 (1975).
18. F. J. Schmidt, J. G. Seidman and R. M. Bock, *JBC* **251**, 2440 (1976).
19. C. Guerrier-Takada, W. H. McClain and S. Altman, *Cell* **38**, 219 (1984).
20. C. J. Green and B. J. Vold, *JBC* **263**, 652 (1988).
21. L. Nichols and F. J. Schmidt, *NARes* **16**, 2931 (1988).
22. W. H. McClain, C. Guerrier-Takada and S. Altman, *Science* **228**, 527 (1987).
23. M. P. Deutscher, *Cell* **40**, 731 (1985).

24. M. P. Deutscher, *TIBS* **13**, 136 (1988).
25. C. Reich, G. J. Olsen, B. Pace and N. R. Pace, *Science* **239**, 178 (1988).
26. B. S. Vold, C. J. Green, N. Narasimhan, M. Strem and J. N. Hansen, *JBC* **263**, 14485 (1988).
27. S. Altman, *Nature NB* **229**, 19 (1971).
28. S. Altman and J. D. Smith, *Nature NB* **233**, 35 (1971).
29. P. Schedl and P. Primakoff, *PNAS* **70**, 2091 (1973).
30. E. K. Bikoff and M. L. Gefter, *JBC* **250**, 6240 (1975).
31. T. Sekiya, R. Contreras, T. Takeya and H. G. Khorana, *JBC* **254**, 5802 (1979).
32. P. Schedl, J. Roberts and P. Primakoff, *Cell* **8**, 581 (1976).
33. R. M. Reilly and U. L. RajBhandary, *JBC* **261**, 2928 (1986).
34. H. D. Robertson, S. Altman and J. D. Smith, *JBC* **247**, 5243 (1972).
35. M. J. Fournier, E. Webb and S. Tang, *Bchem* **16**, 3608 (1977).
36. E. K. Bikoff, B. F. LaRue and M. L. Gefter, *JBC* **250**, 6248 (1975).
37. H. Cudny and M. P. Deutscher, *JBC* **263**, 1518 (1988)..
38. H. Sakano and Y. Shimura, *JMB* **123**, 287 (1978).
39. Y. Shimura, H. Sakano and F. Nagawa, *EJB* **86**, 267 (1978).
40. T. Nomura and A. Ishihama, *EMBO J.* **7**, 3539 (1988).
41. H. Sakano, S. Yamada, T. Ikemura, Y. Shimura and H. Ozeki, *NARes* **1**, 355 (1974).
42. C. Guthrie, *JMB* **95**, 529 (1975).
43. C. Guthrie and C. A. Scholla, *JMB* **139**, 349 (1980).
44. W. H. McClain, *Acc. Chem. Res.* **10**, 418 (1977).
45. J. G. Seidman, F. J. Schmidt, K. Foss and W. H. McClain, *Cell* **5**, 389 (1975).
46. A. N. Maisurian and E. A. Buyanovskaya, *MGG* **120**, 227 (1973).
47. P. K. Asha, R. T. Blouin, R. Zaniewski and M. P. Deutscher, *PNAS* **80**, 3301 (1983).
48. M. P. Deutscher and R. H. Hilderman, *J. Bact.* **118**, 621 (1974).
49. M. P. Deutscher, J. Foulds and W. H. McClain, *JBC* **249**, 6696 (1974).
50. B. Pragai and D. Apirion, *JMB* **153**, 619 (1981).
51. M. Gurevitz and D. Apirion, *Bchem* **22**, 4000 (1983).
52. S. G. Clarkson, *in* "Eukaryotic Genes: Their Structure, Activity and Regulation" (N. MacLean, S. P. Gregory and R. A. Flavel, eds.), p. 239. Butterworths, London, 1983.
53. J. Battey and D. A. Clayton, *JBC* **255**, 11599 (1980).
54. D. Ojala, J. Montoya and G. Attardi, *Nature* **290**, 470 (1981).
55. H. G. Köchel, C. M. Lazarus, N. Basak and H. Kuntzel, *Cell* **23**, 625 (1981).
56. L. Graf, H. Kössel and E. Stutz, *Nature* **286**, 908 (1980).
57. W. Gruissem, D. M. Prescott, B. M. Greenberg and R. B. Hallick, *Cell* **30**, 81 (1982).
58. C. Palleschi, S. Francisci, E. Zennaro and L. Frontali, *EMBO J*, **3**, 1389 (1984).
59. M. Zasloff, *PNAS* **80**, 6436 (1983).
60. J. A. Tobian, L. Drinkard and M. Zasloff, *Cell* **43**, 415 (1985).
61. D. R. Engelke, P. Gegenheimer and J. Abelson, *JBC* **260**, 1271 (1985).
62. D. Frendeway, T. Dingermann, L. Cooley and D. Söll, *JBC* **260**, 449 (1985).
63. R. L. Garber and S. Altman, *Cell* **17**, 389 (1979).
64. O. Hagenbüchle, D. Larson, G. I. Hall and K. U. Sprague, *Cell* **18**, 1217 (1979).
65. R. L. Garber and L. P. Gage, *Cell* **18**, 817 (1979).
66. R. J. Rooney and J. D. Harding, *NARes* **14**, 4849 (1986).
67. H. van Tol, N. Stange, H. J. Gross and H. Beier, *EMBO J.* **6**, 35 (1987).
68. S. Ganguly, P. A. Sharp and U. L. RajBhandary, *MCBiol* **8**, 361 (1988).
69. M. Zasloff, T. Santos, P. Romeo and M. Rosenberg, *JBC* **257**, 7857 (1982).
70. J.-Y. Chen and N. C. Martin, *JBC* **263**, 13677 (1988).

71. M. J. Wang, N. W. Davis and P. Gegenheimer, *EMBO J.* 7, 1567 (1988).
72. D. A. Melton, E. M. DeRobertis and R. Cortese, *Nature* 284, 143 (1980).
73. B. J. Lee, P. de la Peña, J. A. Tobian, M. Zasloff and D. Hatfield, *PNAS* 84, 6384 (1987).
74. R. A. Koski, A. L. M. Bothwell and S. Altman, *Cell* 9, 101 (1976).
75. L. Kline, S. Nishikawa and D. Söll, *JBC* 256, 5058 (1981).
76. C.-J. Doersen, C. Guerrier-Takada, S. Altman and G. Attardi, *JBC* 260, 5942 (1985).
77. M. J. Hollingsworth and N. C. Martin, *MCBiol* 6, 1058 (1986).
78. J. G. Castaño, J. A. Tobian and M. Zasloff, *JBC* 260, 9002 (1985).
79. A. Rice and G. C. Van Tuyle, personal communication, 1989.
80. A. Solari and M. P. Deutscher, *MCBiol* 3, 1711 (1983).
81. S. K. Mukerji and M. P. Deutscher, *JBC* 247, 481 (1972).
82. A. Solari and M. P. Deutscher, *NARes* 10, 4397 (1982).
83. B. M. Greenberg, W. Gruissem and R. B. Hallick, *Plant Mol. Biol.* 3, 97 (1984).
84. D. N. Standring, A. Venegas and W. J. Rutter, *PNAS* 78, 5963 (1981).
85. D. Colby, P. S. Leboy and C. Guthrie, *PNAS* 78, 415 (1981).
86. B. K. Ray and D. Apirion, *EJB* 114, 517 (1981).
87. J. P. Miller, M. E. Hirst-Bruns and G. R. Philipps, *BBA* 217, 176 (1970).
88. T. Kasai, R. S. Gupta and D. Schlessinger, *JBC* 252, 8950 (1977).
89. J. Szeberenyi, M. K. Roy, H. C. Vaidya and D. Apirion, *Bchem* 23, 2952 (1984).
90. R. Zaniewski, E. Petkaitis and M. P. Deutscher, *JBC* 259, 11651 (1984).
91. R. Zaniewski and M. P. Deutscher, unpublished.
92. V. Shen and D. Schlessinger, *Enzymes* 15, 501 (1982).
93. P. F. Spahr and D. Schlessinger, *JBC* 238, PC2251 (1963).
94. P. F. Spahr, *JBC* 239, 3716 (1964).
95. M. F. Singer and G. Tolbert, *Bchem* 4, 1319 (1965).
96. R. S. Gupta, T. Kasai and D. Schlessinger, *JBC* 252, 8945 (1977).
97. H. Cudny and M. P. Deutscher, *PNAS* 77, 837 (1980).
98. N. G. Nossal and M. F. Singer, *JBC* 243, 913 (1968).
99. I. E. Mott, J. L. Galloway and T. Platt, *EMBO J.* 4, 1887 (1985).
100. M. P. Deutscher, J. J. Lin and J. A. Evans, *JMB* 117, 1081 (1977).
101. M. Birenbaum, D. Schlessinger and Y. Ohnishi, *J. Bact.* 142, 327 (1980).
102. W. P. Donovan and S. R. Kushner, *NARes* 11, 265 (1983).
103. W. P. Donovan and S. R. Kushner, *PNAS* 83, 120 (1986).
104. E. T. Lennette and D. Apirion, *J. Bact.* 108, 1322 (1971).
105. J. Zhang and M. P. Deutscher, unpublished.
106. M. P. Deutscher and R. K. Ghosh, *NARes* 5, 3821 (1978).
107. R. K. Ghosh and M. P. Deutscher, *NARes* 5, 3831 (1978).
108. R. K. Ghosh and M. P. Deutscher, *JBC* 253, 997 (1978).
109. H. Cudny, R. Zaniewski and M. P. Deutscher, *JBC* 256, 5627 (1981).
110. J. Zhang and M. P. Deutscher, *NARes* 16, 6265 (1988).
111. H. Cudny, R. Zaniewski and M. P. Deutscher, *JBC* 256, 5633 (1981).
112. R. Zaniewski and M. P. Deutscher, *MGG* 185, 142 (1982).
113. R. T. Blouin, R. Zaniewski and M. P. Deutscher, *JBC* 258, 1423 (1983).
114. J. Zhang and M. P. Deutscher, *JBC* 263, 17909 (1988).
115. J. Zhang and M. P. Deutscher, *J. Bact.* 170, 522 (1988).
116. J. Zhang and M. P. Deutscher, *JBC* 264, 18228 (1989).
117. A. N. Maisurian and E. A. Buyanovskaya, *Genetika* 11, 114 (1975).
118. F. J. Schmidt and W. H. McClain, *NARes* 5, 4129 (1978).
119. P. Roy, H. Cudny and M. P. Deutscher, *JMB* 159, 179 (1982).

120. P. K. Asha and M. P. Deutscher, *J. Bact.* **156**, 419 (1983).
121. D. Neri-Cortes and M. P. Deutscher, unpublished.
122. M. P. Deutscher, *in* "Enzymes of Nucleic Acid Synthesis and Modification" (S. T. Jacob, ed.), Vol. 2, p. 159. CRC Press, Boca Raton, Florida, 1982.
123. M. P. Deutscher, C. W. Marlor and R. Zaniewski, *PNAS* **81**, 4290 (1984).
124. M. P. Deutscher and C. W. Marlor, *JBC* **260**, 7067 (1985).
125. M. P. Deutscher, C. W. Marlor and R. Zaniewski, *PNAS* **82**, 6427 (1985).
126. L. M. Case and M. P. Deutscher, unpublished.
127. L. M. Case, X. Chen and M. P. Deutscher, *J. Bact.* **171**, 5736 (1989).
128. U. Z. Littauer and H. Soreq, *Enzymes* **15**, 518 (1982).
129. M. P. Deutscher, G. T. Marshall and H. Cudny, *PNAS* **85**, 4710 (1988).
130. C. Portier, *MGG* **178**, 343 (1980).
131. L. M. McMurray and S. B. Levy, *J. Bact.* **169**, 1321 (1987).
132. R. V. Krishna, L. Rosen and D. Apirion, *Nature NB* **242**, 18 (1973).
133. J. A. Hautala, C. L. Bassett, N. H. Giles and S. R. Kushner, *PNAS* **76**, 5774 (1979).
134. A. M. Reiner, *J. Bact.* **92**, 1437 (1969).
135. P. Regnier, M. Grunberg-Manago and C. Portier, *JBC* **262**, 63 (1987).
136. P. Regnier and C. Portier, *JMB* **187**, 23 (1986).
137. C. Portier, L. Dondon and M. Grunberg-Manago, *EMBO J.* **6**, 2165 (1987).
138. M. P. Deutscher, R. Zaniewski and H. Cudny, unpublished.
139. K. A. Ost and M. P. Deutscher, unpublished.
140. N. Watson and D. Apirion, *BBRC* **103**, 543 (1981).
141. T. Nomura and A. Ishihama, *EMBO J.* **7**, 3539 (1988).
142. A. Goldfarb and V. Daniel, *NARes* **8**, 4501 (1980).
143. S. Manam and G. C. Van Tuyle, *JBC* **262**, 10272 (1987).
144. M. P. Deutscher, *Enzymes* **15**, part B 183 (1982).
145. A. Marion-Poll, C. S. Hibbert, C. A. Radebaugh and R. B. Hallick, *Plant Mol. Biol.* **11**, 45 (1988).
146. J. Chen and N. C. Martin, personal communication, 1989.
147. M. Aebi, G. Kirschner, J. Chen, U. Vijayraghaven, A. Jacobson, N. C. Martin and J. Abelson, personal communication, 1989.
148. H. C. Cudny, J. R. Lupski, G. N. Godson and M. P. Deutscher, *JBC* **261**, 6444 (1986).
149. L. Zhu, H. Cudny and M. P. Deutscher, *JBC* **261**, 14875 (1986).
150. L. Zhu and M. P. Deutscher, *EMBO J.* **6**, 2473 (1987).
151. H. C. Cudny and M. P. Deutscher, *JBC* **261**, 6450 (1986).
152. P. Masiakowski and M. P. Deutscher, *JBC* **255**, 11233 (1980).
153. G.-H. Wang, L. W. McLaughlin, H. Sternbach and F. Cramer, *NARes* **12**, 6909 (1984).
154. P. Spacciapoli, L. Doviken, J. L. Mulero and D. L. Thurlow, *JBC* **264**, 3799 (1989).
155. L. Zhu and M. P. Deutscher, unpublished.
156. A. Theobald and M. P. Deutscher, unpublished.
157. K. R. Rasmussen, S. M. Whelly and K. L. Barker, *BBA* **970**, 177 (1988).
158. K. R. Rasmussen, S. Whelly and K. Barker, *BBA* **972**, 179 (1988).

The Numerous Modified Nucleotides in Eukaryotic Ribosomal RNA

B. E. H. MADEN

Department of Biochemistry
University of Liverpool
Liverpool L69 3BX, England

Progress in Nucleic Acid Research
and Molecular Biology, Vol. 39

I. Introduction

The ribosome is fundamental, big, and complicated. Its RNA components have retained a common core of secondary structure across the whole range of evolutionary divergence (1–3). The conserved features of the rRNA molecules are thought to be intrinsic to the working machinery of the ribosome (4), which, however, remains enigmatic.

Within the common structural design there are phyletic differences of varying degrees. The deepest differences distinguish the kingdoms of the Eubacteria, Archaebacteria, and Eukaryotes (5, 5a), and also some mitochondrial ribosomes (6, 7). Most of the phyletic differences are manifest at the level of base sequences, and a large database of rRNA sequences has been obtained indirectly by sequencing rDNA (2, 7, 8).

Other striking differences concern the pattern of modified nucleotides in rRNA. Eukaryotic cytoplasmic rRNAs contain many more modified nucleotides than do prokaryotic rRNAs. Human ribosomes contain about 212 modified nucleotides. This is almost three times as many modified nucleotides as the *total* number of nucleotides in a tRNA molecule. rRNAs from several other vertebrate species contain modified nucleotides similar in number to those of human rRNA. rRNA from the yeast, *Saccharmoyces*, contains about 113 modified nucleotides.

Information on the modified nucleotides cannot be obtained simply by sequencing rDNA. Instead, a number of structural and kinetic techniques have been applied to the direct analysis of the modified nucleotides in rRNAs and ribosomal precursor RNAs. The most detailed knowledge has come from studies on vertebrates including man, and from the yeast, *Saccharomyces*. The purpose of this article is to bring together the currently available information on the modified nucleotides, especially in man and the vertebrates and in yeast. Parts of this information have been reviewed (9).

The most important recent advances have been in locating many of the modified nucleotides in rRNA. This has been achieved in most instances by combining RNA oligonucleotide data with rDNA sequence data. This work is summarized in Sections II and III.

Almost all of the modified nucleotides that have been located are in the conserved structural core of rRNA. This brings the modified nucleotides into the central arena of rRNA structure and function. There is no simple theme of primary or secondary structure among the modification sites. The diversity of modification sites is discussed in Sections IV and V, and this diversity raises challenging questions concerning the molecular recognition processes that bring about the modifications.

Further insight into these processes may come from the long-established finding that most modifications occur very rapidly upon ribosomal precursor RNA (Section VI). A related finding, also long established, is that inhibition of methylation of precursors of rRNA is associated with failure of ribosome maturation (Section VI). However, the precise roles of the modified nucleotides in the maturation and working life of the ribosome remain unknown.

Some possible new experimental approaches to rRNA modification are outlined in Section VII where the use of modified nucleotides in estimating whole-body ribosome turnover in man is also briefly outlined.

Throughout this article the terms SSU and LSU rRNA are used to denote the rRNA from the small ribosomal subunit and the major rRNA molecule from the large subunit, respectively. This nomenclature is in line with other recent publications (e.g., 3) and avoids potential confusion from the formerly used range of S values, generally 16–18 S for SSU rRNA, and 23–28 S for LSU rRNA.

II. Types and Numbers of Modified Nucleotides

Table I summarizes the types and numbers of modified nucleotides in rRNA from several vertebrate species and from the yeast, *Saccharomyces carlsbergensis*. The main points relating to the table are as follows: (i) More than 100 nucleotides in vertebrate rRNA are methylated. (ii) Most of these are 2'-*O*-methylated but there are also several types of methylated bases. (iii) In addition, there are almost 100 pseudouridines in vertebrate rRNA. (iv) Most sites are fully modified (i.e., all molecules are modified) although a few are partially modified (i.e., not all molecules are modified). (v) Most of the methylation sites are conserved across the vertebrate species represented in Table I. Many of them are also conserved between vertebrates and yeast; however, there are fewer modified nucleotides overall in yeast than in vertebrates.

The structures of the various modified nucleotides are shown in Fig. 1.

The following discussion outlines the sources of data and some specific points relating to the individual values in Table I.

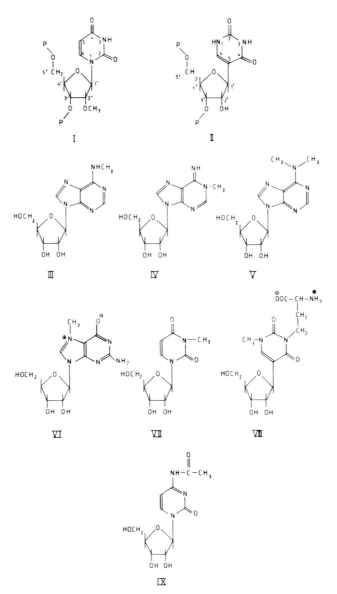

Fig. 1. The modified nucleotides in vertebrate rRNA. (I) An example of a 2'-O-methylated nucleotide: 2'-O-methyluridine (Um) in internucleotide linkage. (II) Pseudouridine (5-ribosyluracil, Ψ), also shown in internucleotide linkage. Both of these types of modification are abundant in eukaryotic rRNA. The remaining compounds are rare, and are shown in the figure as nucleosides. (III) N^6-Methyladenosine (m^{6}A) occurs once in the SSU rRNA of vertebrates, and once in the large subunit (LSU). (See Table IX for the locations of this and the following modifications in the sequences.) (IV) 1-Methyladenosine (m^{1}A) occurs once in the LSU rRNA of vertebrates.

TABLE I

EXPERIMENTALLY DETERMINED NUMBERS OF MODIFIED NUCLEOTIDES IN EUKARYOTIC rRNA[a]

	2'-O-methyl	Base methyl	Pseudo-uridine	Other	Total modified	Total nucleotides	% Nucleotides modified
Human							
SSU	40	5	~36	≥1	~82	1869	4.3
5.8S	2	—	2	—	4	157	2.5
LSU	63–65	5	~57	?	~126	5025	2.5
Total	105–107	10	~95	1–2?	~212	7051	3.0
Mouse							
SSU	40	5	~36	≥1	~82	1869	4.3
5.8 S	2	—	2	—	4	157	2.5
LSU	63–65	5	~57	?	~126	4712	2.7
Total	105–107	10	~95	1–2?	~212	6738	3.2
Rat							
SSU	40	5	~37	≥1	~83	1869	4.3
5.8 S	2	—	2	—	4	157	2.5
(LSU n.d.)							
X. laevis							
SSU	33	5	~44	≥1	~83	1826	4.5
5.8 S	2	—	2	—	4	160	2.5
LSU	62–64	5	~52	?	~121	4110	2.9
Total	97–99	10	~98	1–2?	~208	6096	3.4
S. carlsbergensis							
SSU	18	4	~14	≥1	~37	1798	2.1
5.8 S	—	—	1	—	1	160	0.6
LSU	37	6	~32	?	~75	3393	2.2
Total	55	10	~47	1–2?	~113	5351	2.1

[a] The numbers of modified nucleotides were determined as outlined in Section II, from the sources cited therein. Data on the methylated oligonucleotides in HeLa (human) cell rRNA are summarized in Table III. The hypermodified nucleotide $m^1acp^3\Psi$ (Sections II,D and IV) is included here with the base-methylated nucleotides. The SSU and LSU rRNA sequence lengths are from the following sources: SSU human (35a); mouse (35b); rat (35c); X. laevis (35); Saccharomyces (35d); LSU human (32); mouse (31); X. laevis (30); S. carlsbergensis (37).

(V) N^6-Dimethyladenosine (m^6_2A) occurs twice, at adjacent sites, in SSU rRNA. (VI) 7-Methylguanosine (m^7G) occurs once in SSU rRNA. (VII) 3-Methyluridine (m^3U) occurs once in vertebrate LSU rRNA [and twice in yeast LSU rRNA (22)]. (VIII) 1-Methyl-3-(α-amino-α-carboxypropyl)pseudouridine ($m^1acp^3\Psi$) occurs once in SSU rRNA. (IX) N^4-Acetylcytidine (ac^4C) occurs in SSU rRNA, probably once, at an unknown location. Note that all the substitutions in III to IX are N substitutions. In addition, LSU rRNA contains two base-methylated cytosines (mC) but the positions of the methyl groups on the respective cytosine rings have not been definitively characterized.

A. Sources of Data: Methylation

2'-*O*-Methylated nucleotides were first discovered in rRNA as a result of their conferring resistance to alkaline hydrolysis upon the adjacent phosphodiester bond. Thus many early studies on eukaryotic rRNA methylation were based on the characterization of alkali-stable dinucleotides (*10–13*) and a few trinucleotides (*14*).

A major advance in the analysis of rRNA methylation came with the introduction of oligonucleotide "fingerprinting." The numbers of methyl groups in the rRNAs in Table I were determined by oligonucleotide fingerprinting, in most instances as follows. Cultured cells were grown for two or more generations in medium containing [Me-^{14}C] methionine. [Suitable labeling conditions as applied to HeLa (human-derived) cells are given in *15*.] The SSU and LSU rRNA were purified and enzymically digested, and the resulting methyl-labelled oligonucleotides were separated by electrophoresis in two dimensions.

Three different enzymic digestion procedures were used for generating fingerprints: (i) digestion with ribonuclease T$_1$ (EC 3.1.27.3), either on its own or with alkaline phosphatase; (ii) digestion with combined T$_1$ and pancreatic ribonucleases; (iii) digestion with pancreatic ribonuclease (RNase A) (EC 3.1.27.5) on its own. The characteristics and uses of the three fingerprinting systems are summarized in Table II and are detailed in the references therein. Briefly, complementary use of the T$_1$ and combined T$_1$ plus pancreatic systems, particularly for HeLa (*15, 16, 16a, 17*) and *Xenopus* rRNA (*17a*), yielded the numbers of methylated nucleotides listed in Table I.

These numbers were established in the 1970s before any of the complete SSU or LSU base sequences of rDNA had been determined. They served as the basis, first for examining in detail the kinetics of methylation (particularly in HeLa cells and yeast), and later for placing the methyl groups in the complete sequences. Therefore the numbers of methyl groups determined from fingerprinting are of critical importance. Comments on the individual values are given in the following sections.

B. Numbers of Methyl Groups in Individual rRNA Species

1. SSU rRNA

a. HeLa Cells. The methylated products liberated by digesting HeLa cell SSU RNA with T$_1$ RNase were first characterized in *15*, and the data were refined slightly in *18*. The data on the numbers and molar yields of the products are summarized in Table III, and enable the

TABLE II

RNA Fingerprinting Systems Used for Characterizing Methylated Oligonucleotides

Enzymes(s)	Cleavage sites	Features of system
RNase T_1 (or RNase T_1 plus alkaline phosphatase)	After G residues except 2'-O-methyl-G and some base-methylated G residues (m^7G in eukaryotic SSU rRNA)	Numerous methylated oligonucleotides are resolved in ^{14}C-methyl fingerprints, most in unimolar yield. Some methylated oligonucleotides are fully resolved in ^{32}P fingerprints, others are partly resolved or unresolved from nonmethylated products. RNase T_1 plus alkaline phosphatase digests (*15a*) were used for preferential resolution of uridylate-rich oligonucleotides (*15, 18*). Complete or partial sequence analyses of HeLa cell products, using ^{14}C-methyl-labelled and ^{32}P-labelled material, was carried out as described in *15* (see also *18, 19, 22*).
RNase T_1 plus pancreatic RNase (RNase A)	After all T_1 sites and all pancreatic sites	Nonmethylated regions are degraded to Gp, Up, Cp, and $(Ap)_nGp$, $(Ap)_nUp$, $(Ap)_nCp$, yielding a simple pattern in the fingerprint (*16*). Methylated sequences give numerous short distinctive products due to enzyme-resistant (usually 2'-O-methyl) linkages. Many of these methylated products are fully resolved from nonmethylated material in ^{32}P fingerprints, facilitating absolute quantification of methyl groups (*15, 16, 16a, 17*). Some multiply-methylated products were first sequenced in this system and then identified within corresponding T_1 products (*15*). For a full correlation between the two systems see *17*.
Pancreatic RNase (RNase A)	After all pyrimidines except 2'-O-methyl pyrimidines and some base-methylated pyrimidines (m^3U and $m^1acp^3\Psi$ in eukaryotic rRNA)	Numerous methylated oligonucleotides are resolved in ^{14}C-methyl fingerprints, the majority in unimolar yield. Some methylated products are well resolved in ^{32}P fingerprints, others are partly resolved or unresolved. Nearly all products were fully or partly sequenced in HeLa cell rRNA (*35, 36*). Some methylation sites that occur within short T_1 products occur within longer, encompassing or overlapping RNase A products, enabling assignment to unique locations in the complete RNA sequences (*35, 36*; see also Section III).

TABLE III
Methylated Oligonucleotides in T_1 RNase Digests of HeLa Cell rRNA[a]

Categories	SSU			LSU		
	Numbers of oligonucleotides	Numbers of methyl groups	Notes	Numbers of oligonucleotides	Numbers of methyl groups	Notes
Single oligonucleotides, singly methylated	32	32	b	40–42	40–42	f
Single oligonucleotides, multiply methylated	3	8	c	8	18	g
Multiple yield oligonucleotides, singly methylated	2	4	d	2	11	h
Partially methylated sites	3	3	e	1	1	i
Total methyl groups		47			70–72	

[a] The data are from 18 with subsequent minor adjustments that were made during correlation with the rDNA sequences. Oligonucleotides listed in the following notes are numbered (T30, etc.) as in 18.

[b] T_1 products that gave yields in the range 0.8–1.15 were scored as unimolar. A few T_1 products that gave lower observed yields were also scored as unimolar if the corresponding T_1-plus-pancreatic products were recovered in good yield. [Products that are very A-rich tend to be recovered in low yield due to partial depurination (7% formic acid) of the electrophoretic separation system.]

[c] Products T30, m_2^6A-m_2^6A-C-C-U-G; T68, C-U-A-A-Um-A-Cm-A-U-G; T85, U-Um-C-C-U-U-Um-G.

[d] Products T11, A-A-Cm-G; T24a, A-Gm-G, 2 mol each.

[e] T8 contains Cm-C-C-G unimolar and C-Cm-C-G ~ 0.5 M. T42 is C-U-Um-G ~ 0.5 M. T94 is a long oligonucleotide recovered in about 0.5 M yield due to partial methylation at G(m)-A. This oligonucleotide also contains Um-C. In molecules in which the respective G(m) is unmethylated, Um-C is within T89 instead.

[f] The 5.8-S product T66, ...Gm-C..., is included. Nearly all singly methylated LSU oligonucleotides are well characterized, but two products, T84 and T92b, both possibly containing Gm-U, rest on tentative data.

[g] T14, m^1A and Am-C; T33, mC and A-A-Am-U; T36, ...Gm-A-Am-A-G; T62, Cm-A-Gm-A-U-U-G; T83, ...Um-Gm-U...; T90 ...Gm-U, Um-C, Gm-A...; T92a, ...Um-Gm-Ψ...; T93, ...Am-Gm-Cm-A....

[h] T3, Am-G, 4 mol; T21, Gm-G, ~ 7 mol.

[i] This is the 5.8-S product Um-G, described in Section VII,C. It comigrates with 28-S product T22, which is also Um-G.

following statements to be made. (i) There are 45 methylated nucleotides in HeLa cell SSU rRNA. (ii) Most of these are singly and fully
methylated (i.e., all molecules are methylated) but three are only partially methylated (40–50% of the molecules). (iii) Two nucleotides are
doubly methylated (the two dimethyl-A residues near the 3' end of the
molecule). Thus the total score of methyl groups is 47 per SSU rRNA.

b. *Other Mammalian Cells.* Reference 18 includes a comparative
study of rRNA methylation in vertebrates. As well as the HeLa (human) rRNA data summarized above, the paper contains *methyl*-[14]C
fingerprinting data on rRNA from L cells (mouse) and BHK cells
(Chinese hamster), and the nonmammalian sources, chick and *Xenopus laevis.* The mouse and hamster SSU rRNA fingerprints obtained by
the T_1 and combined T_1 plus pancreatic RNase methods were indistin-
guishable from those of HeLa cells, except that in the mouse two
fractionally methylated components [in spots T8 and T24a (*18*)] appeared to be slightly less methylated than in HeLa cells. Thus the
numbers of methylated nucleotides are the same in SSU rRNA of all
three mammalian species.

Rat SSU rRNA has been subjected to detailed characterization by
T_1 RNase fingerprinting and oligonucleotide analysis using [32]P-
labelled RNA (*19*). There is complete correspondence between the
methylated oligonucleotides identified in that work and in the mammalian sources in *18*, notwithstanding the partly different experimental techniques in the two studies. This correspondence was checked by
the present author in an oligonucleotide-by-oligonucleotide comparison between the two sets of published data. The oligonucleotide fingerprinting data imply high conservation between methylation patterns of SSU rRNA among mammals.

Rabbit reticulocyte SSU rRNA has been examined recently by
rapid sequencing (*20–21*), and also revealed a closely similar methylation pattern to those of the above four mammalian species: see Section III, below.

c. *Nonmammalian Vertebrates.* There are minor differences between the SSU methylation patterns of mammals and the two nonmammalian vertebrate species examined (*18*). There are two fewer methyl
groups in chick and about 6–7 fewer in *Xenopus* than in human SSU
rRNA. The basis of the differences between the *Xenopus* and mammalian SSU methylation patterns is discussed in relation to the sequences
in Section III below.

d. *Saccharomyces.* The *Saccharomyces* values were also obtained
from T_1 fingerprints of [*methyl*-^{14}C]rRNA (*22*). As already mentioned,
there are fewer methyl groups in yeast SSU rRNA than in vertebrate
SSU rRNA.

2. 5.8-S rRNA

5.8-S rRNA is functionally part of the LSU rRNA but is noncova-
lently attached to the major LSU rRNA molecule. It contains about
157–160 nucleotides with minor 5' terminal length heterogeneity [es-
pecially in *Xenopus* (23, 24)]; it is readily detached from LSU rRNA by
mild heat treatment, and lends itself to complete sequence analysis by
classical oligonucleotide procedures. Several 5.8-S sequences were
determined in this way, including those of all the species listed in
Table I. The modified nucleotides in 5.8-S rRNA were discovered
during those studies. (See 8 for a compilation of 5.8-S sequences and
original references.)

3. LSU rRNA

Data on the T_1 oligonucleotides from methyl-labelled LSU rRNA
from HeLa cells were first published, together with the SSU data, in
15, and then with minor refinements in *18*. The latter reference also
contains data for L cells, hamster, chick, and *X. laevis*. As in SSU rRNA,
in LSU rRNA most of the T_1 products are unimolar and singly methylated, but there are also several multiply methylated products and
multiple yield products. The HeLa cell LSU data are summarized in
Table III along with the SSU data. Data from the other mammalian
sources are almost identical to those from HeLa cells. Data from chick
and *Xenopus* are closely similar to those from mammals, with a few
differences. Yeast (*Saccharomyces*) LSU rRNA contains fewer methyl
groups than does vertebrate LSU rRNA.

4. 2'-O-METHYLATION, BASE METHYLATION, AND VARIATIONS BETWEEN METHYLATION PATTERNS

Although 2'-O-methylation is the commonest class of methylation
in eukaryotic rRNA, there are also several base-methylated nucleotides. These are detailed for vertebrates in the context of their encompassing sequences (Section IV). Most but not all of the same
base-methylated nucleotides are present in HeLa and yeast rRNA.
By contrast, most of the differences between the total numbers of
methyl groups are due to differences in 2'-O-methylation. More data
on taxonomic variations of methylation patterns will be of value; see
Section VII.

C. Sources of Data and Numbers of Pseudouridines

Pseudouridine, in contrast to methylated nucleotides, cannot be
selectively labelled *in vivo*; therefore, some methodological discus-

sion of the pseudouridine determinations is in order. Most of the numerical data on pseudouridine in Table I were obtained by labelling cells with $^{32}PO_4$, isolating the RNA, and carrying out alkaline hydrolysis on the separated SSU and LSU rRNAs. In the final step of the analysis, pseudouridine 2'- (3'-)phosphate was separated chromatographically from uridine 2'- (3'-)phosphate (25).

[The results were first calculated as the percentage pseudouridine/(uridine + pseudouridine) × 100. These percentage values were converted to estimated absolute numbers of pseudouridines on the basis of the best derivable estimates of the total numbers of uracil nucleotides, from base composition data, and the approximate sizes of the molecules as then known (25). The values thus originally obtained have been revised slightly in Table I, as the total numbers of uracil nucleotides are now given by the rDNA sequences, assuming that T in rDNA encodes both U and Ψ in rRNA. This assumption is valid at all points at which pseudouridines have been located in the sequences.]

The rat SSU rRNA value in Table I was obtained by a different method, in the study referred to above (19) in which ^{32}P-labelled oligonucleotides were characterized. In that study, *every* T_1 oligonucleotide was analyzed for pseudouridine (19). The rat value is in very good agreement with the mouse and human values derived from alkaline hydrolysates of whole SSU rRNA. This affords confidence that the latter values, and by inference the LSU values, are also fairly accurate.

Whereas the mammalian values in Table I are in very good agreement with each other, the *Xenopus* values differ appreciably from the mammalian ones. The differences, particularly for SSU rRNA, are almost certainly outside the limits of experimental error, and imply that *Xenopus* SSU rRNA possesses several more pseudouridines than does mammalian SSU rRNA. The yeast (*Saccharomyces*) values were from products generated by the combined T_1-plus-pancreatic-RNase method (26). *Saccharomyces* rRNA contains substantially fewer pseudouridines than does rRNA from vertebrates.

D. Other Modified Nucleotides

Unlike tRNA, which contains a wide variety of different nucleotide modifications (27, 27a), eukaryotic rRNA appears to be qualitatively rather conservative in its repertoire of modified nucleotides. Almost all of the modifications fall within the categories already described: numerous 2'-O-methylations, a few base methylations, and numerous pseudouridines. However, 18-S rRNA is known to contain N^4-acetylcytidine [probably one residue but possibly two residues per molecule (28)]. The hypermodified nucleoside, $m^1acp^3Ψ$ (VIII in Fig.

1) (29) is included in Table I with the base-methylated nucleotides (see also Section IV). Possibly one or two other modified nucleotides remain to be discovered. However, the numbers still undiscovered cannot be large as there are no obviously anomalous components in the many base composition studies that have been carried out.

E. Percentage of Nucleotides Modified

The modified nucleotides are expressed in the right column of Table I as percentages of the total numbers of nucleotides in the respective rRNA species. The percentage values afford a measure of the global modification frequencies. About 3–3.4% of the total nucleotides are modified in vertebrate rRNA and about 2.1% in yeast rRNA. It is shown in Section III that the modified nucleotides are distributed very unevenly along the rRNA molecules, with some striking clusters. The substantial interspecies size differences between molecules, particularly for LSU rRNA (Table I) are due to eukaryotic expansion segments (30–32). These contain few if any modified nucleosides, as also discussed in Section III, below.

III. Locations of Modified Nucleotides in the rRNA Sequences

It is clear from the above description that secondary modifications feature prominently in the structure of eukaryotic rRNA. Understanding how the modifications occur and what roles they play requires knowledge of the locations of the modified nucleotides in rRNA. Considerable progress has recently been made in locating the modified nucleotides in rRNA from some eukaryotic species. This progress may be summarized as follows. (i) All of the methyl groups in SSU rRNA from X. *laevis,* man, and some other mammals have been located, with minor exceptions of one or two partial methylations. (ii) Most but not all of the pseudouridines in mammalian SSU rRNA have been located exactly or approximately. (iii) Most of the methyl groups in *Xenopus* and mammalian LSU rRNA have been located. (iv) So far, few of the pseudouridines in LSU RNA have been located. (v) The majority of methyl groups in yeast (*S. carlsbergensis*) rRNA have been located.

A. Mapping Procedures

Crucial to locating the methyl groups was a series of experiments in which methyl-labelled rRNA from cultured cells of X. *laevis* was hybridized to restriction fragments of rDNA and the methylated oligonucleotides that were recovered from the various hybridized regions

were identified (33). These experiments enabled the majority of methylated oligonucleotides to be matched with unique sequences within
the rDNA restriction fragments when the complete rDNA sequences
became known. The X. laevis sequences were determined first for SSU
rDNA (34) and then for LSU rDNA (30). Oligonucleotide data from all
three fingerprinting systems listed in Table II contributed to locating
the methyl groups in the inferred rRNA sequences. Because most of
the methylated oligonucleotides are identical between X. laevis and
human rRNA, and because the sequence data encompassed by the
oligonucleotides (T₁ and/or pancreatic) are sufficient to define unique
sites in rRNA, the methyl group locations could be deduced also for
human rRNA (35, 36).

In a separate study, direct chemical and enzymatic sequencing of
rabbit end-labelled SSU rRNA yielded the locations of methyl groups
as gaps in sequencing gels (20, 21). These results were essentially in
complete agreement with those deduced for Xenopus SSU rRNA by
oligonucleotide mapping, with a few extra, mammalian-specific methylations. The analysis also enabled a few locations that had been
determined only approximately by oligonucleotide mapping to be pinpointed exactly. This technique has not yet been applied successfully
to LSU rRNA.

The methyl group locations in Xenopus SSU rRNA were first reported in 34. Full experimentatal data for Xenopus and human SSU
rRNA were given in 35. Most of the methyl group locations in Xenopus
and human LSU rRNA are detailed in 36. Most of the yeast rRNA
methyl groups are reported in 3 and 37, although in less detail than for
Xenopus and man.

The pseudouridine locations in mammalian SSU rRNA were deduced by matching the rat oligonucleotide data in 19 with the complete mammalian sequence data, as described in 38. This enabled
some 16 pseudouridines to be located exactly and another 14 approximately. The remaining few, which are in short T₁ products, are currently unlocated.

B. SSU rRNA Modification Sites: Methylation and Pseudouridine

Table IV lists the methyl group locations in Xenopus and human
SSU rRNA. All of the sites that are methylated in Xenopus are also
methylated in human, and there are a few additional methylated nucleotides in human SSU rRNA. It can be inferred from oligonucleotide
data that all of the nucleotides homologous to those that are methylated
in human SSU rRNA are also methylated in mouse and hamster rRNA

TABLE IV
METHYLATED NUCLEOTIDES IN SSU rRNA[a]

X. laevis	Human	S. carlsbergensis
Am27	Am27	Am28
Am99	Am99	Am100
Um116	Um116	
Um121	Um121	
	Am159	
Am163	Am166	
	Um172	
	Cm174	
Um393	Um428	
Gm401	Gm436	
Cm427	Cm462	Cm414
Am433	Am468	Am420
Am449	Am484	Am436
Gm474	Gm509	
Am477	Am512	
Cm482	Cm517	
Am541	Am576	
Am555	Am590	Am541
Gm566	Gm601	
Um592	Um627	Um578
Gm609	Gm644	
Am633	Am668	Am619
Gm648	Gm683	
Cm760	Cm797	
Um762	Um799	
		Am796
	Gm867	
Am993	Am1031	Am973
		Cm1006
		Gm1123
$m^1acp^3\Psi1210$	$m^1acp^3\Psi1248$	$m^1acp^3\Psi1187$
Um1250	Um1288	
Um1288	Um1326	Um1265
Gm1290	Gm1328	Gm1267
Am1345	Am1383	
Cm1353	Cm1391	
Um1400	Um1442	
	(Gm1447)	
Gm1448	Gm1490	Gm1425
		Gm1570
m^7G1597	m^7G1639	m^7G1573
	(Um1668)	

TABLE IV (Continued)

X. laevis	Human	S. carlsbergensis
Am1636	Am1678	
Cm1661	Cm1703	Cm1637
Um1761	Um1804	
m^{6}A1789	m^{6}A1832	
m$^6_2$A1807	m$^6_2$A1850	m$^6_2$A1779
m$^6_2$A1808	m$^6_2$A1851	m$^6_2$A1780

^{a} The table contains all of the methylated nucleotides in X. laevis SSU rRNA (except for an unplaced partially methylated Um), all of those in human SSU rRNA (except for an unplaced partially methylated Cm) (35 for both species), and all except two of those in S. carlsbergensis (Table III of 3; see also 22). Nucleotides at homologous sites in the sequences are on the same lines in the table. The two nucleotides in parentheses in the human list are partially methylated. Where gaps appear in the X. laevis list, the same nucleotide is present as in mammals, but is unmethylated, except that Um1668 in human is replaced by C1626 (unmethylated) in X. laevis.

(18) and in rat SSU rRNA (19). Almost all of the same sites are methylated in rabbit SSU rRNA (21).

Table IV also gives the locations of all except one or two methyl groups in yeast SSU rRNA (3). Note that, although there are fewer methyl groups in yeast SSU rRNA than in vertebrates, some nucleotides that are unmethylated in vertebrates are methylated in yeast.

Table V lists the pseudouridines whose locations are known in mammalian SSU rRNA.

Figure 2 shows the locations of the modified nucleotides in mammalian (human) SSU rRNA. The distributions are shown in summarized form in Fig. 3. The distributions are nonuniform, with clusters of methyl groups and pseudouridines. Moreover, the patterns of methyl and pseudouridine clustering do not coincide: methyls are clustered mainly in the 5′ and 3′ regions of the molecule, whereas the greatest cluster of pseudouridines is in the central region. The few extra methyl groups in human and other mammalian SSU rRNAs relative to X. laevis are mainly in the 5′ region of the molecule (Table IV).

The local environments of the modification sites in the sequence and the relation to secondary structure, including domains, are discussed in Sections IV and V. It is shown in Section V that the partial separation of 2′-O-methyl and pseudouridine clusters has interesting consequences in the overall conformation.

TABLE V
PSEUDOURIDINES LOCATED IN MAMMALIAN SSU
rRNA (HUMAN NUMBERING SYSTEM)[a]

Ψ44	Ψ918
Ψ46	Ψ one of 966–969
Ψ105	Ψ1003 or 1004
Ψ109 or 110	Ψ1056
Ψ119 or 120	Ψ1081
Ψ two of 218–220	Ψ1174
Ψ one of 571–573	Ψ1238 or 1239
Ψ681	Ψ1243 or 1244
Ψ688 or 689	m^{1}acp^{3}Ψ1248
Ψ801	Ψ1367 or 1368
Ψ814	Ψ1444 or 1445
Ψ815	Ψ1625
Ψ822 or 823	Ψ1642
Ψ863	Ψ one of 1690–1692
Ψ866	

[a] The pseudouridines were located by matching oligonucleotide data from rat (19) supported in some instances from human SSU rRNA (16, 17a) to the complete sequence derived from rDNA (see 38 for details of the matching). The rat and human sequences differ at only a few points (35a, 35c), none of which correspond to pseudouridine-containing oligonucleotides. Since the SSU methylation patterns are evidently identical between several mammals, it can be assumed provisionally that this is true also for pseudouridine. About eight pseudouridines, in small RNase T$_1$ products, remain to be located in the sequence.

C. LSU rRNA Methylation Sites

Table VI lists most of the methylation sites in *X. laevis* and human LSU rRNA (including 5.8-S rRNA). Almost 60 of the 70–72 methylation sites have been located. Of the remaining 12 or so that are currently unlocated, several are in the short T$_1$ products (G)-Am-G and (G)-Gm-G that occur several times per molecule. The regions where these occur have been determined in *X. laevis* (33) but the precise sites of occurrence in the sequences are not yet known.

```
                                        m        Ψ Ψ
UACCUGGUUG AUCCUGCCAG UAGCAUAUGC UUGUCUCAAA GAUUAAGCCA UGCAUGUCUA    60
                        — 76i —                              C  G     60


                                        m        Ψ     Ψ        m  Ψ
AGUACGCACG GCCGGUACAG UGAAACUGCG AAUGGCUCAU UAAAUCAGUU AUGGUUCCUU   120
                        - -- 93 ·····— -- 9 — — 20 -   120

m
UGGUCGCUCG CUCCUCUCCU ACUUGGAUAA CUGUGGUAAU UCUAGAGCUA AUACAUGCCG   180
A       - -- A   GU                                                 177


          C   C   U   GG C              ΨΨ
ACGGGCGCUG ACCCCCUUCG CGGGGGGGAU GCGUGCAUUU AUCAGAUCAA AACCAACCCG   240
A             ----  ----A         — 71 —    C          U           229


       C UC    U              U
GUCAGCCCCU CUCCGGCCCC GGCCGGGGGG CGGGCGCCGG CGGCUUUGGU GACUCUAGAU   300
  --G    C  -----  ---  -  ------  ------    C                      266


AACCUCGGGC CGAUCGCACG CCCCCCGUGG CGGCGACGAC CCAUUCGAAC GUCUGCCCUA   360
                      U    -   A          U A    G U               325


UCAACUUUCG AUGGUAGUCG CCGUGCCUAC CAUGGUGACC ACGGGUGACG GGGAAUCAGG   420
              C UU  U C                     A                      385


        m          m
GUUCGAUUCC GGAGAGGGAG CCUGAGAAAC GGCUACCACA UCCAAGGAAG GCAGCAGGCG   480
                                             m          m          445


     m
CGCAAAUUAC CCACUCCCGA CCCGGGGAGG UAGUGACGAA AAAUAACAAU ACAGGACUCU   540
                   G        m   m   m                              505


UUCGAGGCCC UGUAAUUGGA AUGAGUCCAC UUUAAAUCCU UUAACGAGGA UCCAUUGGAG   600
                              Ψ   m               m                565
                               A      — 112 —              U


m                   m                    m
GGCAAGUCUG GUGCCAGCAG CCGCGGUAAU UCCAGCUCCA AUAGCGUAUA UUAAAGUUGC   660
                                                    70i            625


      m                Ψ m    Ψ
UGCAGUUAAA AAGCUCGUAG UUGGAUCUUG GGAGCGGGCG GGCGGUCCGC CGCGAGGCGA   720
                      — 1— --23 —         U  A  U                G  685


U
GCCACCGCCC GUCCCCGCCC CUUGCCUCUC GGCGCCCCCU CGAUGCUCUU AGCUGAGUGU   780
 U     U        A     -                 U C              GA        744


                 m m  Ψ           ΨΨ      Ψ
CCCGCGGGGC CCGAAGCGUU UACUUUGAAA AAAUUAGAGU GUUCAAAGCA GGCCCGAGCC   840
-                     — 34 — — 94 —      -58 C        - C U        802


                     U  Ψm*
GCCUGGAUAC CGCAGCUAGG AAUAAUGGAA UAGGACCGCG GUUCUAUUUU GUUGGUUUUC   900
UU                    — 54/56 —            UC                      862


             Ψ
GGAACUGAGG CCAUGAUUAA GAGGGACGGC CGGGGGCAUU CGUAUUGCGC CGCUAGAGGU   960
G                     — 38 —                          U            922
```

FIG. 2. (*continued*)

```
        Ψ                              Ψ
GAAAUUCUUG GACCGGCGCA AGACGGACCA GAGCGAAAGC AUUUGCCAAG AAUGUUUUCA   1020
——— 51 ———           A          A          ——— 24 ———                982

           m                       Ψ
UUAAUCAAGA ACGAAAGUCG GAGGUUCGAA GACGAUCAGA UACCGUCGUA GUUCCGACCA   1080
                                  - —44 —                   —— 99    1042

Ψ          U
UAAACGAUGC CGACCGGCGA UGCGGCGGCG UUAUUCCCAU GACCCGCCGG GCAGCUUCCG   1140
— 99 —        UA        C        ——— 70ii ———          A            1102

                                    Ψ
GGAAACCAAA GUCUUUGGGU UCCGGGGGGA GUAUGGUUGC AAAGCUGAAA CUUAAAGGAA   1200
                                 —12—                                1162

                                             (amΨ)
                                    Ψ      Ψ  Ψ
UUGACGGAAG GGCACCACCA GGAGUGGAGC CUGCGGCUUA AUUUGACUCA ACACGGGAAA   1260
                                  ——— 35 ——— - — 102 ———              1222

                        m
CCUCACCCGG CCCGGACACG GACAGGAUUG ACAGAUUGAU AGCUCUUUCU CGAUUCCGUG   1320
                        A                                   U        1282

  m  m                                     Ψ
GGUGGUGGUG CAUGGCCGUU CUUAGUUGGU GGAGCGAUUU GUCUGGUUAA UUCCGAUAAC   1380
                                            ———52ii———                1342

  m         m
GAACGAGACU CUGGCAUGCU AACUAGUUAC GCGACCCCCG AGCGGUCGGC GUCCCCAAC   1440
            CUC                             -          ———— 113      1398

_m  Ψ  m*
UUCUUAGAGG GACAAGUGGC GUUCAGCCAC CCGAGAUUGA GCAAUAACAG GUCUGUGAUG   1500
——— 113 ———                      A          C                        1458

CCCUUAGAUG UCCGGGGCUG CACGCGCGCU ACACUGACUG GCUCAGCGUG UGCCUACCCU   1560
                                 AC       A          U               1518

ACGCCGGCAG GCGCGGGUAA CCCGUUGAAC CCCAUUCGUG AUGGGGAUCG GGGAUUGCAA   1620
G          A        U          C          G          A          106  1578

   Ψ             m7   Ψ                             *
UUAUUCCCCA UGAACGAGGA AUUCCCAGUA AGUGCGGGUC AUAAGCUUGC GUUGAUUAAG   1680
— 106 —              — 86 —                         C          m     1638

            Ψ                      m
UCCCUGCCCU UUGUACACAC CGCCCGUCGC UACUACCGAU UGGAUGGUUU AGUGAGGCCC   1740
——— 41vii ———                                                 U      1698

UCGGAUCGGC CCCGCCGGGG UCGGCCCACG GCCCUGGCGG AGCGCUGAGA AGACGGUCGA   1800
                      C-                    C          A    A        1757

   m                                            m6   m6
ACUUGACUAU CUAGAGGAAG UAAAAGUCGU AACAAGGUUU CCGUAGGUGA ACCUGCGGAA   1860
                               m6                                    1817

GGAUCAUUA                                                            1869
                                                                     1826
```

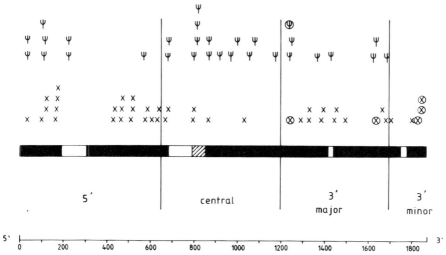

FIG. 3. Summary diagram showing the locations of methyl groups and known pseudouridine residues in mammalian SSU rRNA, from the data in Fig. 2. In the upper section, crosses denote 2′-O-methyl groups, circled crosses denote base-methyl groups, and Ψ symbols denote identified pseudouridines. The circled Ψ is the hypermodified nucleotide m¹acp³Ψ. In the central bar, white regions represent the major eukaryotic expansion segments. The stippled region in the second expansion segment is highly conserved among eukaryotes, but is more complex in secondary structure than the corresponding prokaryotic region (see Fig. 5). Vertical lines indicate domain boundaries. The domains are numbered below the central bar. Adapted from Maden and Wakeman (38).

FIG. 2. Locations of methyl groups and identified pseudouridine residues in mammalian SSU rRNA. The principal sequence is the human SSU sequence in 35a and 38, except that C in position 140 in that sequence is replaced here by U, which appears to be the usual nucleotide (38a). Standard letters above the human sequence indicate definite differences in rat, from the data compilation in 35a. Letters below the sequence indicate differences in *Xenopus laevis*. (V signs indicate extra nucleotides in the rat sequence with respect to human; dashes represent deletions in *Xenopus* with respect to human.) 2′-O-Methylation sites are indicated by m superscripts. Most 2′-O-methylations occur in all three species but those with asterisks occur only in mammals. Base methylations in all three species are as indicated at human positions 1248, 1639, 1832, 1850, and 1851; see also Table IX. Ψ denotes pseudouridine residues identified in mammalian rRNA: a bar above the sequence signifies that one of the indicated uracil residues is pseudouridine. Bars and numbers below the sequence designate pseudouridine-containing RNase-T_1 oligonucleotides, tabulated in 38 and taken originally from 19. About eight pseudouridines in mammalian SSU rRNA remain to be located. Pseudouridines have not yet been systematically located in *Xenopus* SSU rRNA.

TABLE VI
IDENTIFIED METHYLATED NUCLEOTIDES IN LSU rRNA[a]

X. laevis	Human	S. carlsbergensis
5.8 S		
(Um14)	(Um14)	
Gm75	Gm75	
LSU		
m^1A961	m^1A1302	m^1A643
Am965	Am1306	Am647
		Cm648
Cm979	Cm1320	
Gm1186	Gm1501	Gm803
Am1188	Am1503	Am805
Am1198	Am1513	Am815
		Gm865
Am1522	Am1849	Am1131
Cm1844	Cm2328	Cm1435
Am1586	Am2340	Am1447
Gm1587	Gm2341	Gm1448
Cm1588	Cm2342	
Um1908	Um2392	
Cm1915	Cm2399	
Gm1917	Gm2401	
Am2325 or 2327	Am2764 or 2766	
Um2337		
Cm2340	Cm2781	
Am2351	Am2792	
	Cm2801	
Um2372	Um2814	Um1886
Cm2397	Cm2838	
		m^1A2140
Cm2863	Cm3670	Cm2195
Am2880	Am3687	
Am2886	Am3693	Am2218
Gm2906	Gm3713	
Am2922	Am3729	Am2254
mC2944	mC3751	mC2276
		Am2278
Am2947	Am3754	Am2279
		Um2415
Cm2970	Cm3777	
Um2980	Um3787	
Am2987	Am3794	
Am2992	Am3799	
Cm3031	Cm3838	
Cm3049	Cm3856	
Um3087	Um3894	
Gm3106	Gm3913	
Gm3167	Gm4010	
		Um2631
m^6A3341 or 3342	m^6A4179 or 4180	mA2637?

TABLE VI (*Continued*)

X. laevis	Human	S. carlsbergensis
Um3349	Um4187	
Gm3350	Gm4188	
Um3430	Um4266	Um2726
		Gm2788
Gm3496	Gm4330	Gm2790
		Um2840
Gm3552		
mC circa 3570	mC circa 4403	
Gm3621	Gm4454	
Um3625	Um4458	Um2918
Gm2626	Gm4459	Gm2919
Am3650	Am4483	Am2943
		Cm2945
m^{3}U3657	m^{3}U4490	
Cm3663	Cm4496	
Am3695 or 3698	Am4528 or 4531	
Am3717	Am4550	
	Gm4578	
Um3747	Um4580	
Gm3750	Gm4583	
Gm3764	Gm4597	
Cm4032		

28 S tentatively identified

Cm3003 or 3004	Cm3810 or 3811	
Cm3179 or 3182	Cm4022 or 4025	
Cm3583	Cm4416	

[a] The table contains all except about 11–13 of the methylated nucleotides in X. *laevis* and human LSU rRNA (36 for both species) and all except 13 of those in S. *carlsbergensis* (37). Nucleotides at homologous sites in the sequences are on the same lines in the table. Um14 in 5.8-S rRNA is fractionally methylated. Most of the unplaced methylated nucleotides in X. *laevis* LSU rRNA have been mapped to within general regions of the sequence (33, 36), but have so far yielded insufficient flanking sequence data for unique localization. These unplaced nucleotides are as follows: between the 5′ end and *Xenopus* position 842, Am; between 1063–1317, Gm; between 1317–1840, Cm; between 1840–2258, Am; between 2258–2644, Gm; between 2644–2840, Gm; between 2840–3360, Gm; between 3360–3605, Gm(×2). Human LSU rRNA contains similar but unmapped methylated nucleotides. There is probably another Am and there are probably 2–3 further Gm residues in the respective sequences (Table III or 36). The few pseudouridines that have so far been located are in oligonucleotides that also contain methyl groups and are at the following X. *laevis* (and human) positions: 1200 (1515); 3627 (4460) (in Um-Gm-Ψ); 3695 (4492). The numbering systems used here are according to 30 (X. *laevis*), 32 (human), and 37 (S. *carlsbergensis*). The X. *laevis* and human sequences may require renumbering when a few uncertainties in the complete sequences have been resolved.

In *Xenopus* and human LSU rRNA, there are three sites where two or more 2'-O-methyl groups occur on adjacent nucleotides: Am-Gm-Cm; Um-Gm; and Um-Gm-Ψ. These (Table VI) are at human positions 2340–2342, 4187–4188, and 4458–4460, and at the corresponding *Xenopus* locations.

Thirty of the 43 yeast LSU rRNA methyl groups have been located (37) as also shown in the table. As was noted above for SSU rRNA, although there are fewer methyl groups overall in yeast LSU rRNA than in vertebrate LSU rRNA, some nucleotides that are unmethylated in vertebrates are methylated in yeast.

Only a very few pseudouridines in LSU rRNA have yet been located, as noted in the legend to the table.

The distribution of known methyl groups along the sequences of *X. laevis* and human LSU rRNA is shown in summarized form in Fig. 4. The distributions along the aligned sequences are shown in detail in Fig. 3 of 36. That figure is not reproduced here for reasons of space, but the distribution in the human sequence is given in a secondary structure diagram (Fig. 7, below). The distribution of located methyl groups is almost identical between human and *Xenopus* LSU rRNAs. The tendency for clustering into certain regions is even more marked than in SSU rRNA. The most striking feature of the methyl group clustering is in relation to the pattern of core sequences and expansion segments, as outlined below.

D. Clustering of Methyl Groups in the Conserved Core of rRNA

Eukaryotic rRNA may be described as consisting of "core" sequences and "expansion" segments. Core sequences give rise to secondary structure features that are broadly homologous across the three major kingdoms: eubacteria, archaebacteria, and eukaryotes. These sequences have generally evolved slowly and the secondary structure elements to which they give rise include the major long-range interactions between regions that are distant in the primary structure. The conserved structural core is presumed to contain the working machinery of rRNA. The expansion segments are specific to eukaryotic rRNA: they have evolved more rapidly than the core segments; they are (G+C)-rich in vertebrates and are longer in mammals than in lower vertebrates (30, 39; see 40 for representative sequence alignments); hence they are responsible for the different lengths of LSU rRNA from different species, a phenomenon originally observed by Loening (41). [The larger expansion segments in vertebrate LSU rRNA correspond

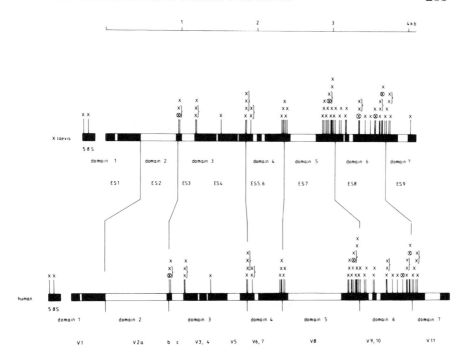

Fig. 4. Distribution of methyl groups in known locations in *X. laevis* and human LSU rRNA. Crosses denote 2'-*O*-methyl groups, circled crosses denote base-methyl groups. Vertical lines connecting the crosses to the bar diagrams indicate the degree of clustering of methyl groups in some regions of the sequences. Brackets indicate the presence of two or more methyl groups within a single T_1 oligonucleotide. In the bar diagrams, the black sections represent conserved core sequences and the white regions represent eukaryotic expansion segments, designated ES1, ES2, etc. in *61* and V1, V2a, etc. in *40*. All sections are drawn to scale, except that the second internal transcribed spacer (ITS 2) which separates 5.8-S rRNA from the major LSU sequence in ribosomal precursor RNA is represented as an arbitrary gap. Domain boundaries are shown as vertical lines. The diagram shows all the methyl groups whose locations are listed in Table VI. For the precise locations of these methyl groups in the human sequence see the secondary structure diagram in Fig. 7. About 11–13 methyl groups remain to be located, including one in domain 1. Diagram adapted from Maden (*36*).

to the well-known hairpin loops that were first visualized by electron microscopy (*42–45*), as shown in a recent systematic correlation between the electron microscopy data and sequence data (*46*).]

All of the methyl groups that have so far been located in LSU rRNA are in core sequences (black in Fig. 4). In fact, 21 of the methylated nucleotides in *Xenopus* and human LSU rRNA are at "invariant" sites of the core regions in the alignment of Gorski *et al.* (*40*). (The term "invariant" in this context indicates that the same base is present in LSU rRNA of man, mouse, *X. laevis, S. carlsbergensis,* and *E. coli.*) The methyl groups at invariant sites are as follows, using the human numbering system (Table VI):

Gm1501, Am1503, Am2340, Cm2342, Am2792, Cm3670, Am3687, Gm3713, Am3729, Am3754, Cm3777, Ψm3787, Am3794, Cm3838, Um3894, Cm4416, Um4458, Gm4459, Am4483, m^3U4490, Gm4597

Most of the other methylated nucleoties are within a three-base distance of an invariant site. It is likely that the remaining, so-far-unlocated methyl groups are also in core sequences, as the small catalogue of unplaced methylated oligonucleotides in LSU rRNA is very similar between *X. laevis* and man (*36;* see also the legend to Table VI) despite considerable differences in length between the *Xenopus* and human expansion segments.

It should be noted that the presence of a methyl group at an invariant nucleotide does not necessarily imply phylogenetic conservation of methylation itself, even among eukaryotes. This is reflected in the overall statistic that the total number of methyl groups is lower in yeast than in vertebrates. It will be noticed that several invariant nucleotides that are methylated in vertebrates, listed above, are not methylated in yeast (Table VI).

The SSU rRNA methyl groups are also concentrated predominantly in core sequences. In human SSU rRNA the following methyls are on nucleotides that are invariant or almost so in the eukaryotic, archaebacterial, and eubacterial sequences in the database in *7:*

Am159, Um172, Cm462, Am484, Am590, Gm601, Um627, Gm644, Am668, Gm683, m^7G1639, Cm1703, m^6A1832, m^6_2 A1850, m^6_2A1851

In fact the great majority of the methylation sites listed in Table IV are on nucleotides that are conserved among all known eukaryotic sequences. Again, however, the presence of a methyl at an invariant nucleotide does not imply phylogenetic conservation of methylation itself.

The expansion segments amount to a smaller proportion of the total sequence in SSU than in LSU rRNA. The shaded region in Fig. 3 is not clearly homologous to prokaryotic SSU rRNA but is quite highly conserved among eukaryotes and contains a few methyl groups. (This region is discussed again in relation to secondary structure; see Section V.)

The pseudouridines that have been located are also mainly in core regions, although interestingly, again, several are in the "conserved" SSU eukaryotic-specific region in Fig. 3.

Clearly, the modification sites are somehow generated within structural features of the conserved, mainly core regions. With these considerations in mind, we turn to the local environments of the modified nucleotides in the primary and secondary structure.

IV. Diversity of Modification Sites in Relation to Local Primary Structure

In contrast to the generalization that modified nucleotides occur in the conserved core sequences, there is great diversity and no unifying feature of the modification sites at the level of primary structure. This diversity is characteristic of each of the three major classes of modification, as described below.

A. Diversity of 2'-O-Methylation Sites

Early evidence that the 2'-O-methylated sites occur in numerous different local sequence environments came from the observation that all 16 possible alkali-stable 2'-O-methylated dinucleotides are present in alkaline hydrolysates of mammalian rRNA (12, 13). A novel way of describing the diversity of methylation sites is shown in Table VII. Of the 64 theoretically possible trinucleotide sequences in which the central nucleotide is 2'-O-methylated, some 46 are actually present in various frequencies in vertebrate rRNA as revealed by sequencing.

In an attempt to search for possible patterns and preferences in 2'-O-methylation sites, the data in Table VII have been further summarized in Table VIII into purine–pyrimidine combinations. 2'-O-Methylated triplets of the type R-Rm-R are the most abundant, followed by those containing two purines and one pyrimidine, followed by those with three pyrimidines, and finally those with two pyrimidines and one purine. However, no combinations are excluded at this purine–pyrimidine level of grouping, and therefore no clearcut rules emerge.

When the sequence data encompassing the 2'-O-methylation sites are extended beyond the trinucleotide range, there is very little duplication. (G-A-Am-C-G occurs twice in SSU rRNA and once in LSU rRNA.) The trinucleotides G-Am-G and G-Gm-G, which are multiply represented in LSU rRNA, occur in several different, larger pancreatic

TABLE VII
Frequencies of Triplets Encompassing 2'-O-Methylation Sites in Human rRNA[a]

SSU

1st	3rd	Um	Cm	Am	Gm
U	U	3	1	2	
	C		1	2	
	A	3	1	2	
	G			1	2
C	U				
	C			1	
	A				
	G		1		
A	U	1		2	
	C			2	1
	A	1			1
	G		2		3
G	U			1	1
	C		1	1	
	A	2		1	
	G	1	1	1	1

LSU

1st	3rd	Um	Cm	Am	Gm
U	U	1	2		3
	C		1		1
	A				
	G	1		1	1
C	U	1	1	1	
	C		1		1
	A				
	G			2	1
A	U		1	2	1
	C		1	3	1
	A		1	2	2
	G	2		1	1
G	U	1	2	2	2
	C	3	1		
	A		3		
	G		1	4	7

SSU plus LSU

1st	3rd	Um	Cm	Am	Gm
U	U	4	3	2	3
	C		2		1
	A			2	
	G	4		2	3
C	U	1	1	1	
	C		1	1	1
	A				
	G		1	2	1
A	U	1	1	4	1
	C		1	5	2
	A	1	1	2	3
	G	2	2	1	4
G	U	1	2	3	3
	C		2		
	A	2	3	1	
	G	4	2	5	8

	Um	Cm	Am	Gm	Um	Cm	Am	Gm	Um	Cm	Am	Gm
	11	7	13	9	9	15	18	21	20	22	31	30
Total 2'-O-methyl different triplets				40				63+4				103+4
	7	7	9	6	6	11	9	11	9	13	13	11
Total *different* triplets				29				37				46

[a]The triplets are written in the standard "genetic code" form except that the second nucleotide of each triplet is 2'-O-methylated. The numbers of the different 2'-O-methylated triplets are given (e.g., U-Um-U does not occur in SSU rRNA but U-Um-C occurs three times). The locations of the triplets in the sequences are in Figs. 2 and 7; see also the oligonucleotide data in 35 and 36. C-Cm-C in SSU rRNA is fractional and unlocated. The LSU grid includes two 2'-O-methylated nucleotides in 5.8-S rRNA and also includes several unlocated methyl groups, in particular G-Am-G (three unlocated occurrences) and G-Gm-G (seven occurrences) but excludes four 2'-O-methylated nucleotides that cannot yet be assigned unambiguously to specific triplets. These are denoted "+4" on the "total 2'-O-methyl" line. Multiply-methylated tracts in LSU rRNA are treated as in the following example: G-Um-Gm-U is assigned one occurrence each to G-Um-G and U-Gm-U.

267

TABLE VIII
DISTRIBUTION OF 2'-*O*-METHYLATION SITES IN
HUMAN rRNA AMONG PURINE- AND PYRIMIDINE-
CONTAINING TRIPLETS[a]

R-Rm-R	24
R-Rm-Y	18
R-Ym-R	17
Y-Rm-R	12
Y-Ym-Y	11
R-Ym-Y	8
Y-Rm-Y	7
Y-Ym-R	6

[a] The data are summarized from Table VII and include all 2'-*O*-methylation sites in human rRNA except for four that cannot yet be assigned unambiguously to specific triplets.

RNase products and hence in different larger sequences. Most of the yeast 2'-*O*-methylation sites are also in unique oligonucleotides (22).

B. Diversity of Base Methylation Sites

The relatively small number of methylated bases also occur in an array of unique sequences (Table IX). Most of the base-methylated nucleotides were identified in specific oligonucleotides in HeLa cell rRNA as described in 15, with reliance on previous characterization of the free bases (47). (The positions of substitution of the two base-methylated cytosines in LSU rRNA are currently uncharacterized.) Most of the base-methylated nucleotides in yeast were identified in 22. The hypermodified nucleoside 1-methyl-3(α-amino-α-carboxypropyl)-pseudouridine (symbolized $m^1acp^3\Psi$ by analogy to $acp^3\Psi$ in tRNA, 48) was first identified by Saponara and Enger (29). It was then identified in a specific oligonucleotide in yeast and HeLa SSU rRNA (49). [This hypermodified nucleoside has been abbreviated $am\Psi$ (18, 65) or sometimes $m^1cap^3\Psi$ (19)].

These base-methylated sequences are totally conserved among the vertebrates for which sequence data are available, and most are conserved between vertebrates and yeast.

C. Contrast with DNA Methylation

The diversity of sequences that are methylated in eukaryotic rRNA contrasts greatly with the methylation pattern of DNA. In vertebrates, DNA methylation occurs on the C-5 atom of cytosines, generally

TABLE IX
DIVERSITY OF SEQUENCES ENCOMPASSING
BASE-METHYLATION SITES IN VERTEBRATE rRNA
(HUMAN NUMBERING)[a]

SSU rRNA

1248	G-A-C-m¹acp³Ψ-C-A-A-C-A-C-G[e]
1639	G-m⁷G-A-A-U-Ψ-C-C-C-A-G[e]
1832	G-U-A-m⁶A-C-A-A-G
1850,1	G-m²⁶A-m²⁶A-C-C-U-G[e]

LSU rRNA

1302[b]	G-m¹A-A-A-C-Am-C-G[f]
3754	G-C-mC-A-A-Am-U-G[g]
4179 or 4180[c]	G-U-(m⁶A,A)-C-G
~ 4403[d]	G-A-U-C-C-U-U-C-G; one mC
4490	G-m³U-U-Ψ-A-G

[a] The table lists the T_1 RNase products from vertebrate rRNA that contain base-methylated nucleotides, together with the locations of the methylated bases in the human numbering system. All vertebrate species so far examined yield the same base-methylated T_1 products.

[b] It was not certain in 36 which of the three adjacent A residues is base-methylated, but it is likely to be the first one by homology with the same sequence in *S. carlsbergensis* (37).

[c] It is not yet known which of the two A residues is methylated.

[d] It is not yet known which of three nearby C residues is methylated.

[e] These three sequences are present and similarly modified in *S. carlsbergensis* rRNA.

[f] This sequence in *S. carlsbergensis* contains Am-Cm-G.

[g] This sequence in *S. carlsbergensis* contains Am-Um-G.

within the diad-symmetrical sequence CpG (50). (DNA, which lacks 2′ hydroxyl groups, is not susceptible to sugar methylation.)

D. Diversity of Pseudouridine-Containing Sites

Pseudouridines also occur in a wide variety of local sequence environments. This conclusion comes from the analysis of pseudouridine-containing oligonucleotides in rat SSU rRNA (19) and extensions of the original oligonucleotide sequences that were obtained by matching with the complete SSU rRNA base sequence derived from rDNA (38; see Section III). Nine of the 16 possible trinucleotides in which the central nucleotide is pseudouridine have so far been identified from the rat SSU rRNA data, as summarized in Table X. It is likely that the range will be extended when the remaining pseudouridine-containing sequences in SSU and LSU rRNA become characterized.

In summary, there is no obvious evidence for consensus recognition sequences for any of the three main types of nucleotide modification in eukaryotic rRNA: 2'-O-methylation, base methylation, or pseudouridine.

V. Modified Nucleotides in the Secondary Structure

Given the great diversity of modification sites at the level of primary structure, the question arises whether there are unifying features

TABLE X
FREQUENCIES OF TRIPLETS ENCOMPASSING
PSEUDOURIDINES AT KNOWN SITES IN
MAMMALIAN SSU rRNA[a]

	Ψ	
U		U
	2	C
	3	A
		G
C		U
	2[b]	C
		A
		G
A	1	U
	2	C
	2	A
	2	G
G	1	U
	1	C
		A
		G

[a] Of the ~ 38 pseudouridines detected by analysis of all the T_1 oligonucleotides from rat SSU rRNA (19), these 16 can currently be located exactly in the sequence (38) (Fig. 2).

[b] Includes the hypermodified nucleotide $m^1acp^3\Psi$.

at the level of secondary structure. For example, one might imagine that 2'-O-methylation sites are recognized for modification through presenting the 2'-hydroxyl group at a particular angle with respect to the local conformation. Similarly, pseudouridines might be formed at a specific type of recognition site in the conformation. Base-methylation sites, being fewer in number and different chemically from 2'-O-methylations, might follow individual rules of their own. In this section the locations of the modification sites in the rRNA conformation are examined.

Much effort has gone into refining secondary structure models for SSU and LSU rRNA from many species. There is now substantial agreement as to the main secondary structure features of the conserved core regions, especially the long-range interactions including those that define domain boundaries. As noted above, most of the modified nucleotides in SSU rRNA and all of those so far located in LSU rRNA are in the conserved core regions.

A. SSU rRNA

Figure 5 shows a secondary structure model for human SSU rRNA. The model conforms in most of its interactions to a recent model for rabbit SSU rRNA (51), whose primary structure is closely similar to that of human SSU rRNA. The rabbit model is based in turn on a phylogenetically derived model (1) but includes proposed secondary structures for the eukaryotic expansion segments, not included in the phylogenetic (1) model. Although most of the interactions in Fig. 5 are those of the Rairkar model, parts of the central domain are based on an earlier model (52) for *Xenopus* rRNA, particularly the long-range interaction between nucleotides 675-684/1025-1034, which is a key feature in the earlier model. In Fig. 5 the helices are generally numbered according to the Brimacombe (52) system; this is useful when describing the path of SSU rRNA in the small subunit (see below).

SSU rRNA comprises structural domains defined by phylogenetically conserved long-range interactions. In the human model the domain-defining interactions are as follows:

5' domain	22-31/643-652 (helix 3)
5' plus central domains	12-15/1196-1199 (helix 2)
3' major domain	1204-1214/1685-1694 (helix 28)
3' minor domain	3' to the 3' major domain

These interactions contribute to or are close to a system of base-pairing

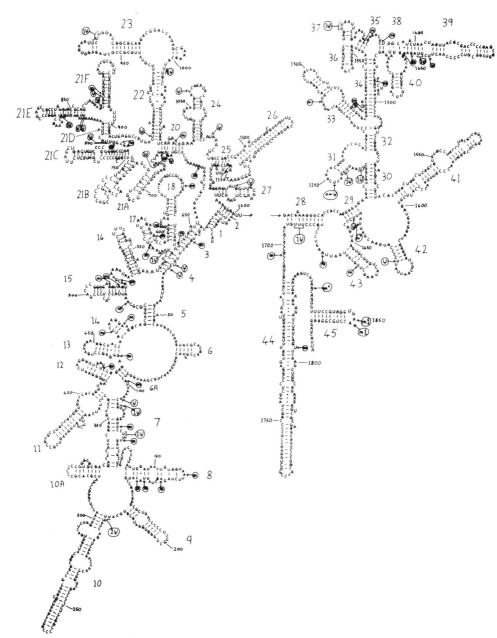

FIG. 5. Secondary structure diagram of human SSU rRNA with locations of modified nucleotides. The model is based on 51 and 52 (see Section V,A). Small arabic numerals denote nucleotide numbering from the 5′ end; large arabic numerals denote

termed the "pseudoknot" (53), which holds the origins of the domains together in the overall conformation.

One further general point may be noted. Several of the putative helices are quite short or are destabilized by imperfections (for example, helices 14, 31, 35–38). Also G·U pairs are quite common. References will be made to these features in the following description of the environments of the modified nucleotides.

1. 2'-O-METHYLATION

2'-O-Methylation sites occur in all domains, with the largest number in the 5' domain. It is immediately apparent that 2'-O-methylations occur in a wide variety of local secondary structures (Fig. 5). To illustrate this diversity in local secondary structure environments, a "guided tour" may be taken of the 2'-O-methylation sites in the 5' domain.

Am27. This occurs in the 5' limb of the long-range interaction (helix 3) that defines domain 1. It occurs internally in the helix. However, the next nucleotide downstream is the U residue of a conserved U·G pair. Thus the features of this Am are its participation in a long-range interaction and its location next to a U·G pair.

Am99. This occurs at the start of a short single-stranded region at the intersection of several short or imperfect helical elements: 6A, 7, 11, and 12.

Um116 and Um 121. These occur in the 5' limb of the moderately long-range helix 7. There has been some difficulty in modelling a best fit to account for the various phylogenetic base-pairing possibilities in this region. In the mammalian version shown in Fig. 5, Um116 is in a short base-paired segment, and Um121 is in a short looped-out tract. These proposed secondary structure environments should still be regarded as tentative in detail.

*Am159, Am166, *Um172, and *Cm174. These four methylated nucleotides occur in a region that can be written in the form of a highly imperfect local hairpin helix (number 8) as shown. Remarkably, the three starred nucleotides are methylated in mammals but not in *Xeno-*

---

helix numbering, generally according to 52. The locations of the methyl groups are indicated by a circled "m" connected by an arrow to the respective nucleotide; "m" on its own denotes 2'-O-methylation; m^7, etc. denotes base methylation (see also Table IX). Ψ connected by an arrow to a U residue denotes pseudouridine. 1Ψ (or 2Ψ) connected by an arrow to two or more nearby U residues indicates that one (or two) of these is pseudouridine.

pus, although the sequence comprising the entire helix is conserved between *Xenopus* and mammals. [The three mammalian-specific methylations underlie differences between the mammalian and *Xenopus* SSU rRNA methyl fingerprints in *18;* they were first located in the mammalian sequence in *21* (see also *35*).] Am159 is at the tip of the helix, the other three are in the 3′ limb: Am166 immediately 3′ to a bulged G, Um172 immediately 5′ to a bulged A, Cm immediately 3′ to the same bulged A. Given the identity of the primary structure of the entire helix between *Xenopus* and mammals, there is no obvious local basis for the three extra methylation sites in mammals.

Um428. This occurs in the 3′ limb of the local helix 12, immediately 3′ to a bulge, and in a U·G pair. (This representation, from *51*, replaces an earlier representation of this helix in *52*.)

Gm436. This occurs at the entry to the 5′ limb of the local hairpin 13.

Cm462 and Am468. These occur in a small, imperfect local hairpin helix number 14. It is of interest that in *E. coli* the corresponding helix is perfect with four contiguous base-pairs (and unmethylated). However, in eukaryotes from *Saccharomyces* to vertebrates, the imperfections and methyl groups are conserved.

Am484. This occurs in a single-stranded region between helices 14 and 15.

Gm509 and Am512. These both occur in the 3′ limb of the imperfect local hairpin helix 15. Gm occurs immediately after a bulged A. Am occurs near the 3′ end of the helix, or in the terminal base-pair if the following G is depicted as not pairing with U (*52*).

Cm517. This is in a single-stranded region following helix 15.

Am576 and Am590. These both occur in a short region that probably represents a truncated version of *E. coli* helix 17. Different representations of this region are given in *51* and *52*. The two versions place the respective methyl groups in different local conformations. The later version (*51*) is shown in Fig. 5.

Gm601 and Um627. These occur in a large, phylogenetically highly conserved local helix, number 18, that possesses a sizeable lateral bulge in the 5′ limb and a large hairpin loop. Gm is in the lateral bulge and Um is in the hairpin loop. The general secondary structure of this imperfect hairpin is conserved between *E. coli* and eukaryotes, but *E. coli* does not possess the 2′-*O*-methylated nucleotides. There is, however, a m^7G in the hairpin loop in *E. coli*.

Gm644. This occurs just after the start of the 3′ limb of the long-range interaction, helix, 3, that defines domain 1. The base-pair in which it is involved is three base-pairs away from that in which Am27, mentioned above, is involved.

In summary, examples of 2'-O-methyl groups in domain 1 occur in long-range and local helices, in apparently single-stranded regions, and in a few instances at sites where the local secondary structure is unresolved. In the helical elements, 2'-O-methyl groups are in the 5' or 3' limbs, generally near imperfections, or occasionally in the loop of a local hairpin. Where a 2'-O-methyl group is associated with a lateral bulge, it may be (in different instances) 5', within, or 3' to the bulge.

This bewildering diversity of 2'-O-methylation sites is repeated elsewhere in SSU rRNA, although as noted above, domain 1 is the most heavily 2'-O-methylated. The distribution of 2'-O-methyl groups among the domains and among the different types of local conformational environments is summarized in Tables XI and XII.

2. BASE METHYLATIONS

The five methylated bases in SSU rRNA occur toward the 3' end of the molecule in the 3' domain. Three of them are in hairpin loops, the other two in single-stranded regions between helices.

*am*Ψ*1248.* This occurs in the 3' major domain in the loop of an unusual hairpin helix (*31*) in which three of the four base-pairs are U·G pairs. Interestingly, not only is the same modification present at the corresponding site in yeast SSU rRNA; the sequence encompassing the entire hairpin element, including the three U·G pairs is also totally

TABLE XI
MODIFIED NUCLEOTIDES AND DOMAINS IN HUMAN SSU rRNA[a]

| Domain | Numbers of nucleotides | | Located pseudouridines[b] | Total nucleotides |
	2'-O-Methyl	Base-methyl		
5'	21	0	8	652
Central	6	0	14	550
3' Major	10	2 ($m^1acp^3\Psi$, m7G)	8	481
3' Minor	2	3 (m^6A, $m_2^6A \times 2$)	0	186

[a] For simplicity the 5' domain is defined as the first 652 nucleotides, although strictly speaking, nucleotides 1–21 are not within the domain as defined by the encompassing long-range interaction. Similar simplifications are used for the other entries under "total nucleotides."

[b] Eight pseudouridines are unlocated.

TABLE XII

Methylated Nucleotides and Local Conformations in Human SSU rRNA[a]

Conformation		Total
Single-stranded link tract	Am99, Am484, Cm517, Am668, Cm797, Um799, m⁷G1639, Am1678, Cm1703, m⁶A1832	10
Long-range interaction	Am27, Um116, Um121, Gm644, Gm683, Am1031, Um1326, Gm1328, Am1383, Gm1490	10
Local helical system: 5′ limb	Gm436, Cm462, Am576, Gm601, *Gm867, Um1288, Cm1391	7
Local helical system: hairpin loop	*Am159, Um627, m¹acp³Ψ1248, m⁶₂A1850, 1851	5
Local helical system: 3′ limb	Am166, *Um172, *Cm174, Um428, Am468, Gm509, Am512, Am590, Um1442, *Gm1447, *Um1668, Um1804	12
		44

[a] Long-range interactions are defined here as including those interactions where two or more local helices separate the 5′ and 3′ limbs of the interacting tracts. They include the domain-defining interactions and several other interactions as well (see Fig. 5). Many of the methylated nucleotides in local helical systems are in bulges or irregularities: see the text and Fig. 5. Nucleotides with asterisks are methylated in human SSU rRNA but not in *Xenopus* SSU rRNA. The base-methylated nucleotides are underlined.

conserved. This is one of many instances in which U·G pairs are conserved across wide phylogenetic range in rRNA. Further examples are given under LSU rRNA, below.

m^7G1639. This occurs in a single-stranded region of the 3′ major domain in the secondary-structure model, between low helix 42 and long-range helix 29. Again, the modification and the encompassing single-stranded sequence are conserved in yeast.

m^6A. This occurs in a single-stranded region of the 3′-minor domain between helices 44 and 45. The sequence is conserved in yeast but apparently the modification is not (3) (Table IV).

m^6_2A1850 and 1851. The two adjacent dimethyl-A residues occur in the loop of the 3′ terminal hairpin helix 45. The whole structure including the two dimethyl-A residues is very highly conserved, being present and containing the two dimethyl-A residues also in prokaryotic rRNA (54).

3. Pseudouridines

Although not all pseudouridines in SSU rRNA have yet been located, there are sufficient data to generate an emerging picture. Pseudouridines that have been located occur in the greatest numbers in the central domain, with others in the 5' and 3' major domains. Pseudouridines, like 2'-O-methyl groups, occur in a wide variety of local environments, with examples in single-stranded tracts, long-range interactions, and local helical systems (Fig. 5, Table XIII).

B. Modified Nucleotides and the Path of SSU rRNA in the Small Ribosomal Subunit

Recently, two descriptions have been published of the three-dimensional arrangement of SSU rRNA in the small ribosomal subunit of *E. coli* (55, 56). Because the conserved structural core of rRNA consists of secondary-structure features common to prokaryotes and eukaryotes, it follows that much of the three-dimensional structure must be broadly similar between prokaryotes and eukaryotes. Therefore, the distribution of modified nucleotides in the three-dimensional structure of eukaryotic (specifically, human) SSU rRNA can be inferred

TABLE XIII

Pseudouridines and Local Conformations in Human SSU rRNA[a]

Conformation		Total
Single-stranded link tract	Ψ105, Ψ(688 or 689), Ψ801, Ψ1081, Ψ(1238 or 1239)	5
Long-range interaction	Ψ44, Ψ46, Ψ(109 or 110), Ψ(119 or 120) Ψ681, Ψ1643, Ψ(1690-2)	7
Local helical system: 5' limb	Ψ,Ψ(218–220), Ψ(571–573), Ψ814, Ψ815, Ψ(822 or 823), Ψ863, Ψ866, Ψ918, Ψ1174, Ψ(1243 or 1244)	11
Local helical system: hairpin loop	Ψ1056, m^{1}acp$^3\Psi$1248, Ψ(1367 or 1368)	3
Local helical system: 3' limb	Ψ(966–969), Ψ(1003 or 1004), Ψ(1444 or 1445), Ψ1625	4
Unlocated in sequence		~8
		~38

[a] Nucleotide numbers in parentheses indicate pseudouridines for which the respective T$_1$ oligonucleotide has been located in the sequence but the modification site has not yet been pinpointed within the oligonucleotide (see 38).

in outline by reference to the *E. coli* structure, a brief description of which now follows.

The three-dimensional models are based on extensive experimental evidence, including rRNA–rRNA cross-links and rRNA–protein cross-links (55), protein footprinting (56), and the centers of mass of the individual ribosomal proteins in the small subunit (57). The two models are similar in outline; they differ in several details, but the differences do not fundamentally affect the present discussion. For descriptive purposes, it is convenient to use Brimacombe's numbering system for helices (Fig. 5) and to refer to the morphological features that had previously been identified by electron microscopy (58): the head, body, cleft, and platform.

In both models the "pseudoknot," from which the three domains spring, occupies a central location in the subunit. The 5' domain comprises much of the RNA of the body of the subunit (Fig. 6). The central domain sends helices into the cleft and platform and a long helix (number 21) that extends down the length of the body. The 3' major domain is self-contained and occupies the head. The 3' minor domain has only two helices: helix 44 extends down into the body and the 3' terminal helix 45 is in the platform. The locations of single-stranded regions are broadly constrained by their bounding helices, but there is uncertainty as to the precise paths of the longer single-stranded regions. The main differences between the models concern the detailed placements and orientations of some helices. For example, helices 13 and 14 of the 5' domain are placed on the solvent side of the subunit in 55 but on the interface with the large ribosomal subunit in 56.

The eukaryotic structure must accommodate expansion segments into the above framework. The major expansion segment of the 5' domain comes after the conserved helix 8 at the base of the body. The expansion segment in helix 44 of the 3' minor domain is also accommodated at the base of the body. The eukaryotic-specific material in the central domain is more complicated and is important to this description: several helices designated 21A–F replace the long prokaryotic helix 21. It can be surmised that these helices occur in roughly the same overall region as prokaryotic helix 21, on the side of the body below the platform, but that they spread over a larger area (probably interfacing extensively with parts of the 5' domain). If this interpretation is correct, then the whole of this system of eukaryotic helices extends downward from the platform on the side of the body that faces the large subunit. Finally, some eukaryotic expansion material occurs in the 3' major domain in the head.

The locations of the three major classes of modified nucleotides can

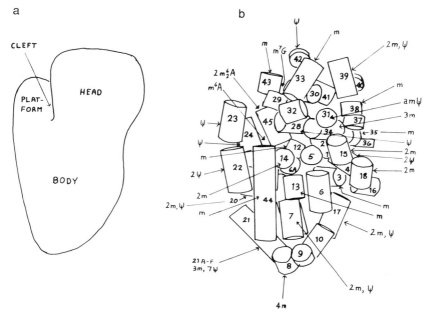

FIG. 6. Distribution of modified nucleotides in the inferred three-dimensional structure of mammalian SSU rRNA in the ribosome. The overall shape and large-scale features of the small subunit (58) are given in (a). The inferred disposition of most of the helices, viewed from the same orientation as (a) and redrawn from Fig. 4(b) of Brimacombe *et al.* (55) is shown in (b). The figure is based on *E. coli* SSU rRNA. Most of the mammalian helices in Fig. 5 correspond in their numbering and approximate sizes to the respective *E. coli* helices. The main differences are as follows. At the base of the body, mammalian helices 10 and 44 are lengthened by eukaryotic expansion segments. Also, on the lower part of the body, helix 21 of *E. coli* rRNA is replaced by the 21A-F complex in mammalian rRNA. Helices bearing one or more 2′-*O*-methyl groups are marked m, 2m, etc. Helices bearing one or more pseudouridines are marked Ψ, 2Ψ, etc. The positions of the base-methyl groups are indicated by their specific abbreviations, e.g., m^6_2 for 6-dimethyladenosine, etc. A few modified nucleotides that are in single-stranded regions adjacent to helices are indicated with their respective helices in this diagram. A few others that are relatively remote from helices are not included. Also a few helices are not well visualized in this orientation because they are buried, or on the opposite surface. For example, helix 45 is part of the platform, but this is not clearly seen in this orientation.

now be described in relation to the three-dimensional model. (See Figs. 5 and 6 and Table XIV in relation to the following description.)

2′-*O*-methyl groups are clustered principally in the body and head; there are a few in or near the cleft but none in the platform.

In the body, helix 3 near the center of the subunit contains Am27 and Gm644. Helix 12 is a related key feature: in the *E. coli* structure a

TABLE XIV

DISTRIBUTION OF MODIFIED NUCLEOTIDES IN THE INFERRED OVERALL STRUCTURE OF
MAMMALIAN SSU rRNA IN THE RIBOSOME[a]

Feature	2'-O-Methyl	Base-methyl	Located pseudouridines
Body	28	0	16
Head	10	2 ($m^1acp^3\Psi$, m^7G)	8
Cleft	2	1 (m^6A)	1
Platform	0	2 ($m_2^6A \times 2$)	5

[a] The body contains helices 1–18, 20, 21A–F (by inference from prokaryotic helix 21), and helix 44, together with the single-stranded tracts that are closely associated with these helices. The head contains helices 28–43 and their associated single-stranded regions, and is identical to the 3' major domain (Table XI), thus containing the same modified nucleotides as that domain. The platform comprises principally helices 22–24 with their associated single-stranded regions and helix 45. Insofar as the cleft is walled by parts of the above features, its component material is partly arbitrarily defined in this table. The following tracts are so assigned, being probably in the base of the cleft (see 55): helix 19 and associated single-stranded regions (including Am668), helices 25–27, the interhelix single-stranded region linking helices 28 to 44 (containing Cm1703) and the single-stranded region linking helices 44 to 45 (containing m^6A1832). Figures 5 and 6 give further information on the locations of individual modified nucleotides within the structural features.

tertiary cross-link brings helix 12 via its characteristic loop-out into proximity with a bulged G in helix 3. The loop-out occurs at the same position in eukaryotic helix 12 and immediately precedes Um428. It can therefore be inferred that Um428 in helix 12 is in close proximity to helix 3. 2'-O-Methyl groups also occur in or near several helices (14, 15, 17, 18) that spring from this central region. Other 2'-O-methyl groups occur in two conserved helices, 7 and 8, that extend consecutively down to the base of the body. Four more 2'-O-methyl groups occur in material of the central and 3' minor domains that is associated with the body: Cm797, Um799, and Gm867 in the 21D-F complex of helices in the central domain, and Um1804 in a looped-out location toward the base of helix 44 of the 3' minor domain.

Most of the 2'-O-methyl groups in the head are in a system of interconnected helices (34, 35, 38, and 39); two others (Um1668, Am1678) are in or near helix 43.

2'-O-Methyl groups in or near the cleft are Am668 and Cm1703. The latter is two bases 3' to the "universal" C1400 (E. coli numbering system) that is involved in binding the anticodon region of tRNA to the ribosome (59), and that has been shown by DNA hybridization electron microscopy to be located in the cleft (59a).

The platform helices 22, 23, and 24 and their interconnecting single-stranded tracts lack 2'-O-methyl groups. In the Brimacombe secondary structure models (52, 55), this overall structure is particularly highly conserved in its general shape between prokaryotes and eukaryotes, including the looped-out regions of the helices and the approximate lengths of the connecting single-stranded tracts. The long-range helix 20, which connects the platform helices with the helix 21 complex, does contain 2'-O-methyl groups: Gm683 and Am1031.

It is not yet possible to state with confidence which 2'-O-methyl groups are internal and which are external with respect to the overall structure of SSU rRNA in the subunit. This is due to uncertainties in the precise locations of some of the helices, in their orientations around their helical (cylindrical) axes, and the largely unknown locations of the eukaryotic ribosomal proteins. However, nuclease S_1 (EC 3.1.30.1) probing experiments (60) and more recent chemical probing experiments (51), carried out on isolated rRNA, indicate that some 2'-O-methyl groups are in protected environments whereas others are exposed. Further work is required to extend these observations, but it does appear that there is no general "inside" or "outside" rule for 2'-O-methylation in the isolated rRNA.

Methylated bases occur in the following locations. $m^1acp^3\Psi$ protrudes from the short hairpin helix 31 in the head. m^7G is in a short single-stranded region between the hairpin helix 42 and the long-range helix 29 near the topmost part of the head. m^6A is in a single-stranded region connecting the bases of helices 44 and 45, and is thus in the cleft. The m^6_2A sequence at the tip of helix 45 is on the lip of the platform overlooking the cleft. (Only a single projection of Brimacombe's model, that corresponding to Fig. 4b of 55, is shown here. The association of helix 45 with the platform is shown more clearly in 3e of 55.)

All four of these base-methylated sequences are highly sensitive to nuclease S_1 (60), consistent with their exposed locations in the model.

Pseudouridines, like 2'-O-methyl groups, are widely distributed in the model. However, as is implicit from their distribution in the primary structure (Fig. 2 and 3), the pattern of pseudouridine distribution does not closely parallel that of 2'-O-methyl groups in the three-dimensional structure. In particular, the platform helices 22, 23, and 24 contain five of the located pseudouridines. Helices 20 and the 21D to F complex contain eight more located pseudouridines. It was proposed above that the helix 21 complex extends down the side of the body below the platform. If this is correct, there is considerable clustering of pseudouridines in the platform and subplatform region of the body, which together constitute the interface with the large ribosomal sub-unit. Other pseudouridines are dispersed at various locations in the body and head, ranging from helix 7, far down in the body, to helix 42, in an exposed location at the top of the head.

The following conclusions can therefore be drawn on the basis of the reasonable assumption that mammalian SSU rRNA adopts a three-dimensional structure generally similar to that of *E. coli*. (i) 2'-O-Methyl groups are intimately interwoven into many of the conserved structural elements in the body and head; a few occur in the vicinity of the cleft but none in the platform. (ii) Base-methylated nucleotides occur in two exposed locations in the head, another occurs in the cleft, and the dimethyl-A sequence is at the tip of the platform. (iii) Pseu-douridines are widely distributed in the structure but not in parallel fashion to 2'-O-methyl groups. In particular, there are several pseu-douridines in the platform and several more in the region of the body below the platform; these features together constitute the side of the small subunit that makes contact with the large subunit. These conclu-sions represent a major step forward in integrating the modified nu-cleotides into our perception of the overall structural organization of eukaryotic SSU rRNA.

C. LSU rRNA

Figure 7 shows the secondary structure model of human LSU rRNA of Gutell and Fox (2). The model is based on a wide phylogenetic comparison and resolves several uncertainties and discrepancies be-tween previous models for vertebrate LSU rRNA (40, 61, 62). The model does not show secondary structures for the eukaryotic expan-sion segments; these require considerable extra space for human LSU rRNA and are omitted as they do not contain any known modified nucleotides (Section III,D). Helices are not numbered as there is not yet a widely agreed numbering system for LSU rRNA.

Methyl groups in LSU rRNA, like those in SSU rRNA, occur in a wide variety of local secondary-structure environments, including single-stranded tracts, long-range interactions, and local helical sys-tems, as summarized in Table XV. Some features of the distribution in LSU rRNA are of particular interest and are as follows. (i) The greatest cluster of methyl groups is toward the 3' end of the molecule, in the core regions of domains 5 and 6 (corresponding to domains 4 and 5 in the prokaryotic numbering system). (ii) Other clusters occur near do-main boundaries: see also Fig. 4. (iii) There are several tracts where two or more methyl groups occur on closely spaced nucleotides. The char-

TABLE XV
LOCATED METHYLATED NUCLEOTIDES AND LOCAL CONFORMATIONS IN HUMAN
LSU rRNA[a]

Conformation		Total
Single-stranded link tract	m¹A1302, Am1306, Gm1501, Am1503, Am1513, Am2340, Gm2341, Cm2342, Am(2764 or 2766), Cm2838, Ψm3787, Am3794, Cm3856, Gm4010, Gm4188, <u>mC(~4403), m³U4490</u>, Am(4528 or 4531), Am4550, Um4580	20
Long-range interaction	5.8-S <u>Um14</u>, Cm2328, Cm2781, Cm2801, Um2814, Am3799	6
Local helical system, 5' limb	Cm1320, Um2392, Cm3670, Am3687, Am3693, Cm3838, Um3894, Gm3913, Gm4454, Cm4496, Gm4583, Gm4597	12
Local helical system: hairpin loop	5.8-S <u>Gm75</u>, Cm2399, Gm2401, Am2792, Am3729, <u>mC3751</u>, Am3754, <u>m⁶A(4179 or 4180)</u>, Um4266, Um4458, Gm4459	11
Local helical system: 3' limb	Am1849, Gm3713, Cm3777, Um4187, Gm4330, Am4483, Gm4578	7
Tentatively located or unlocated		14–16
		70–72

[a] Methylated bases and the two 2'-O-methylated nucleotides in 5.8-S rRNA are underlined. (The tentatively located and unlocated methylated nucleotides are listed in Table VI and the legend to that table, and in Table III of 36.)

acteristic triply methylated sequence Am-Gm-Cm (human nucleotide numbers 2340–2342) occurs in a relatively long and highly conserved single-stranded tract that links domains 3 and 4. It can be speculated that this tract is constrained in a rather characteristic conformation. Two other sites, each with pairs of adjacent methylated nucleotides, are at human positions 4187–4188 (Um-Gm, emerging from the 3' limb of a helix in domain 6) and 4458–4459 (Um-Gm-Ψ, in a universally conserved hairpin also in domain 6). (iv) Many 2'-O-methyl groups in helical regions are at imperfections, as also noted for SSU rRNA, or are in close proximity to conserved G·U pairs. Several examples of the latter are to be found in the highly conserved and highly methylated tract that occurs towards the 3' end of domain 5 (nucleotides approximately 3600–3800 in Fig. 7).

There is presently insufficient information on the path of LSU rRNA in the large ribosomal subunit to allow detailed comment on the

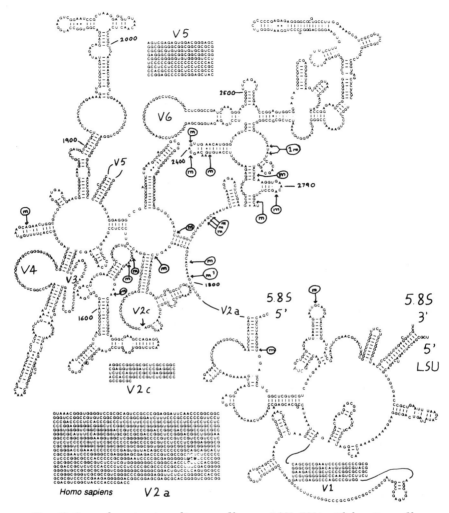

FIG. 7. Secondary structure diagram of human LSU rRNA with locations of known methylated nucleotides. The diagram is adapted from 2. All methyl groups whose locations have been determined are included in the figure. About 13 methyl groups remain to be located in the sequence (see Table VI). The domains in LSU rRNA can be described as radiating from the central "clockface" of single-stranded regions. Domain 1 includes 5.8-S rRNA and radiates from "6 o'clock" in the left-hand half of the figure. Domain 2 is the eukaryotic-specific expansion segment V2a. Domains 3 and 4 spring from the long-range helices at approximately "9 o'clock" and "12 o'clock" in the left-hand half of the figure. Domain 5 springs from "12 o'clock" in the right-hand half of the figure. Domain 6 springs from "3 o'clock" in the right-hand half of the figure, and domain 7 comprises the remaining material 3' from domain 6. V1, V2a etc. through V11 are eukaryolic expansion segments.

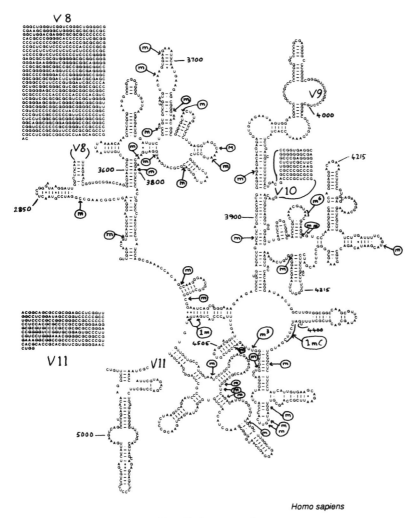

FIG. 7. (continued)

distribution of methylated nucleotides in the three-dimensional structure. However, because many methyl groups occur in fairly close proximity to domain boundaries, and because some of the domain boundaries are linked together by relatively short single-stranded tracts (as in SSU rRNA), it can be inferred that subsets of methyl groups that are distant in the primary structure are brought together in the three-dimensional conformation into a region where phylogenetically conserved helical elements spring from a central system of long-range interactions.

D. Diversity of Modification Sites at the Level of Secondary Structure

Just as nucleotide modification is not associated with unique or consensus sequences at the level of primary structure, so also the findings summarized above do not point to any simple or recurrent theme with respect to the distribution of modified nucleotides among local features of secondary structure. Moreover, for many instances where modified nucleotides are associated with specific secondary structure features, such as bulges in helices or single-stranded linking tracts between helices, many examples can be found elsewhere in the rRNA molecules where apparently comparable features are unmodified. It was hinted at in the previous paragraph that nucleotide modification is associated with relatively complex features in the overall tertiary structure. This may indeed turn out to be correct, but may pose further conceptual difficulties. These difficulties concern the extreme rapidity with which many modifications occur upon ribosomal precursor RNA, as discussed in the final two sections. To anticipate: do the modifications occur before or after the three-dimensional conformation of mRNA has formed?

VI. rRNA Modification and Ribosome Maturation

Long before the locations of any of the modified nucleotides within the rRNA molecules became known, it was established that most nucleotide modifications occur very early during ribosome maturation. These and related findings take on considerable new interest in the light of the new structural knowledge on the environments of the modified nucleotides described in the preceding two sections. In summary, the early findings were as follows. (i) Most methylation occurs on the primary ribosomal transcript during or immediately after transcription. (ii) Methylation of the primary transcript is confined to the ribosomal sequences; the transcribed spacers are unmethylated. (iii) There are a few delayed methylations in both the SSU and LSU rRNA sequences, most conspicuously the SSU base methylations. (iv) Inhibition of methylation is associated with complete or partial inhibition of rRNA maturation. (v) Pseudoridine is also introduced at the level of 45-S ribosomal precursor RNA. Points (i)–(iii) have been established for mammals and yeast, and points (iv) and (v) for mammals.

A. Methylation on Nascent Ribosomal Precursor RNA

The structure of the primary transcript is shown in Fig. 8. It consists of the SSU, 5.8-S and LSU sequences, and transcribed spacers. The lengths (and sequences) of the transcribed spacers and hence the overall lengths of the primary transcripts show great phyletic variation. Because many of the studies described below were carried out on HeLa cells or other mammalian cells, it is convenient to use the classical mammalian nomenclature for the primary transcript and intermediates in rRNA maturation. This nomenclature is based on the approximate S values of the molecular species in mammals: 45 S for the primary transcript, 32 S for the major intermediate that contains the 5.8-S, and LSU rRNA sequences (63). These precursor rRNA species occur only in the nucleolus.

Greenberg and Penman, more than 20 years ago (64), observed the following on the uptake of methyl label into ribosomal precursor RNA. When HeLa cells were labelled for 10 minutes with methyl-labelled methionine, 45-S rRNA was the only nucleolar RNA species that was labelled. During longer labelling periods, or following a chase with excess unlabelled methionine, label was observed to flow into 32-S, cytoplasmic SSU, and finally LSU rRNA. Following very short labelling periods (3–6 minutes), an appreciable fraction of incorporated methyl label sedimented heterogeneously and more slowly than 45-S RNA. These findings led to the conclusions that: (i) the more slowly sedimenting material, seen only after very short labelling, is nascent 45-S RNA; (ii) methylation therefore commences upon nascent 45-S

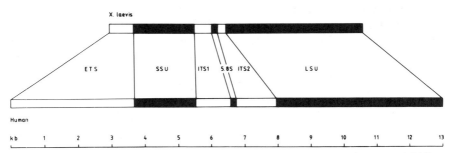

FIG. 8. The primary transcripts of *X. laevis* and human ribosomal precursor RNA. ETS, ITS1, and ITS2 denote the external transcribed spacer and the first and second internal transcribed spacers. The diagrams are to scale. Note the great differences in length between the *Xenopus* and human transcribed spacers. Most methylations occur upon the primary transcript, and all of these early methylations are within the ribosomal sequences. For further details, see Section VI.

RNA; (iii) methylation is practically complete upon newly synthesized 45-S RNA.

Subsequent chemical analysis (12) showed that most of the methylation of 45-S RNA is in alkali-stable (2'-O-methyl) dinucleotides, and that the distribution of label between individual dinucleotides from 45-S RNA resembles that from LSU plus SSU rRNA, whereas the distribution in 32-S RNA resembles that in LSU RNA. Thus, most or all of the 2'-O-methylation of rRNA occurs very rapidly on 45-S RNA. A second implication of the analytical data is that the transcribed spacers are unmethylated.

These findings were confirmed and extended when rRNA fingerprinting was applied to ribosomal precursor RNA (15). The conclusion that the transcribed spacers are unmethylated was upheld; all of the methylated oligonucleotides in fingerprints of 45-S rRNA can be accounted for within the SSU, 5.8 S and LSU rRNA sequences (15, 65). The conclusion that the 2'-O-methylations occur very rapidly was supported by an actinomycin-chase experiment; uptake of methyl label was blocked at nearly all 2'-O-methylation sites within 5 minutes or less of blocking transcription (15). An exception was discovered subsequently: Gm in the universal Um-Gm-Ψ sequence of LSU rRNA is methylated later at the level of 32-S rRNA (66). The base-methylations in SSU rRNA occur later than the 2'-O-methylations; labelling at these sites continues during an actinomycin chase (15, 67) and the modifications occur at or after the time when the largely completed small subunits emerge into the cytoplasm (15, 65, 68).

Meanwhile, uptake of methyl label into nascent 45-S RNA of rat liver was observed (69). In a subsequent study with isolated nucleoli from Novikoff (rat) hepatoma cells (70) it was demonstrated that in nascent chains of intermediate length (20-30 S) the pattern of alkali-stable dinucleotides is predominantly that of SSU rRNA, whereas in the longer nascent chains the pattern approximates that of SSU-plus-LSU rRNA. This provided evidence that the SSU sequence precedes the LSU sequence in the transcription unit, a point that was in dispute at the time (42) but that has been resolved subsequently (as depicted in Fig. 8) by abundant data obtained mainly from analysis of the rRNA genes. More importantly for the present discussion, the findings in 70, and by implication in 64 and 69, suggest that the SSU sequence can be recognized for methylation within nascent ribosomal precursor RNA before completion of transcription of the LSU sequence. Just how close to the growing point of the primary transcript methylation occurs is unknown. Information on this point would contribute greatly to our understanding of the temporal relationship between methylation and folding (see Section V,D) and of the molecular recognition processes involved, as discussed in Section VII.

B. Essential Role of Methylation in rRNA Maturation

Soon after the initial discovery that methylation occurs mainly upon ribosomal precursor RNA (12, 64) a series of experiments was carried out whose results strongly suggested that methylation plays an essential role in ribosome maturation. Those experiments were as follows.

When suspension cultures of HeLa cells were deprived of methionine, complete failure of the final stages of rRNA maturation ensued (71). 45-S RNA continued to be synthesized and to undergo initial processing to 32-S RNA, but the precursor RNA species were submethylated, as shown by analysis for alkali-stable dinucleotide content. The steady-state levels of ribosomal precursor RNA in the nucleolus remained approximately constant; this fact together with continued synthesis, and failure of maturation, indicated that the rRNA sequences are degraded at a relatively late stage in the maturation pathway. The submethylated precursor molecules could be rescued, at least to some extent, by reversal of methionine starvation. This was demonstrated by following the fate of these molecules during an actinomycin chase with methionine restored. (However, rescue may not be quantitative.) The findings were specific for methionine. Deprivation for valine (72) or other essential amino acids led to a slow-down in transcription and processing of ribosomal precursor and in some instances a mild imbalance in subunit maturation (73), but only methionine deprivation led to complete failure of maturation. The findings strongly implied that normal methylation is necessary for successful rRNA maturation.

A subsequent study (74), showed that when methionine is limiting but not totally absent (i.e., present at about 1/20 of the normal concentration) there is incomplete early uptake of methyl label into 45-S RNA, assayed by steady-state labelling experiments. However, this RNA becomes fully methylated during maturation and is quantitatively processed into rRNA. In the presence of ethionine, a competitive inhibitor of S-adenosylmethionine biosynthesis, methylation and maturation become abortive (74), in agreement with the earlier studies.

It is not unanimously agreed that submethylation of precursor RNA leads to complete failure of ribosome maturation. Cycloleucine, another inhibitor of S-adenosylmethionine biosynthesis, allows some residual maturation of rRNA in Chinese hamster ovary cells, indicating that extensive inhibition of ribosome maturation from submethylated ribosomal precursor RNA is the cumulative result of partial inhibitions at several individual processing steps (75).

In summary, the current balance of evidence is that methylation plays a direct and essential role in maturation, but it is not clear to what extent partial submethylation can be tolerated, or exactly at what stages methylation is essential. Some ideas on possible effects and functions of 2'-O-methylation are discussed in Section VII,C.

C. Pseudouridine in Ribosomal Precursor RNA

Pseudouridine has been detected in 45-S and 32-S RNA by base composition analysis (76), and then by analysis of a rather limited sample of oligonucleotides obtained by the combined T_1 plus pancreatic RNase fingerprinting method (16). The yields of pseudouridine in the base composition analyses and in the T_1 plus pancreatic RNase products were consistent with the hypothesis that pseudouridine formation, like 2'-O-methylation, occurs rapidly at specific sites within the ribosomal sequences of ribosomal precursor RNA. However, the timing of the many individual pseudouridine modifications needs to be fully examined by fingerprinting or by other techniques that can locate pseudouridines within specific sequences. Only then will it become possible to view the pseudouridine modifications with the same degree of precision as for methylation.

VII. Outlook

On surveying our current knowledge of the numerous modified nucleotides in eukaryotic rRNA, one can discern both progress and remaining problems.

To summarize the progress: only in the last few years have the locations of substantial numbers of modified nucleotides been determined in the rRNA of any eukaryotic species. Those that are now located include about 130 of the 210 or so in human and rodent RNA (based on some degree of cross-inference between species as described in Section III); about 100 in *Xenopus,* in which the pseudouridines have not yet been studied, and about 70 out of 113 or so in the yeast *Saccharomyces.*

The general facts to emerge from these findings are that the modified nucleotides are in the conserved structural core of rRNA, and that they are in diverse local environments. An initial attempt in this article to trace the distribution of modified nucleotides along the path of rRNA in the small ribosomal subunit reveals that the modified nucleotides occur in much of the three-dimensional structure, with some interesting features, notably an apparently preferential distribution of pseudouridines on the side of the small subunit that makes contact with the large subunit.

Major problems include: extending the database on the locations of the modified nucleotides, understanding the molecular recognition processes involved in the modification events, defining the functions of the modified nucleotides, and applying this knowledge in a biomedical context. These topics are briefly discussed in this final section.

A. Extending the Database

The database of modified nucleotides needs to be extended in two ways. First, it is necessary to complete the task of locating all of the modified nucleotides in the rRNA of one or more chosen species, such as man and *Xenopus*. Second, it will be illuminating to extend the analysis among a diverse array of eukaryotes.

Achieving the first of these objectives will serve a number of purposes. It will provide a complete basis for describing how the modification patterns fit into the three-dimensional structure of rRNA in the ribosome of that species, and it will provide the basis for experimental study of the molecular recognition events in rRNA modification and for studying the functions of the modified nucleotides.

Achieving the second objective will serve a role analogous to that already attained by comparative sequencing. Just as comparative sequencing (usually of rDNA) has revealed conserved and variable features of primary and secondary structure in rRNA, so comparative analysis of modification patterns will reveal whether modifications at some sites are more highly conserved than at others, as indeed is true of tRNA (27, 27a). There are some preliminary indications that this may be the case for eukaryotic rRNA but much more data are needed. The identification of, for example, a subset of 2'-O-methylation sites that are particularly highly conserved phylogenetically would have an obvious bearing upon attempts to understand the factors (structural or other) that determine this type of methylation.

The analysis of certain types of taxon-specific variations in modification patterns may also be informative, as in the following example. Mammalian LSU rRNA contains (as already described) two alkali-stable trinucleotides, each with two consecutive 2'-O-methyl groups (Um-Gm-U and Um-Gm-Ψ), and an alkali-stable tetranucleotide with three 2'-O-methyl groups (Am-Gm-Cm-A). In contrast, wheat LSU rRNA contains seven alkali-stable trinucleotides (14). It is reasonable to suppose that these sites of consecutive 2'-O-methylation are in some way particularly unusual structurally. Where do the alkali-stable trinucleotides fit into the wheat sequence, and how do wheat and mammalian LSU rRNA differ (in sequence and/or conformation) at the respective multiply-methylated sites?

The principal obstacle that impedes extending the database is technical. So far, progress has depended largely on matching rRNA oligonucleotide sequences derived by classical methods against corresponding, unique tracts in the complete sequences derived from rDNA. Greater speed should be attainable using procedures based on "rapid" rRNA sequencing by polyacrylamide gel methods, as pioneered for rabbit SSU rRNA (20, 21).

Application of these methods to detect all the modified nucleotides will always remain more difficult than sequencing rDNA. However, currently available rDNA sequences will facilitate the direct analysis of rRNA by giving the "background" primary structure upon which the modified nucleotides are to be placed. The resulting database on modified nucleotides will be of great value in relation to topics such as those outlined below.

B. Molecular Recognition in rRNA Modification

The experiments establishing that 2'-O-methylation occurs extremely rapidly upon 45-S rRNA focus attention upon the interrelationship between transcription, methylation, and folding of the RNA. As detailed in Section V, 2'-O-methylation sites occupy diverse conformational environments. Some are contained within apparently local features such as (imperfect) hairpin helices—for example, Cm462 and Am468 (human numbering) in helix 14 of SSU rRNA. Others occur in regions where the conformation is established by long-range interactions—for example, Am27 and Gm644 in helix 3 of SSU rRNA. Others occur where the local structure is apparently single-stranded, but in these regions the final conformation may be constrained by the overall tertiary structure of the molecule—examples are Am668, preceding the long-range helix 20 in SSU rRNA, and Am-Gm-Cm between domains 3 and 4 in LSU rRNA.

Does methylation precede or follow the formation of the respective long-range interactions and tertiary structure? Does it precede or follow the binding of ribosomal proteins? Are all of the 2'-O-methylations catalyzed by a single 2'-O-methylase, or are there multiple enzymes? What about the pseudouridines?

Such questions are at the heart of what I have here termed molecular recognition. By analyzing modification at specific sites in nascent transcripts it should be possible to determine whether 2'-O-methylations occur close to the growing point of the primary transcript or at some distance behind, after secondary and perhaps tertiary inter-actions have occurred. Another approach is to use *in vitro* transcripts generated by bacteriophage T7 RNA polymerase as substrates for studying the requirements for modification. Considerable success has been achieved in this way in studying the methylation of *E. coli* SSU rRNA (77, 78), and the approach is potentially promising for eukaryotic rRNA transcripts. Progress has been made in the purification of nuclear 2'-O-methylating enzyme systems, and some progress in their applica-tion to RNA substrates synthesized *in vitro* (79). Chemical specificity of 2'-O-methylation has been obtained, but site-specificity in the RNA sequences remains to be achieved (79). Further progress in under-standing the molecular basis of eukaryotic rRNA modification, both methylation and pseudouridine formation, should come from such experiments.

C. Function

What are the functions of the numerous modified nucleotides in eukaryotic rRNA? The phenomenon is complex, as has been conveyed in this article. Several relevant considerations, some deriving from simpler systems, are outlined below.

1. MODIFIED NUCLEOTIDES AND "FINE-TUNING"

Kersten (27) has reviewed evidence on the biological functions of modified nucleotides in tRNA: in particular, ribosylthymine (T) at position 54, isopentenyl derivatives at position 37, and queuine deriv-atives at position 34. The modifications do not confer all-or-none ef-fects upon the ability of the respective tRNAs to participate in protein synthesis. Instead they exert a variety of subtle effects. These include: for T54, increasing the efficiency of interaction of elongator tRNAs with the A site of the ribosome, decreasing errors in amino acid incor-poration in protein synthesis, and adjusting the relative frequency of initiation of the different proteins in (eubacterial) polycistronic mRNAs; for isopentenyl modifications at position 37, achieving ac-curacy in codon recognition, especially by specific suppressor tRNAs (27 and references therein); for Q in a lower eukaryote (*Dictyostelium discoideum*), increasing tolerance to starvation during the develop-ment cycle. A key link exists between pseudouridine modification in the anticodon loop of tRNA and the regulation of synthesis of enzymes of amino-acid biosynthetic operons (80), by a mechanism in which pseudouridine in tRNA is thought to be required for efficient attenu-ation (81).

In rRNA, the most intensively studied modifications are those of the two adjacent m^6_2 residues near the 3' end of SSU rRNA. The m^6_2 A modifications are common to prokaryotes and eukaryotes, in contrast to most of the modifications described in the present article, which are specific to eukaryotes. There is a mutant *E. coli* whose phenotype is resistant to the antibiotic kasugamycin, and which lacks the m^6_2A modifications. Absence of the m^6_2A modifications does not result in gross defects in protein synthesis. However, the mutant *E. coli* is deficient in growth in comparison with wild-type, is detectibly deficient in interaction between ribosomal subunits and initiation of protein synthesis (82), and shows increased "leakiness" of nonsense and frameshift mutations (83).

2. NUCLEOTIDE MODIFICATIONS AND EUKARYOTIC RIBOSOME BIOSYNTHESIS

The quantitatively major groups of modifications in eukaryotic rRNA, the numerous 2'-O-methylations and pseudouridinations, occur rapidly upon ribosomal RNA precursor as described above. The methionine deprivation experiments (71), also described above, strongly imply a role for 2'-O-methylation in ribosome biosynthesis. What might such a role be?

3. POSSIBLE ROLES FOR 2'-O-METHYLATION

An early and speculative suggestion for a role for 2'-O-methylation was that this type of modification protects specific phosphodiester bonds against accidental nucleolytic cleavage during ribosome maturation (15, 47). Underlying this proposal was the idea that sites that are 2'-O-methylated occupy exposed locations. The recently inferred path of SSU rRNA in the small subunit indicates that only some 2'-O-methylation sites are exposed in the mature, fully folded rRNA. However, as also discussed above, the temporal relationship between synthesis, 2'-O-methylation, and folding needs further clarification. At present the structural data neither support nor eliminate the protection hypothesis.

Another possibility is that 2'-O-methylation may "fine-tune" the conformation of rRNA during and after maturation. Such methylation affects the stability of model polyribonucleotides (84). Those studies were carried out upon homopolyribonucleotides containing from at least several percent to 100% 2'-O-methyl substituents. Thus the model systems afford only a partial approach to the actual complexities of 2'-O-methyl group distribution in eukaryotic rRNA sequences. Nevertheless the findings from the model systems may have a useful bearing upon 2'-*O*-methyl groups in naturally occurring RNA. The findings were as follows: 2'-*O*-Methylation enhanced the ordered self-structure of single-stranded polymers, but either decreased slightly or increased the stability of polynucleotide duplexes, depending on which strand was alkylated; poly(Am·poly(U) showed slightly decreased stability relative to poly(A)·poly(U) whereas poly(A)·poly(Um) showed increased stability.

Extrapolating the findings from model systems to methylation sites in rRNA, it can be hypothesized that a 2'-*O*-methyl group in a single-stranded region stabilizes to some extent the conformation at that particular phosphodiester bond. Within helical regions (usually imperfect ones), the precise effects of 2'-*O*-methylation are difficult to predict from the model studies, and may depend on the local base composition and sequence. Observations by Nazar and co-workers on a partially methylated site in 5.8-S rRNA, described below, are of interest in this regard (85).

4. EFFECTS ASSOCIATED WITH A PARTIALLY
   METHYLATED SITE IN 5.8-S rRNA

Mammalian 5.8-S rRNA is methylated at two sites: Um14 and Gm75. The latter is always methylated but the former is methylated in some but not all molecules. Um14 is in a tract that is thought to participate (alternatively) in internal base-pairing in isolated 5.8-S rRNA and in bonding with LSU rRNA in the complex (see Fig. 7). 5.8-S rRNA methylated at Um14 migrates slightly more slowly on polyacrylamide gels than does the molecule that is unmethylated at this site. This implies that the methylated form possesses a more open conformation in isolated 5.8-S rRNA, that is, weaker internal base-pairing in the vicinity of U14. Similarly, the methylated form appears to be destabilized in its interaction with LSU rRNA, the melting temperature being evidently reduced by about 2 to 3° through methylation at U14 (85). Both observations thus indicate weaker base-pairing by the 2'-*O*-methylated than the unmethylated form.

From the above studies it can be imagined that 2'-*O*-methylation exerts many individually small local effects that, collectively, modulate the overall conformation of rRNA substantially. It is less easy to predict whether the overall direction of this modulation is toward increased or decreased structural stability. Further insight into the conformational effects of 2'-*O*-methylation, and hence into the possible biological role of this type of modification, may be afforded by experiments in which the properties of natural rRNA are compared with RNA transcibed *in vitro* using cloned rDNA and bacteriophage

RNA polymerase. In such experiments it must be born in mind that natural rRNA also contains pseudouridine.

5. PSEUDOURIDINE

Pseudouridine is the Cinderella of modified nucleotides in rRNA. Its presence to the extent of some 95 residues per mammalian ribosome is frequently ignored in discussions of ribosome biosynthesis and function. Yet 95 pseudouridines must be there for a purpose.

In pseudouridine, the uracil ring is linked via its C-5 atom to the C-1 of ribose, in contrast to the normal glycosyl bond in uridine, between the N-1 and the C-1 (85*a*). Some consequences of this arrangement are depicted in Fig. 9. It confers extra hydrogen bonding capability upon pseudouridine, because N-1 and N-3 are both potentially available for hydrogen bonding. In line with this extra bonding capacity, polypseudouridylic acid possesses an ordered self-structure, unlike poly(U), and increased stability relative to poly(U) in binding to poly(A), forming a triple helix 2 poly(Ψ)·poly(A) (85*b*). When pseudouridine forms Watson-Crick base pairs with adenine it can theoretically do so in either the *anti*- or the *syn*-conformation. It is not known which conformation is preferred in rRNA. Extensive efforts have been made to resolve the question in the anticodon arm of tRNA by physical means; recent evidence based on NMR favors the *anti* conformation (86). In either conformation the resulting "edge" of the base pair in the major groove differs from that of a standard A·U pair, and is therefore potentially recognizable by (for example) a protein.

Because only some pseudouridines in rRNA have been located, it is possible to make only preliminary comments upon the involvement of pseudouridine in base pairing. Table XVI classifies those pseudouridines that have been located in mammalian rRNA with respect to whether they are involved in (inferred) base pairs. The table includes the 16 pseudouridines that have been located in SSU rRNA and the two in 5.8-S rRNA. (The 14 pseudouridines in SSU rRNA that have been localized to within a few nucleotides but not precisely pinpointed, Table V, are not included because it cannot yet be inferred that they are base-paired.) As can be seen, of those listed, eight are in (inferred) A·U pairs; interestingly three are in (inferred) G·U pairs, and the rest are in single-stranded tracts or bulges. This classification shows that pseudouridines occur in diverse environments with respect to actual or potential base-pairing.

There are as yet no specific indications as to the functions of the many pseudouridine residues in the biosynthesis or function of eukaryotic ribosomes. No experiments have yet been devised for inhibit-

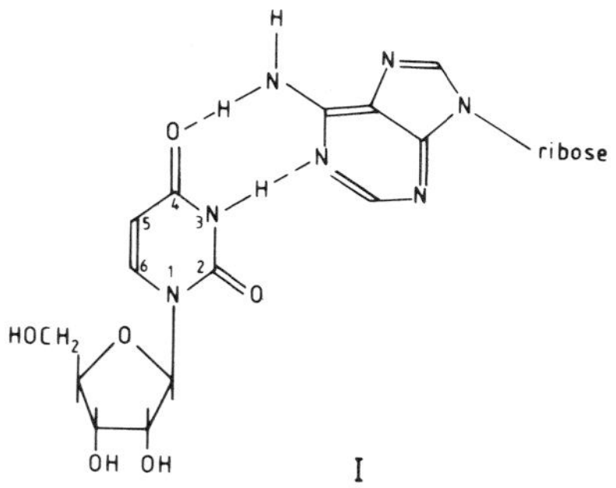

FIG. 9. Uridine and pseudouridine in RNA. Pseudouridine, like uridine, occurs in single-stranded or double-stranded regions. In the latter, pseudouridine (also like uridine) can base-pair with adenosine or guanosine (Table XVI). The figure shows: (I) uridine base-paired with adenosine; (II and III) pseudouridine base-paired with adenosine. In II, pseudouridine is in the *anti*-conformation; in III it is in the *syn*-conformation. In Ψ·A base-pairs in tRNA, the *anti*-conformation of pseudouridine is believed to be favored (86). In either conformation, the pattern of atoms lining the major groove, on the left of the uracil ring (II or III), differs from that in a U·A pair (I).

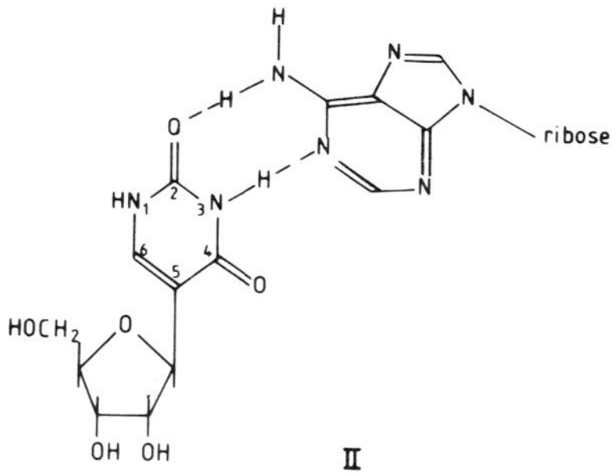

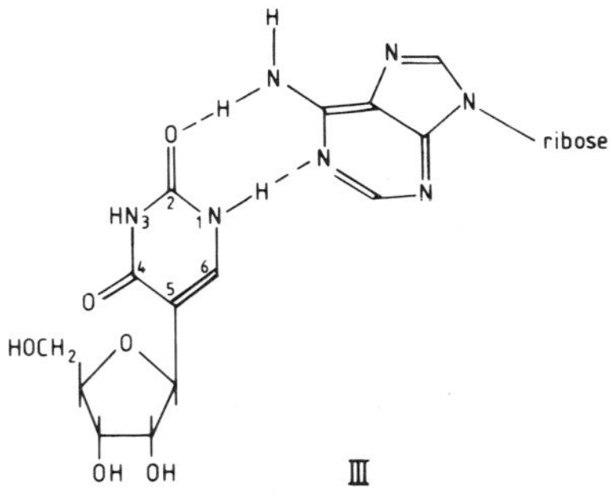

TABLE XVI

INVOLVEMENT OR OTHERWISE OF PRECISELY LOCATED PSEUDOURIDINES WITH BASE-
PAIRING PARTNERS IN SECONDARY STRUCTURE MODELS OF HUMAN rRNA[a]

| RNA | Residue | Partner? | Secondary structure | | Notes[b] |
			Feature	Distance	
SSU	Ψ44	Bulge	Helix 4	Long-range	
	Ψ46	A564	Helix 4	Long-range	
	Ψ105	Single-stranded	Precedes helix 7	Long-range	
	Ψ681	A1028	Helix 20	Long-range	
	Ψ801	Single-stranded	Between helices 21C and 21D		
	Ψ814	G915	Helix 21E	Local helix	c
	Ψ815	A914	Helix 21E	Local helix	c
	Ψ863	G894	Helix 21F	Local helix	d
	Ψ866	G891	Helix 21F	Local helix	d
	Ψ918	A1023	Helix 22	Semilocal	e
	Ψ1056	Single-stranded	Helix 24 loop	Local helix	
	Ψ1081	Single-stranded	Between helices 24 and 25		
	Ψ1174	Bulge	Helix 27	Local helix	
	m¹acp³Ψ1248	Single-stranded	Helix 31 loop	Local helix	f
	Ψ1625	A1614	Helix 42	Local helix	
	Ψ1643	A1223	Helix 29	Long-range	
5.8 S	Ψ55	A48	Helix stem	Local helix	
	Ψ69	A82	Helix stem	Local helix	
LSU	Ψ1515	A1602	Helix stem	Semilocal	
	Ψ4460	Single-stranded	Helix loop	Local helix	g
	Ψ4492	Single-stranded	Between two helices		

[a] The table lists the pseudouridines that have so far been exactly located in human rRNA and indicates: whether or not they are base-paired in phylogenetically derived secondary structure models; the base-pairing partner (where appropriate) and the secondary structure feature. Helices in SSU rRNA are numbered as in Fig. 5.

[b] Entries under "distance" denote whether the respective helix is formed by local hairpin folding or long-range interaction. (See Fig. 5 for this and the following notes.)

[c] These two base-pairs are at the base of a local helix, with an imperfection just above.

[d] This local helix possesses the two indicated Ψ·G pairs, an mG·U pair, and another U·G pair.

[e] This helix is semilocal in that it is attached via single-stranded regions to helix 23, which is a local helix.

[f] m¹acp³Ψ cannot participate in base pairing because both N atoms in the uracil ring are blocked by substituents (Fig. 1).

[g] This is in the "universal" Um-Gm-Ψ sequence of LSU rRNA.

ing pseudouridine formation *in vivo* in ribosomal precursor RNA; consequently no conclusions can be drawn as to whether pseudouridine formation, like 2'-*O*-methylation, is essential for ribosome maturation. The partial clustering of pseudouridines on the side of SSU rRNA that interacts with the large subunit is intriguing in the light of the extra hydrogen-bonding capacity of pseudouridine mentioned above. It will be interesting to discover whether the converse is true of the distribution of pseudouridine in LSU rRNA. If so, it might be inferred that some pseudouridines contribute to interaction between ribosomal subunits. Further experimental approaches to pseudouridine in ribosome biosynthesis and function are available in principle, as for methylation, by using unmodified RNA transcribed from cloned genes by bacteriophage RNA polymerase.

D. Applications: Modified Nucleotides and Ribosome Turnover in Man

The carbon–carbon bond that links the uracil ring to ribose in pseudouridine is particularly stable chemically; pseudouridine is nonmetabolizable physiologically and is quantitatively excreted in urine (87, 88). Thus, urinary pseudouridine affords a measure of the rate of whole-body turnover of RNA species that contain pseudouridine, namely rRNA, tRNA, and lesser amounts of small nuclear RNA. Other nonmetabolizable derivatives of modified nucleotides include the base m^6_2Gua, which is specific for tRNA, and m^7Gua which occurs in tRNA, rRNA, and mRNA. These compounds are also excreted in the urine.

Advantage has been taken of these facts to develop a procedure for estimating the rates of whole-body turnover of rRNA, tRNA, and mRNA in man (89). The results are summarized in Table XVII. The data are expressed in micromoles of RNA/kg/day and also, for rRNA and tRNA, in milligrams of RNA/kg/day. The findings show that the turnover of all three rRNA species is considerably more rapid (about threefold) in preterm infants than in adults. This is in good quantitative agreement with findings on rates of muscle protein turnover measured by 3-methylhistidine excretion, which is also some threefold higher in preterm infants than in adults (90).

The measurements are performed by liquid chromatography on samples of urine and are straightforward to carry out. They are likely to be used increasingly to complement ^{15}N tracer studies that have been used classically to estimate whole body protein turnover. Related measurements of RNA turnover based on urinary excretion of modified

TABLE XVII

CALCULATED TURNOVER RATES FOR rRNA, tRNA, AND mRNA IN
PRETERM INFANTS AND ADULTS[a]

	Turnover rates	
	Preterm infants	Adults
Micromoles of rRNA/day/kg	0.1	0.037
Milligrams of rRNA/day/kg	223	82.5
Milligrams of ribosomes/day/kg	402	149
Micromoles of tRNA/day/kg	1.93	0.63
Milligrams of tRNA/day/kg	48	15.8
Micromoles of mRNA 5' ends/day/kg	2.44	0.62

[a] Adapted from Sander et al. (89).

nucleotide metabolites have been carried out in various pathological conditions (summarized in 89).

In conclusion, the study of the numerous modified nucleotides in eukaryotic rRNA probes deeply into the molecular biology of the eukaryotic ribosome, and is finding applications in the investigation of RNA turnover in man. This is a fascinating interface between molecular biology and medicine.

ACKNOWLEDGMENTS

I thank Richard Brimacombe and Jane Wakerman for helpful discussions during the preparation of this article, Julie McGreavey for her typing of the manuscript, and Pauline Dickinson and Maureen Wilde for help with the illustrations. The secondary structure diagrams were adapted from figures that were kindly provided by Robin Gutell and Asha Rairkar. I thank the MRC, SERC, and Wellcome Trust for support of research in my laboratory.

REFERENCES

1. R. R. Gutell, B. Weiser, C. R. Woese and H. F. Noller, This series 32, 155 (1985).
2. R. R. Gutell and G. E. Fox, NARes 16, (Suppl.), r175 (1988).
3. H. A. Raue, J. Klootwijk and W. Musters, Prog. Biophys. Mol. Biol. 51, 77 (1989).
4. P. B. Moore, Nature 331, 223 (1988).
5. G. E. Fox, E. Stackebrandt, R. B. Hespell, J. Gibson, J. Maniloff, T. A. Dyer, R. S. Wolfe, W. E. Balch, R. S. Tanner, L. J. Magrum, L. B. Zablen, R. Blakemore, R. Gupta, L. Bonen, B. J. Lewis, D. A. Stahl, K. R. Luehrsen, K. N. Chen and C. R. Woese, Science 209, 457 (1980).
5a. N. R. Pace, G. J. Olsen and C. R. Woese, Cell 45, 325 (1986).
6. I. C. Eperon, S. Anderson and D. P. Nierlich, Nature 286, 460 (1980).
7. E. Dams, L. Hendriks, Y. Van de Peer, J.-M. Neefs, G. Smits, I. Vandenbrempt and R. De Wachter, NARes 16 (Suppl.), r87 (1988).

8. V. A. Erdman and J. Wolters, *NARes* **14** (Suppl.), r1 (1986).
9. B. E. H. Maden, *in* "Chromatography and Modification of Nucleosides" (C. W. Gehrke and K. C. Kuo, eds.), pp. B265–301, Vol. 2. Elsevier, Amsterdam 1990.
10. H. Singh and B. G. Lane, *Can. J. Biochem.* **42**, 87 (1964).
11. H. Singh and B. G. Lane, *Can. J. Biochem.* **42**, 1011 (1964).
12. E. K. Wagner, S. Penman and V. M. Ingram, *JMB* **29**, 371 (1967).
13. T. Tamaoki and B. G. Lane, *Bchem* **7**, 3431 (1968).
14. B. G. Lane, *Bchem* **4**, 212 (1965).
15. B. E. H. Maden and M. Salim, *JMB* **88**, 133 (1974).
15a. G. G. Brownlee, "Determination of Sequences in RNA," Elsevier/North-Holland, Amsterdam, 1972.
16. B. E. H. Maden and J. Forbes, *FEBS Lett.* **28**, 289 (1972).
16a. B. E. H. Maden, C. D. Lees and M. Salim, *FEBS Lett.* **28**, 293 (1972).
17. B. E. H. Maden and M. S. N. Khan, *BJ* **167**, 211 (1977).
17a. M. S. N. Khan and B. E. H. Maden, *JMB* **101**, 235 (1976).
18. M. S. N. Khan, M. Salim and B. E. H. Maden, *BJ* **169**, 531 (1978).
19. Y. C. Choi and H. Busch, *Bchem* **17**, 2551 (1978).
20. R. E. Lockard, J. F. Connaughton and A. Kumar, *NARes* **10**, 3445 (1982).
21. J. F. Connaughton, A. Rairkar, R. E. Lockard and A. Kumar, *NARes* **12**, 4731 (1984).
22. J. Klootwijk and R. J. Planta, *EJB* **39**, 325 (1973).
23. P. J. Ford and T. Mathieson, *EJB* **87**, 199 (1978).
24. L. M. C. Hall and B. E. H. Maden, *NARes* **8**, 5993 (1980).
25. D. G. Hughes and B. E. H. Maden, *BJ* **171**, 781 (1978).
26. J. Klootwijk and R. J. Planta, *Mol. Biol. Rep.* **1**, 187 (1973).
27. H. Kersten, *This Series* **31**, 59 (1984).
27a. R. W. Adamiak and P. Gornicki, *This series* **32**, 27 (1985).
28. G. Thomas, J. Gordon and H. Rogg, *JBC* **253**, 1101 (1978).
29. A. G. Saponara and M. D. Enger, *BBA* **349**, 61 (1974).
30. V. C. Ware, B. W. Tague, G. C. Clark, R. L. Gourse, R. C. Brand and S. A. Gerbi, *NARes* **11**, 7795 (1983).
31. N. Hassouna, B. Michot and J.-P. Bachellerie, *NARes* **12**, 3563 (1984).
32. I. L. Gonzalez, J. L. Gorski, T. J. Campen, D. J. Dorney, J. M. Erickson, J. E. Sylvester and R. D. Schmickel, *PNAS* **82**, 7666 (1985).
33. B. E. H. Maden, *Nature* **288**, 293 (1980).
34. M. Salim and B. E. H. Maden, *Nature* **291**, 205 (1981).
35. B. E. H. Maden, *JMB* **189**, 681 (1986).
35a. F. S. McCallum and B. E. H. Maden, *BJ* **232**, 725 (1985).
35b. F. Raynal, B. Michot and J.-P. Bachellerie, *FEBS Lett.* **167**, 263 (1984).
35c. R. Torczynski, A. P. Bollon and M. Fuke, *NARes* **11**, 4879 (1983).
35d. A. S. Mankin, K. G. Skryabin and P. M. Rubstov, *Gene* **44**, 143 (1986).
36. B. E. H. Maden, *JMB* **201**, 289 (1988).
37. G. M. Veldman, J. Klootwijk, V. C. H. F. de Regt and R. J. Planta, *NARes* **9**, 6935 (1981).
38. B. E. H. Maden and J. A. Wakeman, *BJ* **249**, 459 (1988).
38a. B. E. H. Maden, C. L. Dent, T. E. Farrell, J. Garde, F. S. McCallum and J. A. Wakeman, *BJ* **246**, 519 (1987).
39. A. A. Hadjiolov, O. I. Georgiev, V. V. Nosikov and L. P. Yavachev, *NARes* **12**, 3677 (1984).
40. J. L. Gorski, I. L. Gonzalez and R. D. Schmickel, *J. Mol. Evol.* **24**, 236 (1987).
41. U. E. Loening, *JMB* **38**, 355 (1968).

42. P. K. Wellauer and I. B. Dawid, *PNAS* **70**, 2827 (1973).
43. P. K. Wellauer and I. B. Dawid, *JMB* **89**, 379 (1974).
44. P. K. Wellauer, I. B. Dawid, D. E. Kelley and R. P. Perry, *JMB* **89**, 397 (1974).
45. U. Schibler, T. Wyler and O. Hagenbuchle, *JMB* **94**, 503 (1975).
46. J. A. Wakeman and B. E. H. Maden, *BJ* **258**, 49 (1989).
47. M. Klagsbrun, *JBC* **248**, 2612 (1973).
48. R. P. Singhal, E. F. Roberts and V. N. Vakharia, *This Series* **28**, 217 (1983).
49. B. E. H. Maden, J. Forbes, P. de Jonge and J. Klootwijk, *FEBS Lett.* **59**, 60 (1975).
50. Y. Gruenbaum, R. Stein, H. Cedar and A. Razin, *FEBS Lett.* **124**, 67 (1981).
51. A. Rairkar, H. M. Rubino and R. E. Lockard, *Bchem* **27**, 582 (1988).
52. J. Atmadja, R. Brimacombe and B. E. H. Maden, *NARes* **12**, 2649 (1984).
53. C. W. A. Pleij, K. Rietveld and L. Bosch, *NARes* **13**, 1717 (1985).
54. P. H. van Knippenberg, J. M. A. van Kimmenade and H. A. Heus, *NARes* **12**, 2595 (1984).
55. R. Brimacombe, J. Atmadja, W. Steige and D. Schüler, *JMB* **199**, 115 (1988).
56. S. Stern, B. Weiser and H. F. Noller, *JMB* **204**, 447 (1988).
57. P. B. Moore, M. Capel, M. Kjeldgard and D. M. Engelman, *in* "Structure, Function and Genetics of Ribosomes" (B. Hardesty and G. Kramer, eds.), pp. 87–100. Springer-Verlag, New York, 1985.
58. J. A. Lake, *ARB* **54**, 507 (1985).
59. J. B. Prince, B. H. Taylor, D. L. Thurlow, J. Ofengand and R. A. Zimmerman, *PNAS* **79**, 5450 (1982).
59a. M. I. Oakes, M. W. Clark, E. Henderson and J. A. Lake, *PNAS* **83**, 275 (1986).
60. M. S. N. Khan and B. E. H. Maden, *EJB* **84**, 241 (1978).
61. C. G. Clark, B. W. Tague, V. C. Ware and S. A. Gerbi, *NARes* **12**, 6197 (1984).
62. B. Michot, N. Hassouna and J.-P. Bachellerie, *NARes* **12**, 4259 (1984).
63. B. E. H. Maden and J. S. Robertson, *JMB* **87**, 227 (1974).
64. H. Greenberg and S. Penman, *JMB* **21**, 527 (1966).
65. R. C. Brand, J. Klootwijk, R. J. Planta and B. E. H. Maden, *BJ* **169**, 71 (1978).
66. E. Eladari, A. Hampe and F. Galibert, *NARes* **6**, 1759 (1977).
67. E. F. Zimmerman, *Bchem* **7**, 3156 (1968).
68. R. C. Brand, J. Klootwijk, T. J. M. van Steenbergen, A. J. de Kok and R. J. Planta, *EJB* **75**, 311 (1977).
69. M. Muramatsu and T. Fujisawa, *BBA* **157**, 476 (1968).
70. M. C. Liau and R. B. Hurlbert, *JMB* **98**, 321 (1975).
71. M. H. Vaughan, R. Soeiro, J. R. Warner and J. E. Darnell, *PNAS* **58**, 1527 (1967).
72. B. E. H. Maden, M. H. Vaughan, J. R. Warner and J. E. Darnell, *JMB* **45**, 265 (1969).
73. B. E. H. Maden, *BBA* **281**, 396 (1972).
74. S. F. Wolf and D. Schlessinger, *Bchem* **16**, 2783 (1977).
75. M. Caboche and J.-P. Bachellerie, *EJB* **74**, 19 (1977).
76. P. Jeanteur, F. Amaldi and G. Attardi, *JMB* **33**, 757 (1968).
77. J. Ofengand, D. Negre and C. Weitzman, *J. Cell. Biochem.* **13D** (Suppl.), 207 (1989).
78. D. Nègre, C. Weitzman and J. Olergand, *PNAS* **86**, 4902 (1989).
79. D. C. Eichler, N. K. Raber, C. M. Shumard and S. J. Eales, *Bchem* **26**, 1639 (1987).
80. C. Singer, G. Smith, R. Cortese and B. Ames, *Nature NB* **238**, 72 (1972).
81. H. M. Johnston, W. M. Barnes, F. G. Chumley, L. Bossi and J. R. Roth, *PNAS* **77**, 508 (1980).
82. B. Poldermans, H. Bakker and P. H. van Knippenberg, *NARes* **8**, 143 (1980).
83. C. P. J. J. van Buul, W. Visser and P. H. van Knippenberg, *FEBS Lett.* **177**, 119 (1984).
84. F. Rottman, K. Friderici, P. Comstock and M. K. Khan, *Bchem* **13**, 2762 (1974).

85. R. N. Nazar, A. C. Lo, A. G. Wildeman and T. O. Sitz, *NARes* **11**, 5989 (1983).

85a. W. E. Cohn, *JBC* **235**, 1488 (1960).

85b. F. Pochon, A. M. Michelson, M. Grunberg-Manago, W. E. Cohn and L. Dondon, *BBA* **80**, 441 (1964).

86. R. H. Griffey, D. Davis, Z. Yamaizumi, S. Nishimura, A. Bax, B. Hawkins and C. Dale-Poulter, *JBC* **260**, 9734 (1985).

87. S. Weissman, A. Z. Eisen, M. Lewis and M. Karon, *J. Lab. Clin. Med.* **60**, 40 (1962).

88. A. Dlugajczyk and J. J. Eiler, *Nature* **212**, 611 (1966).

89. G. Sander, H. Topp, G. Heller-Schoch, J. Wieland and G. Schoch, *Clin. Sci.* **71**, 367 (1986).

90. G. Sander, J. Hulsemann, H. Topp, G. Heller-Schoch and G. Schoch, *Ann. Nutr. Med.* **30**, 137 (1986).

Damage to DNA and Chromatin Structure from Ionizing Radiations, and the Radiation Sensitivities of Mammalian Cells[1]

J. T. LETT

Department of Radiology and
Radiation Biology
Colorado State University
Fort Collins, Colorado 80523

Cellular radiation biology is in a process of transition. It has reached the stage common to the development of all sciences when the inadequacies of classical terminology and theory are no longer conducive to remedy by further *ad hoc* assumptions (*1–3*). Historically, such

---

[1] A glossary of terms pertinent to radiobiology is included at the end of this article (p. 346).

Progress in Nucleic Acid Research
and Molecular Biology, Vol. 39

conditions have produced periods of stagnation caused by entrenched resistance to innovation. With regard to the subject of this article—the basis of cellular lethality caused by ionizing radiations—the situation has been exacerbated by three unusual circumstances. First, theories of cellular radiation sensitivity that preclude post-irradiation modification of radiation damage by cellular metabolic processes are demonstrably unsound (4, 5), yet one of them is still being utilized, and even taught, despite the caveats expressed by its progenitors (see, e.g., 5). Second, the lack of utility of one of two phenomenological (operational) interpretations of cellular radiosensitivity (6) first introduced more than 20 years ago has been stultifying for the reasons such abstractions often are, even on the grandest scale.[2] The third circumstance concerns the notion that most of the DNA damage responsible for cell death is caused by diffusing radicals, usually ·OH, resulting from the irradiation of bulk water. That process is called *indirect* action because the radiant energy responsible for the biologically significant damge to DNA is deposited neither in the macromolecule itself nor in adjacent molecules with which it is directly associated (bound).

Arguments favoring indirect action, which has received strong, but latterly waning, support for many years, have been detailed twice in this series recently (7, 8), so further elaboration here is unnecessary. As a long-time proponent (9–13) of the opposite view, that energy deposited in DNA chromatin—that is, *direct* action—causes most of the biologically significant radiation damage, I present it now while remaining cognizant of the fact that, under special conditions, radiation damage not involving DNA could be of crucial importance. The case is made mainly in light of recent developments in the radiation chemistry of DNA (chromatin) and the probable role of such chemistry in a general theory of cellular radiosensitivity (5) that overcomes the fundamental deficiencies outlined above (4, 5).

Of the two presentations of the other viewpoint, the first (8) seems extreme, given the knowledge of radiation chemistry extant at the time it was published. Assumptions on which that article was based have been challenged recently in a comprehensive text treating in detail the radiation chemistry of DNA in dilute aqueous solution (14; for arguments in a similar vein, see 15, 16). The second review (7) is more appropriate, but must be balanced by evaluation of the information presented here. My own bias is revealed by sympathy (17) with the assertion, "It is perhaps a consequence of the acceptance of the pos-

---

[2] "Einstein showed that time and space must be defined in terms usable to scientists . . . . They had to be quantities that ordinary men using ordinary tools could measure—not scientifically useless abstractions." (John Boslough, *Stephen Hawking's Universe*).

tulate that ˙OH is the dominant damaging species involved in cellular radiation lethality that the absorption, migration and dissipation of excitation energy have largely been neglected in molecular radiobiology" (18). Presently, that situation is changing, and increasing acceptance of a unique role for hydration water (17, 19) in the radiation responses of DNA and nucleoprotein is reducing the distinction between direct action and indirect action. Cellular radiation biology, therefore, is also experiencing a period of consolidation (1).

Formal efforts to explain the lethal effects of ionizing radiations at the cellular level (only ionizing radiations are considered here) began more than half a century ago with the physical concepts of lethal hits within targets (4, 5). General target theory thus was born. It two foremost proponents were D. E. Lea in Britain and K. G. Zimmer in Germany, and both of them were cognizant of the fact that general target theory is inapplicable if post-irradiation metabolism modifies the cellular response (20, 21). In fact, target theory can be applied to biological entities and cells only if (1) recovery (repair) is inherently absent, (2) inherent recovery (repair) is rendered ineffective. Those postulates of hit and target theories "can be said to describe the ideal case in radiobiology just as Einstein's postulate [of photochemical equivalence] does in photochemistry" (21).

Adequate applicability of target theory to enzymes, to viruses not repaired well in their hosts, etc. has long been known, so the first of the above stipulations is correct. Recent examination of the cell-cycle responses to densely ionizing radiations of the cell-cycle-dependent, repair-deficient, "S/S" variant of the L5178Y murine leukemic lymphoblast has demonstrated the validity of the second stipulation (5). In both situations, the surviving fraction, S, is related to dose, D, by the simple exponential function

$$S = e^{-kD} \tag{1}$$

that appears on the usual "semi-log" plot as a straight line, the slope of which, k (a constant), is a measure of cellular radiosensitivity. Furthermore, with the S/S variant as the test vehicle, it has been shown that *any* general theory of cellular radiosensitivity that precludes post-irradiation recovery (repair) is intrinsically unsound (4, 5), and that survival curves with shoulders (Fig. 1; Fig. 2, Curve D) as well as other survival curves without shoulders that obey Eq. (1) (Fig. 1; Fig. 2, Curve C) result from the modulation of radiation damage by enzymatic repair (recovery) systems (4, 5). Since the *concept* of a vital cellular radiation target is neither required nor invalidated by rigorous theories of radiation action, however, it is retained here as a convenient shorthand for these discussions.

Efforts to fit equations derived from general target theory to survival curves with shoulders have persisted for the last 30 years, despite the caveats of Lea (20) and Zimmer (21), the discoveries of cellular and molecular (DNA) repair mechanisms, and strenuous efforts by Zimmer to halt the trend even until his recent death (21, 22). Often, the mathematical modelling has been tantamount to approximating curves by general polynomials, procedures not without precedent, as they derive from the development of calculus (see e.g., 23). The trend continued even after the discovery of the variation through the cell cycle of cellular radiation sensitivity to sparsely ionizing radiations (24, 25), and hence the implicit illustration of the inadequacies of prior fits of equations to survival curves for cell populations in exponential growth. However, at long last, "consideration of the theoretical implications of the responses of the S/S variant of the L5178Y murine leukaemic lymphoblast to X-photons and heavy ions finally should bring to an end this unusual episode in the history of modern science" (5).

I. Some Considerations of Single Cell Survival Curves

Cellular survival curves with shoulders and linear limiting slopes have been approximated by general target theory with a formulation requiring that a cell is inactivated by hits in multiple targets and dies from a lethal accumulation of sublethal events (hits) (for a brief review see 4). Cellular responses to sparsely ionizing radiations, however, are not compatible with that notion. Dose fractionation, long known to be of therapeutic benefit (e.g., 26), was found, first with algae (27), and then with mammalian cells (28), to increase cellular survival. Such split-dose recovery was believed to involve processes underlying the shoulder on a cell-survival curve but not the limiting slope, while the converse applied to various forms of post-irradiation manipulation: liquid-holding recovery, delayed-plating recovery, etc. (reviewed in 4 and 5). In 1979, those cellular responses were described with formal operational definitions called the repair of sublethal and potentially lethal damage, respectively (6). Unfortunately, the distinction between the two expressions of cellular recovery is not only arbitrary but also fallacious, particularly since the first definition is derived conceptually from target theory. Subsequently, much effort has been expended in proving that the "repair of sublethal damage" is but a part of the repair of potentially lethal damage (e.g., 29–33).

Qualitative interpretation of the shapes of survival curves sufficient for our present purposes can be elicited from the adumbrated example

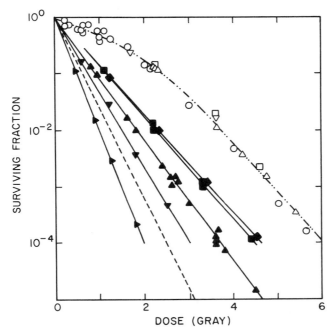

FIG. 1. Effects of post-irradiation temperature (12 hours) on the survival of synchronous L5178Y S/S cells exposed to X-photons. After the temperature treatment, the cells were incubated at 37°C for survival assay. Temperature (°C): G_1 cells, 25, ◆; 31, ■; 34, ▲;35, ▼; 40, ▶; 37, ---. G_1 cells propagated to G_1 + 8 hours before irradiation, 31, □; 34, △; 35, ▽; 37, ○. [Reproduced with permission from Nagasawa *et al.* (4).]

of the responses of the L5178Y S/S lymphoblast to X-photons (4) shown in Fig. 2, coupled with the influence of $LET_∞$. (5). A limiting survival curve (A), generated by the amount and spatial distribution of deposited radiant energy (Zimmer's ideal case) is converted by fast chemical reactions of DNA (34, 35) involving transient species (radical ions, radicals, excited states, etc.) into the cellular survival curve (B) that would pertain in the absence of enzymatic repair processes. Fast chemical reactions involving DNA and immediately adjacent compounds often elicit *chemical* protection, repair, and fixation (34, 35), which can vary in kind and quantity among cell types and affect the position of curve (B) relative to curve A (Fig. 2). Curves of type C can be produced from curve B of the S/S variant by enzymatic processes that obey *first-order* reaction kinetics (19) and are temperature dependent at certain stages in the cell cycle (4, 5) (Fig. 1). Curve D can be

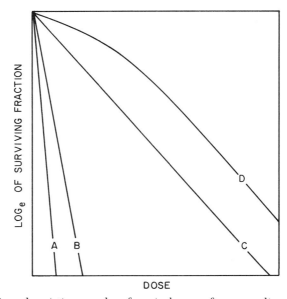

FIG. 2. Some heuristic examples of survival curves for mammalian cells after single acute doses of sparsely ionizing radiations. A, Survival determined by pattern of energy deposition (track structure), the ideal case of Zimmer. B, Survival after completion of rapid chemical reactions. C, Survival after operation of enzymatic repair (and fixation) processes obeying first-order kinetics. D, Survival after (subsequent) operation of enzymatic repair processes obeying "Michaelis–Menten" kinetics; the actual limiting slopes of D will depend upon the processes involved, see text.

generated from curve C by other enzymatic processes that change from about *first-order* to *zero-order* kinetics as the dose (substrate concentration) increases. As the limiting reaction rate is approached, such processes appear to become saturated or overwhelmed (4). Examples of such reaction kinetics were reported for enzymatic catalysis long ago and explained in the classical paper by Michaelis and Menten in 1913. Enzymes in cells need not behave classically, of course.

Comprehension of the inadequacy of target theory to explain the radiosensitivity of mammalian cells requires knowledge of both the existence of cellular recovery processes and the corollary that the constants in general survival equations represented by Eq. (1) (see Fig. 1 and Curve C in Fig. 2) are not direct measures of the intrinsic sensitivities of radiation targets (4). Refutation of the use of target theory for cells by the classical method of *reductio ad absurdum* (19) then suffices, as the following illustration shows. From target theory, the constant in Eq. (1) can be expressed in terms of the geometrical dimensions of the target (5): the steeper the slope of the survival curve, the bigger the target. Two competing first-order reactions (e.g., 19) can reduce the slope of the survival curve, still give an equation of type 1 (Figs. 1 and 2) and, according to target theory, thus reduce the size of the target. The better the repair, the smaller the target. In the limiting (theoretical) case of a completely repair-proficient cell, the slope of the survival curve will become vanishingly small and so will the size of the target. Hence, according to target theory, cells with fully proficient repair systems survive because they do not contain targets that can be hit (5, 19).

In this article, the DNA chemistry related to radiation damage expressed in curve B is examined, together with the accuracy of the basic (implicit) tenet that the damage must be directly proportional to dose. Otherwise, a simple exponential curve requires a complicated explanation. Emphasis is upon double-strand breaks in DNA, however, because such damage, unrepaired or otherwise, is widely believed to be the main cause of cell death (e.g., 7, 14), since normally radioresistant cells seem proficient in the repair of other kinds of DNA damage. Except for specific examples considered later, the kinetics of recovery processes are not within the current purview, but appropriate mathematical treatments can be found in standard textbooks. Note, however, that termination of enzymatic reactions by cellular processes unrelated to repair must be considered (19, 36), as must the effect of linear energy transfer on repair proficiency (5, 36), since a component of intrinsically *irreparable* damage encountered from exposure to any ionizing radiation can determine the upper limit of the curve. Kinetic equations become complex for two, or more, processes operating concurrently, consecutively, etc., but curve fitting by general polynomials should be avoided. The method of choice is to dissect features of specific processes by the use of special experimental conditions and/or the employment of mutants with different efficiencies of repair mechanisms that are under genetic control (4, 5).

From the above, the counterproductive effect of the abstraction, the repair of sublethal damage, can be seen. In the sense considered, *all* the damage is potentially lethal damage, and the cellular responses are distinguished mostly by the differing kinetics of recovery processes that operate after any radiobiologically significant dose of sparsely ionizing radiation. Once the notion of sublethal damage is rejected, however, the term "potentially lethal damage" becomes a tautology, and the matter reduces to the simple concept that ionizing radiation causes a spectrum of damage in cells that is lethal unless it is

repaired—by processes that can be delineated with the rigorous termi-
nologies of the physical and life sciences (1, 4, 5). Judicious simplifi-
cation with respect to "potentially lethal damage" has the approval of
the originator of the term, L. J. Tolmach (personal communication).

For a field responsible for the discovery of cellular and molecular
repair mechanisms, and the established definition of the cell cycle
(25), the sad situation of the last 25 years is, I hope, over. Historians of
science may ponder why utilization of patently unsound theories and
an experimentally untestable abstraction persisted when the very
need for examination of quantitative reaction kinetics was so obvious,
and has found expression in various models (37).[3] From the practical
standpoint, of course, large sums of public monies have been expended on entrenchment rather than solution, and part of the basic
teaching matter for radiotherapy residents has been ambiguous and
unscientific.

II. Mechanisms of Energy Transfer

A. Basic Terminology

To simplify discussion of current knowledge of the radiation-
induced chemical events in the immediate environment of irradiated
mammalian genomic DNA, the following convention is used. Initial
ionization events in bulk, i.e., normal, water are:

$$H_2O \rightarrow H_2O^{\cdot+} + e^- \text{ (dry)} \tag{2}$$

$$H_2O^{\cdot+} + H_2O \rightarrow OH^{\cdot} + H_3O^+ \tag{3}$$

$$e^- \text{ (dry)} + nH_2O \rightarrow e^- \text{ (aq)} \tag{4}$$

Reactions (3) and (4) are less likely to occur in the hydration water
surrounding such polar macromolecules as DNA (38), so e^- (dry) will
henceforth be called an electron, which it is. Comparable initial events
in anhydrous DNA are described by Eq. (5) because radiant energy is
deposited in localized concentrations sufficient

---

[3] One physicist noted for the development of theories of track structure "persisted in
the use of target theory precisely because it is quantitative and testable. When particle
beams interact with matter, that interaction is reported as a cross-section. Target theory
makes it possible to calculate these cross-sections. When experimental data are quantitative, we must demand that models also be quantitative. If experimental data yield
cross-sections, models must yield cross-sections. Qualitative abstractions that are not
testable, and that are typically phrased with such words as 'could be' or 'might be,' are
not worth consideration, as 'might be' could equally well be replaced with 'might not
be' " (R. Katz, personal communication).

$$DNA \rightarrow DNA^{\cdot +} + e^- \tag{5}$$

to break any covalent bond in DNA. In standard quantum-mechanical semiconductor terminology, reaction (5) produces electrons and "holes" in DNA. Both can migrate to other points in the macro-molecule where energetic and structural considerations, such as the energy sink provided by thymine for electrons, determine that they be trapped. Other compounds or structures attached to the DNA can provide traps to localize energy transferred through the macro-molecule and (deoxyribo)nucleoprotein.

Generally speaking, the lives of excited states, radical ions and radicals etc., are so ephemeral at ambient temperature that it is neces-sary to use very short examination periods after a radiation pulse, and/or very low temperatures, in order to examine their behavior. In the latter case, information about subsequent reactions is obtained by raising the temperature (annealing) throughout the range over which radical species can persist.

B. Hydration of DNA

Three decades ago, serious consideration was given first to the role of DNA hydration in cellular radiosensitivity. It stemmed from the question: what serve better as models for the situation of DNA *in situ:* dilute solutions of DNA; DNA gels composed of DNA fibers, or films, hydrated to extents comparable to the local aqueous environments of cellular DNA? The initial studies with dry DNA and DNA gels (9–12), examined in Section II,G, demonstrated important roles for water of hydration in the induction of double-strands breaks (DSB) and anoxic DNA crosslinking reactions, and prompted also the measurement of the hydration curve of DNA (12). Subsequently, the basic characteris-tics of the DNA hydration curve have been substantiated, (e.g., 39), and critical facets of the binding of the water molecules to DNA have been revealed (e.g., 40, 41).

As DNA hydration proceeds under conditions of increasing relative humidity at ambient temperature (12, 39, 40), transition occurs from the A to the B form of the duplex, the most common form of nuclear DNA in animate systems. At that juncture, the bound water molecules lie mostly in the grooves of the duplex, and the zig–zag configuration of the water chain in the minor groove seems necessary for the stability of B DNA (40). Water molecules in this initial layer are bound strongly to the DNA in a crystalline state different from the semicrystalline state of liquid water, and are thought to represent a discrete primary layer of water (41) in which 10–12 H_2O molecules per nucleotide are bound to phosphate groups, sugars, and bases. Many of those water molecules, and some of their outlying neighbors, form bonds with the nitrogen and oxygen atoms of the bases, and even form bridges from one DNA strand to the other (40). Given the strength of the binding, and the fact that initial reactive species formed in the primary hydration layer (7) [Eq. (2)], are already adjacent to the DNA, and vice versa, the primary hydration layer is involved in *direct* action insofar as energy deposition is concerned (e.g., 1, 19).

Even though the transition may not be abrupt, and a solvation layer approaching 20 H_2O molecules per nucleotide could still have strong binding, further hydration of the DNA begins to introduce water molecules into positions where the binding energies are more likely to be those of liquid (bulk) water. From such bulk water, reactive species formed by indirect action may migrate to the DNA. Distinction between the behavior of water molecules in the initial hydration layers and those in further levels of hydration is revealed by the radiation-induced conductivity of hydrated DNA.

C. Conductivity Induced by Pulsed Radiation

During the 50 years since it was suggested that the semiconductive properties of proteins might play an important role in biological processes (42), such properties have received extensive examination. Intrinsic (dark) conductivities of pure, dry polymers generally are very low, yet significant increases can occur upon hydration (43). Radiation-induced conductivity is critically dependent on the level of hydration when DNA is exposed to high-energy electrons at very low temperatures (Fig. 3). From the decay of the induced conductivity detected within one microsecond following 2–50-ns radiation pulses (44, 45), the charge carriers seem to be electrons. The hydration threshold (0.79 g H_2O/g DNA) for radiation-induced conductivity (Fig. 3) corresponds well with the level of hydration needed to form B DNA. Although in that configuration the stacked DNA bases have an optimal overlap for the internal delocalized π-orbital (46, 47), charge (electron) migration seems to occur through the hydration water (48), but whether the B configuration of DNA is required for the process is not known. Electron migration is limited in frozen dry DNA (9 nm; 30 base-pairs). However, in DNA hydrated to 1.65 g H_2O/g DNA, migration seems possible over long distances (micrometers) with mobilities 10^3 to 10^4 times those of ions in aqueous solution. Yet once ionization has occurred [Eq. (5)] recombination of the charged species is hindered, either energetically or spatially (45, 48).

Comparable conduction behavior is exhibited by collagen (Fig. 3)

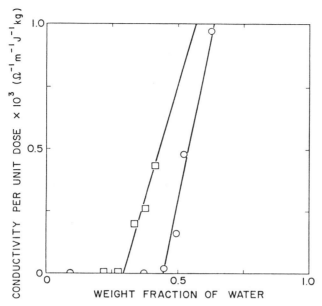

FIG. 3. Effect of hydration on the radiation-induced conductivity of DNA (○) and collagen (□) at 77 K. [Reproduced in revised form, with permission, from van Lith *et al.* (*45*).]

and other proteins. For a polysaccharide, both dark and radiation-induced conductivities showed discontinuities at the same critical water content (*49*). Generally, therefore, charge carriers formed within the bound water regions are immobile or become localized in less than one nanosecond, whereas fully hydrated polymers do not behave as effective trapping sites for mobile electrons in adjacent ice regions (*49*).

Energy transfer via the outer hydration water seems possible over extended distances throughout nucleoproteins *in situ* even if the water in the grooves of the DNA helix, and other strongly bound water in proximal macromolecules, do not contribute to the process. Mechanistic models utilizing such possibilities for DNA are currently under development (*49a*). Hydration water should envelope the nucleosome, so energy transfer could "short-circuit" passage along the DNA molecule by moving laterally between the DNA windings with 2.7-nm separations (*50*). Furthermore, the packing of nucleosomal structures into 10- and 30-nm fibers (*7*) will also help to determine the extent to which hydration water contributes to the local aqueous DNA environment in cells. Energy traps, or charge-transfer complexes, present in biological macromolecular configurations would provide important focal points for energy localization.

D. Pulse Radiolysis of Solid (Hydrated) DNA

Short-lived light emissions (luminescence) are caused by fast chemical events involving transient species present during (in-pulse), and after, a pulse of radiation. From early studies of such processes (e.g., 51), it was concluded that energy transfer can extend over 100 DNA base-pairs. Those experiments involved the use, as incident radiation, of pulsed electrons with energies sufficient to cause the concomitant emission during the pulse of Cerenkov radiation, which is emitted when a relativistic electron enters a medium at a speed greater than the speed of light in that medium.

Subsequent use of 30-ns electron pulses at energies ($\leq$ 260 keV) below the Cerenkov threshold permits facile observation of the very fast events occurring in-pulse (52, 53). In behavior consistent with the conductivity phenomenon, the in-pulse spectra obtained *in vacuo* from dry fibrous DNA, which were independent of temperature (77 K, 293 K), were weak and short-lived ($<$0.1 μsec), but hydration up to 1.4 g H_2O/g DNA caused a response indicative of increased electron mobility. At ambient temperature, oxygen (1 atm) quenched the luminescence spectrum in dry DNA by 35–40%, but only if the freeze-dried samples were maintained under vacuum for at least 48 hours and then purged with oxygen for 3 hours prior to irradiation, the time for oxygen to diffuse into the sample. Energy transfer over a mean distance of 25 base-pairs (provisional) was determined by use of the electron-affinic compound, misonidazole, as an energy trap. Oxygen quenching, presumably by electron scavenging, was equivalent to that of 1 misonidazole molecule per 15 DNA base-pairs. All these observations are pertinent to the subsequent comparisons with the original studies of hydrated DNA (9–12).

Recent adaptation of pulse photolysis to the examination of opaque and highly scattering systems (54) has permitted its use as "time-resolved diffuse reflectance pulse radiolysis" for the examination, also at ambient temperature, of the transient, but longer-lived species, appearing in irradiated hydrated DNA (55). After an electron pulse long enough (5 μsec) for the mobile charge carriers and excited states to disappear, a weak transient, but long-lived, absorption pattern decayed by 35% in 30 msec. Removal of oxygen did not affect this response but hydration (1 g H_2O/g DNA; 20 H_2O molecules/nucleotide) did, and once again, misonidazole seemed to quench electron-gain centers by scavenging electrons. Important information about radiation effects in DNA can be expected when the full potential of this new and powerful technique is exploited fully.

Thus far, evidence has been presented about the involvement of hydration water in the initial events occurring in irradiated DNA and the migration (transfer) of the transient species. Another important source of modulation is the modification of the response of cellular DNA by the constituent proteins in nucleoprotein.

E. Energy Transfer in Nucleoprotein from Protein to DNA

Establishment of the occurrence of inter- and intramolecular energy transfer upon irradiation of solid synthetic polymers (56) soon was followed by the demonstration of such processes in irradiated proteins by measurements of electron spin resonance (ESR) (57, 58). Use of that technique then provided evidence for the transfer, at 77 K *in vacuo*, of energy deposited in protein to DNA in an highly condensed nucleoprotamine (DNA : salmine, 7 : 3), the fish sperm head (13), isolable by simple plasmolysis in a relatively nonswollen condition (~50% water). Differences in the ESR spectra from the nucleoprotein and its constituents were interpreted to mean that energy was transferred efficiently from protein to DNA by primary processes before the formation of the radicals detectable by ESR measurements. That interpretation was supported by further examination of sperm heads and DNA–protein complexes (59), and it was noted that the DNA protected the protein from the effects of direct deposition of energy.

Similar conclusions, reached by analysis of radiation-induced luminescence in irradiated nucleohistone (60), prompted examination of the transfer of electronic excitation energy from protein to DNA in calf thymus nucleohistone by pulsed electron (1.6 μsec) luminescence spectroscopy (61). After irradiation at 93 K, the excitation energy was transferred with 40% efficiency via the release of energy from histone trapping sites.

Although energy transfer from protein to DNA has been confirmed sporadically in the intervening years, and can now be considered an established phenomenon, a recent illustration of it is of particular interest here because of the conditions under it was measured. In frozen solutions of natural chromatin and reconstituted complexes, a large increase in DNA thymyl radicals, ˙TH, (see Fig. 5) indicated a significant transfer of electrons generated in the histone proteins (62) to DNA (~60%) but there was no evidence of the transfer of hole centers (*63*, *64*). Hence histone proteins act as DNA sensitizers to direct action (*63*), or DNA protects proteins.

F. Radiation Responses of Frozen Solutions of DNA

Notwithstanding environmental modulation where the responses of DNA in nucleoproteins are concerned, it is appropriate now to consider DNA models that may simulate better the cellular situation than either hydrated DNA fibers (films) or dilute DNA solutions, namely, frozen solutions of DNA. Much of what is presented below is a liberal paraphrase of an article (*38*) that contains an extensive evaluation of preceding research, supports my long-held concepts (*1, 9–12, 19*), and is necessary to the development of the thesis of this article.

In the cell nucleus, the local concentrations of DNA, RNA, protein, and smaller molecules make the environment of the genetic material more a gum-like paste than a dilute aqueous solution. Around such polar macromolecules as DNA, the properties of the (hydration) water are profoundly altered and the perturbation can extend for several nanometers from the polarizing molecule. The hydration water possesses an ordered, ice-like, structure; has restricted rotational and translational mobility compared to bulk water above 273 K but retains considerable mobility down to 193 K when the bulk water is totally immobilized; and undergoes anisotropic diffusion. Most nuclear water is hydration water. Profound changes also occur in the chemical response to radiation by hydration water. In the structured layer around the DNA helix the "dry charges" from the radiolytic reaction described by Eq. (2) are likely to reach and react with the DNA before solvation and the production of long-lived intermediates [e.g., Eqs. (3) and (4)] can occur. A 100-fold increase in the solvation times of $H_2O^{\cdot+}$ and e^- lengthens their presolvation distances to 8.5 and 35 nm, respectively. Most of the damage to cellular DNA is initiated by the formation of DNA ion-radicals (see below) irrespective of whether the primary energy deposition occurs in the "naked" DNA molecule or in the hydration volume (*38*).

Frozen solutions of DNA are essentially phase-separated systems because the ice freezes into crystallites separate from the DNA molecules, which are left with local environments composed essentially of hydration water situated in the interstices of the ice crystals. As the temperature of this system is raised to 135 K after irradiation at 77 K, ·OH radicals formed in bulk water recombine because they cannot cross the phase boundary and attack the DNA. On warming to ambient temperature, the H_2O_2 formed by that recombination will not harm the DNA unless redox-active transition metal ions are present (*65*). Those cations can catalyze further ˙OH radical formation by the Haber–Weiss reaction (Fenton's reagent) (*14*).

The overall response of frozen solutions of DNA irradiated at 77 K is represented in Fig. 4. In that figure, the upper curve represents the total radical yield at 77 K in the DNA and *all* the water. Annealing to 135 K (middle curve) reveals the yield of DNA-located radicals not produced by indirect action because the water radicals trapped in the ice crystallites recombine (hatched regions). The yield of DNA-located radicals is twice that from dry DNA (slope of lower curve), so the difference is due to the hydration water, which would have a mass about equal to that of the anhydrous DNA if the efficiencies of the processes are similar. That value (~18 H_2O molecules per nucleotide) fits well with the known features of hydration water as reported here. For the DNA of the supercoiled plasmid pBR322 discussed below, the

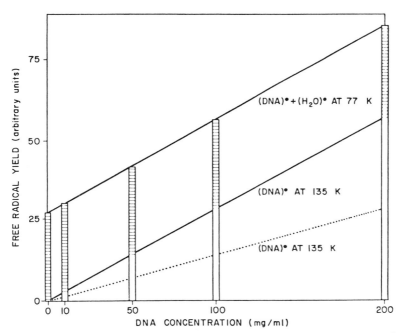

FIG. 4. Schematic illustration of damage caused to DNA in frozen aqueous solution by γ-photons. Upper curve, hatched columns: $(H_2O)˙$ radical yield at 77 K. Middle curve: linear $(DNA)˙$ radical yield at 135 K, the annealing temperature for ˙OH radicals trapped in ice crystallites. Lower curve: the absence of hydration water halves the linear yield of $(DNA)˙$ in dry DNA samples. [Reproduced in modified form, with permission, from Gregoli *et al.* (*38*).]

value is ~15 H_2O molecules per base molecule, ignoring the spine water (66). With this interpretation of the radiation effects, hydrated DNA can be considered as a system in which DNA is affected by roughly twice the energy absorbed by anhydrous DNA, because events in hydration water result in the transfer of energy (charge) to the DNA. Such *water-mediated* irradiation effects result from direct action, since they do not involve diffusing species from bulk water, e.g., $\cdot$OH (38).

Utilization of a system of frozen solutions of supercoiled pBR322 DNA by Cullis, Symons, and their colleagues in a series of (still ongoing) studies is providing valuable insights into the chemistry of radiation processes in DNA. Early radiation events caused by direct action in plasmid DNA and detected by ESR measurements have been assessed on the basis of computer subtraction analysis of the ESR spectra (38, 62–65, 67–70).

Primary ion radicals are formed at random at 77 K, and, through charge migration, approximately equal yields of $G^{\cdot+}$ cations and $T^{\cdot-}$ anions are obtained because guanine and thymine are the eventual energy sinks for short-range hole migration and long-range electron migration, respectively. The yields are influenced little by overall DNA base composition. Annealing above 130 K, when the $\cdot$OH radicals in the ice crystallites are eliminated, causes $T^{\cdot-}$ to react irreversibly with surrounding molecules of hydration water to form 5-thymyl radicals by protonation (Fig. 5), whereas $G^{\cdot+}$ reacts by processes not yet understood.

At 77 K, oxygen scavenges electrons, and O_2^- ions are formed close to the DNA at the expense of $T^{\cdot-}$. As annealing proceeds, the solvation of the O_2^- ions is altered and some are protonated to $HO_2^{\cdot}$, and around

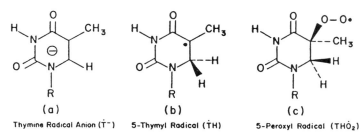

FIG. 5. Thymine derivatives formed by γ-photon irradiation of frozen aqueous solutions of plasmid pBR322 DNA. [Reproduced in modified form, with permission, from Symons (63) and from Boon *et al.* (67).

193 K they are lost concomitantly with the appearance of $RO_2^\bullet$ radicals formed by reaction with $T^{\bullet-}$, or the thymyl radical (Fig. 5), or indirectly from $G^{\bullet+}$. The yield of $RO_2^\bullet$ depends on the availability of oxygen, and if peroxylation saturates, an excess of thymine radicals is formed.

Use of the supercoiled plasmid (pBR322) permitted subsequent analyses of the irradiated DNA by gel electrophoresis for formation of both double- and single-strand breaks (DSBs and SSBs) (38, 63, 65, 67–69) under oxic and apoxic conditions, without evidence of cross-linking (66), and also in the presence of cellular radiosensitizers and other compounds. Both DSBs and SSBs were formed *as a linear function of dose* by Co-60 γ-irradiation at efficiencies (see extrapolation to ~273 K in the frozen state, in Fig. 6, and Section II,b) comparable to those found in other DNA studies at ambient temperature, especially in mammalian cells (*14, 71*) (see also Section IV); the effect of oxygen on strand breakage was small.

Electron spin resonance can be used only to detect certain kinds of intermediates in the reactions leading to (stable) chemical end products that include strand breaks (67). A major difficulty has been the lack of overt evidence for the formation of sugar radicals that, on the basis of the radiation chemistry of dilute solutions of DNA, are known to result in the rupture of the sugar–phosphate backbone (*14*). However, analysis of the reactions of additives is leading toward the identification of the intermediate species arising from the direct deposition of energy in

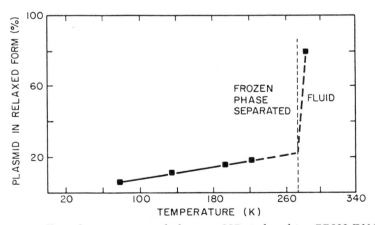

FIG. 6. Effect of temperature and phase on SSBs induced in pBR322 DNA (~80 μg/mol) by γ-photons (~100 Gy). Analysis for SSBs was conducted at 293 K. The phase difference is due to $^\bullet$OH radicals formed in bulk water. [Reproduced with permission from Boon *et al.* (67).]

hydrated DNA at low temperatures (63, 65, 69). Iodoacetamide bound to, and hydrogen peroxide in the hydration water of, plasmid DNA both sensitize the molecule to γ-irradiation (63, 65, 69). Hydrogen peroxide yields $^{\cdot}$OH radicals in the hydration shell by reaction (6) together with the anticipated reduction in $T^{\cdot-}$ (TH$^{\cdot}$) and, to a lesser extent, $G^{\cdot+}$. Concentrations

$$H_2O_2 + e^- \rightarrow {}^{\cdot}OH + OH^- \tag{6}$$

of $^{\cdot}$OH formed in the hydration water under normal circumstances are very low, of course (38, 65). The ESR spectra accompanying the reactions involving iodoacetamide and hydrogen peroxide are indicative of the formation of alkyl radicals that, although unidentified as yet, seem likely to be sugar-centered radicals involved in strand breakage. Those radicals cannot usually be detected because they decay at temperatures at which the $G^{\cdot+}$ and $^{\cdot}$TH persist; hence their spectra are obscured in the absence of additives that modify the normal reaction pathways and/or their rates (63, 65, 69). Hydroxyl radicals formed from hydrogen peroxide in the hydration water of pBR322 plasmid DNA cause increases in both DSB and SSB (63, 65), yet the induction frequency is still *linear* with dose (65).

Radicals of bases, such as the thymyl radical formed in DNA [Fig. 5(B)], can, if the electron density is appropriate, abstract an hydrogen atom from an adjacent sugar (Fig. 7) to yield a sugar radical and 5,6-dihydrothymine (TH$_2$), which is isolable as a major product from

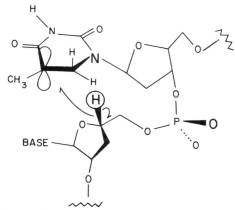

FIG. 7. Possible transfer mechanism for a neighboring C–H hydrogen atom to a $^{\cdot}$TH center in irradiated DNA. The resulting sugar-centered radical can be responsible for strand breaking. [Reproduced in modified form with permission from Symons (63).]

frozen aqueous solutions of *Escherichia coli* DNA after γ-irradiation at 77 K (72). In the presence of oxygen, base peroxyl radicals may play an analogous role. Under aerobic conditions, there is no evidence for sequence specificity of strand breakage in DNA or oligonucleotides; the 3' and 5' termini are simple phosphates (70), and a strand-breaking mechanism involving hydrogen atom abstraction from C-1' and C-2' sites of neighboring sugars by base radicals has been suggested (70) (cf. Fig. 7). From the radiation chemistry of dilute aqueous solutions of DNA, it has long been established that the formation of sugar radicals through hydrogen abstraction leads to strand breakage (14, 72a), but the sugar radicals are thought to be formed primarily from attack on the sugar by ·OH radicals (14, 73). Hydrogen abstraction by base radicals from neighboring sugars may occur to a limited extent, but the chemistry is different from that for direct action (70).

Other useful information comes from observations of spin-labelled DNA irradiated at ambient temperatures in solution (74, 75). Analysis of the attack on the spin-label delineates the type of attack as a function of distance: probes with short tethers (0.7 nm) react mainly with DNA base radicals; longer probes (1.5 nm) react mainly with water and sugar radicals (74, 75).

G. Intermediate Summary and Some Caveats

With respect to the influence of the proximal nuclear environment on its responses to radiation exposure *in situ*, DNA is far from a dormant macromolecule awaiting attack by marauding ·OH radicals created by the deposition of radiant energy in bulk water. Energy deposited directly in the DNA migrates through the delocalized π-orbital of the stacked bases and/or the hydration shell to sites determined by DNA structure and chemical composition. Chromatin proteins and hydration water both can influence and even compound the radiation damage to the DNA. Thus, the cellular radiation target for direct action is at least the nucleoprotein skeleton plus its water of hydration (1, 19). Questions can be raised, however, about the relevance of DNA reactions occurring after irradiation at *low* temperature to the DNA chemistry resulting from direct action at *ambient* temperature. Nevertheless, charge (energy) transfer processes do occur also at ambient temperature, and in the case of DNA strand breakage, hydration water produces formally comparable effects (9–12, 15), which are examined here in light of the recent findings.

Intermolecular crosslinking caused in "dry" DNA under aerobic conditions by large doses of high-energy electrons was attributed to the exhaustion of oxygen in the fibrous DNA samples and its slow replacement by diffusion (*9, 10*), as is confirmed by the evidence noted in Section II,D (*53*). Pronounced increases in crosslinking caused in DNA under anoxic conditions by hydration water can now be explained by the enhanced electron (charge) migration registered by radiation-induced conductivity and other phenomena (*44, 45, 48, 51–53, 55, 63*). Reductions in anoxic crosslinking at high levels of hydration are attributable now, as then, to ˙OH radical attack. Oxygen can reduce or even eliminate crosslinking by electron scavenging or peroxidation, but the effect of oxygen on DSB induction is small (*9–12*). Intermolecular DNA crosslinking occurs in solid (hydrated) fibers and films, phage heads, nucleoproteins and cells (e.g., *9–12, 14, 76*), and cellular DNA–protein crosslinking (*14*) is also an intrinsic response of exposure to UV light. Links composed of small peptides, amino acids, or their derivatives that are impervious to proteolytic enzymes would *imitate DNA–DNA crosslinks.*

Aerobic DSB formation deduced from analyses, complicated by overt crosslinking, of combined measurements of light scattering parameters and intrinsic viscosities of initially linear DNA molecules, was approximately linear with dose up to 4 g H_2O per g DNA (*12*). Presentation of those data in terms of dose delivered to, or *total energy deposited* in, the hydrated fibers (Fig. 8) shows that the efficiencies of DSB formation caused by energy deposited in the hydration water or dry DNA are about equal until the water content exceeds the DNA content, which supports the construction of Fig. 4 (*38*) insofar as a *final outcome* of energy deposition at *ambient* temperature, DSB formation, is concerned.

Responses of plasmid and viral DNA under specific conditions also are particularly informative in this regard. The G value obtained for DSB formation (1.6×10^{-11} DSB/Gy/Da) when the pBR322 plasmid was γ-irradiated aerobically at ambient temperature in hydrated salt films at 75% relative humidity (*15*) is close to that expected from Fig. 8. For SSB induction the G value was 1.6×10^{-10} SSB/Gy/Da, but note that the SSB/LET_∞ response is unusual in such films (*71*) and that salt can affect the responses of fibrous DNA (*9*). Analogous G values can be determined from the responses of the plasmid DNA in frozen solution. Although an assessment of the temperature dependence for DSB formation in the pBR322 plasmid comparable to that for SSB induction (Fig. 6) has not been undertaken as yet, only a small increase in the SSB/DSB ratio was found in the range 77–220 K (*66*). With that knowledge, the information in 67, the size of pBR322 DNA (4.3 kbp), and the extrapolation in Fig. 6, the aerobic strand-breaking efficiencies in *frozen* solution at 273 K are $\sim 1.6 \times 10^{-11}$ DSB/Gy/Da and $\sim 1.6 \times 10^{-10}$

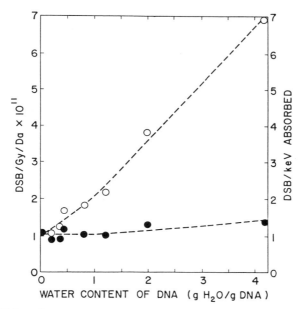

FIG. 8. Effect of water content on aerobic DSB induction by high-energy electrons at ambient temperature in hydrated DNA fibers, and based on dose delivered (○, left ordinate) and energy absorbed (●, right ordinate). For increased accuracy, the scale on the right ordinate should be increased by 4%. [Data from (12), corrected according to information in (71).]

SSB/Gy/Da. Such provisional values are consistent (Fig. 8) with the level of plasmid hydration, 15 H_2O per nucleotide (neglecting the spine water) (66). Also, the G values of 1.9×10^{-11} DSB/Gy/Da and 2.0×10^{-10} SSB/Gy/Da for SV40 DNA irradiated in infected cells, but not incorporated into the genome, see 15 and p. 330, are indicative of full hydration, ~1 g H_2O per g DNA. Furthermore, since the ratio of SSB:DSB was about 10:1 in all three instances, the genome of the SV40 virus behaved, *in situ*, as though it were *a hydrated DNA molecule responding to direct energy deposition*.

Recently, a G value of ~2.5 (~40 eV/SSB) has been determined for SSB induction in viral DNA under ambient conditions in dilute aqueous solution that "protect" it fully from ˙OH-radical attack, i.e., from direct action (J. F. Ward, personal communication). Overall, there is a welcome consistency in the conclusions reached from investigations of direct radiation effects on DNA spanning a period of 30 years and performed in various laboratories with different techniques. Yet the comparisons also serve to emphasize specific caveats implicit to all that follows. (1) Absence of intermolecular DNA crosslinking (with the above proviso) must have been demonstrated unequivocally if estimations of efficiencies of anoxic DNA strand breakage (DSBs and SSBs) in nucleoproteins and cells are to be accepted without reservation. Overt gel formation (9–12) need not have occurred. Numerous efforts to examine the molecular basis of the well-known oxygen effect in cells (77) have yielded differing results (14, 71) that may be related to the actual level of oxygen involved (78). Use of commercial oxygen-free nitrogen, for example, does not guarantee anoxia (78). (2) The relative magnitude of a given biophysical property of a linear DNA molecule compared to a crosslinked, branched, bifurcated, circular, or super-coiled molecule of the same total length (mass) is a function of the property examined (9–12, 63, 67 and Section IV,F). Without consideration of such factors, proper evaluation cannot be made of putative changes in the masses of the very large DNA molecules extractable from mammalian cells by the techniques of gel electrophoresis, neutral sucrose sedimentation, or neutral elution. Mammalian DNA contains looped structures maintained by proteins and may consist of large rings.

Before results obtained *in vitro* can be compared in more detail with those for cellular DNA *in situ*, further description of the environment of that DNA is necessary.

III. Chemical Protection and Radical Scavengers

Protection of DNA against attack from diffusing ($^{\bullet}$OH) radicals by the protein component of nucleoprotein was demonstrated by perceptive early investigations of the radiation responses of nucleoproteins in aqueous solutions (79, 80). Analysis of those results, the status of knowledge of radiation damage to DNA current in 1966, and the genesis of original ideas have been given prior review (34), which serves as the basis for extension here. However, for one interested in an adaptation of the phenomenon of protein protection to modern techniques, its use in the "footprinting" of DNA by $^{\bullet}$OH radical damage (81) is worthy of examination. In the cell nucleus, many molecules of different kinds, large and small, can react with diffusing radicals and, by such scavenging action, eliminate most of them before they can even reach the deoxyribonucleoprotein. One important class of such chemicals, sulfhydryl compounds, has received extensive survey in a recent encyclopedic review (82). Specific examples of reactions of sulfur compounds situated in the hydration water of DNA in frozen aqueous solutions are of relevance here.

Low concentrations of cysteine and glutathione (RSH) leave the initial yields of DNA radicals unaffected, but annealing to 200–210 K causes a marked decrease in the level of DNA radicals and a concomitant rise in ESR spectra characteristic of RSSR$^-$ radical anions. Reduction of strand breakage by *chemical repair* seems to occur under these conditions (63). Disulfides (RSSR), however, give rise to RSSR$^-$ radical anions directly at 77 K and the concentrations of T$^{\cdot-}$ and $^{\cdot}$TH are reduced, which is indicative of *protection (by electron scavenging)* rather than chemical repair (63). Formally analogous mechanisms probably modify the effects of oxygen.

Reactions of sulfur compounds, which can also be representative of amino-acid components in nucleoproteins, can affect DNA responses to irradiation (see also above) in at least three general ways through: (1) fast chemical reactions involving

$$DNA^{\cdot} + RSH \rightarrow DNA + RS^{\cdot} \tag{6}$$

$$DNA^{\cdot} + RS^- \rightarrow DNA^- + RS^{\cdot} \tag{7}$$

$$DNA^- + H^+ \rightarrow DNA \tag{8}$$

chemical repair and fixation, Eqs. (6)–(8); (2) protection against direct and indirect action by scavenging radicals; and (3) effects on subsequent metabolic processes (82). As might be expected, the concept of chemical repair and fixation stemmed from synthetic polymer chemistry and was adopted for DNA chemistry (34, 35, 82a). Such processes will not be examined further here because, henceforth, cellular DNA will be considered *in toto* with respect to its immediate molecular environment, except for special modulations associated with superstructural features that may mitigate damage different from that in bulk DNA. Effects of energy transfer, hydration water, chemical protective agents, strategically located multivalent metallic cations, etc. are assumed to be complete before *enzymatic* repair and fixation begin (34, 35) (see discussion of Fig. 2, Curve B, in Section I).

IV. Strand Breakage in Cellular DNA

A. General Perspective

Whereas DSBs and SSBs can be measured with reasonable facility in extracted DNA, plasmids, viruses, bacteria, and yeasts, radiobiologically significant DNA damage in higher eukaryotic cells, and especially mammalian cells, has proved more refractory to evaluation. There are three main reasons for this: biophysical techniques suffer reductions in, and even loss of, resolution as the masses of linear DNA molcules approach those of the DNA contents of mammalian chromosomes; such molecules are especially sensitive to hydrodynamic shear and/or enzymatic degradation; and the actual configurations of DNA molecules in the architecture of mammalian nucleoproteins still are not properly understood. The use of biophysical techniques has persisted, of course, because currently only those techniques have the potential sensitivity needed for examination of the formation and fate of DNA damage in *survivors* from irradiated populations of proliferative mammalian cells. Fortunately, it is the ability to process DSBs that seems to be the major determinant in the retention of reproductive integrity by normally radioresistant mammalian cells.

Mammalian cells completely deficient in enzymatic repair (Fig. 2, Curve B) need only absorb a dose of 0.025 Gy of X-photon energy (LET$_\infty$ ~1 keV μm^{-1}) if, on average, a DSB in *one* of 40 chromosome-sized DNA molecules of relative mass 10^{11} Da is lethal. Currently, however, the limiting dose for resolution by gel electrophoresis of DSB induction in mammalian cells by X-photons is $\geq$1 Gy (83, 84), which would cause on average one DSB in *each* of the 40 chromosome-sized DNA molecules. By contrast, the limiting resolution of reoriented gradient alkaline sucrose sedimentation in zonal rotors is ~0.02 Gy, and although the exact damage cannot be identified, it probably consists of some 20 total strand breaks (TSBs) affecting half of the chromosome-sized DNA molecules. Analogous considerations apply if, on average, one *unrejoined* DSB kills a cell and unrejoined DSBs are responsible for survival curves of the types illustrated in Fig. 2 (Curves C and D). A worst-case scenario for extant biophysical techniques occurs if all DSBs are rejoined, but *incorrectly* rejoined DSBs are lethal. Cytological approaches to that problem are considered briefly in Section IV,G.

Especially informative in these regards is the behavior of the radiosensitive, diploid mutant *rad 54.3* of *Saccharomyces cerevisiae* (85), the survival of which is determined mostly by the formation and fate of DSBs (33). Rejoining of DSBs in the cell is temperature-conditional and can be examined under growth or nongrowth conditions (33). Under optimal conditions, recovery from low doses can be complete (33). Mutant cells irradiated with 30 MeV electrons (LET$_\infty$ ~0.1 keV μm^{-1}) and treated sequentially under different conditions gave (33) a series of simple exponential survival curves comparable to those in Fig. 1 that are transitional between Curves B and C in Fig. 2, and a series of curves with decreasing slopes but increasing shoulders. With the exception of complete recovery, the range of the latter sequence of curve-shapes (Fig. 2, Curves B–D) encompasses that defined by the behavior of the S/S variant at 37°C at two phases of the cell cycle (Fig. 1) and is simulated closely by the S/S variant during cycle progression (86). Quantitation of the repair kinetics for the *rad 54-3* mutant will prove useful in resolving the underlying bases of cellular radiosensitivity. Temperature-sensitive mutants (variants) clearly are powerful research tools.

Chemical methods for analyzing cellular DNA damage (72, 72a) are orders of magnitude less sensitive than biophysical techniques for DSB detection. With proliferative mammalian cells, supralethal doses are needed and the relevance of examining repair (?) processes in dying cells is moot. At present, the experimental problem posed by the possible lethality of one damaged base per mammalian genome seems insuperable, but that possibility also is unlikely to occur except in very rare circumstances. Another abiding concern is the relevance of base and sugar damage produced in aqueous solutions of DNA by ˙OH radicals to the corresponding classes of damage induced by ionizing radiations in mammalian cells (17). Restoration of base damage in surviving mammalian cells can be examined indirectly through the accompanying formation of SSBs (e.g., 86a), by exploiting the sensitivity of the zonal centrifugation technique, or by introducing specific DNA damage within plasmids that then is incorporated into the mammalian genome (87, 87a). Enzymatic analysis of cellular DNA damage also is useful when the true enzymatic specificities are not in doubt, and enzymatic endgroup analysis may resolve the difficulty of break clusters (88).

Despite the nature of current experimental difficulties, anticipated innovations could produce an emulation of the excitement of two decades ago when the ability of cells to rejoin strand breaks was demonstrated: for DSBs with *Micrococcus radiodurans* (89) (prokaryotes) and Chinese hamster ovary cells (90) (eukaryotes); for SSBs with *E. coli* mutants (91) (prokaryotes) and with the L5178Y S/S variant (eukaryotes) (92).

B. High Doses of Sparsely Ionizing Radiations

For DNA preparations, small biological entities, prokaryotes, lower eukaryotes, and mammalian cells exposed to such large (supralethal) aerobic doses of sparsely ionizing radiation D that the broken DNA molecules have been reduced to sizes where the validity of the experimental procedure for strand-break analysis is unequivocal, the following are true:

$$n_{SSB} = K_1 D \tag{9}$$

$$n_{DSB} = K_2D \tag{10}$$

where n is the number of strand breaks. Such results have been demonstrated repeatedly (see *1, 14, 34, 67, 71* and the numerous references provided therein). When DNA is irradiated in dilute aqueous solution, the response is different [Eqs. (11) and (12)], see (*34, 71*), because SSBs

$$n_{SSB} = K_3D \tag{11}$$

$$n_{DSB} \sim K_4D^2 \tag{12}$$

produced randomly in DNA by ˙OH radical attack do not cause DSBs unless they occur within a few nucleotides of each other on opposite strands of the duplex (*34, 72a, 93*). Mathematical analysis of such SSB distributions was undertaken 35 years ago to explain DSB induction by a nuclease (*94*). Reactions of ˙OH radicals cause analogous DNA responses when produced by hydrogen peroxide in cells and aqueous solution (*7, 17*) but not in hydration water in frozen DNA solutions (*65*). Additionally, recent computer simulations (*73*) of the paths of the diffusing ˙OH radicals (*7, 95*) have confirmed the repeated experimental observation that induction of SSBs in irradiated cells is insufficient to cause the experimentally determined numbers of DSBs by random processes, e.g., by the diffusion of ˙OH radicals.

On the evidence considered thus far, DSBs are induced by high doses of sparsely ionizing radiations under aerobic conditions in DNA, including plasmid DNA, gels with limited water contents (*9–12, 15, 71*), plasmid DNA in frozen aqueous solution (*63–65, 67–69*), viral DNA in the mammalian cell nucleus when not incorporated into the genome (R. Roots, personal communication; *96*), and bulk genomic DNA in prokaryotes and eukaryotes (*14, 71*), by discrete ionizing events through *mechanisms different from those by which the majority of them are formed in aqueous solution at ambient temperatures.* Moreover, the *efficiencies* with which strand breaks are induced at (near) ambient temperatures under these various conditions are also *similar*, although special circumstances may apply to damage at specific sites in cellular (chromatin) structures (*1, 17*), see Section IV,E.

Consolidation of the significant array of aerobic data for a "standard" sparsely ionizing radiation (LET$_\infty$: 1 keV/μm) can be assisted with the following *broad* approximations and generalizations. They are presented with the implicit understanding that some variations in strand-breaking efficiencies will be expected over the LET$_\infty$ range, ~0.1–10 keV/μm, and that a spectrum of other local damage is associated with the strand breaks measured by biophysical techniques, which cannot resolve closely located clusters of breaks (*71*), and that

DSBs may be produced from SSBs by hydrodynamic shearing. First, in anhydrous DNA the strand breaking efficiencies are ~1000 eV/DSB ($\sim 10^{-11}$ DSB/Gy/Da) (Fig. 8) and ~ 100 eV/SSB ($\sim 10^{-10}$ SSB/Gy/Da), a ratio of SSB : DSB of 10 : 1. Second, those efficiencies are doubled by water-mediated direct effects for DNA and, small biological entities, hydrated to 1 g H_2O per g DNA *in vitro*, and for DNA *in situ* when not incorporated into the mammalian genome. Third, for genomic DNA under normal cellular conditions, the efficiency of DSB formation also is ~1000 eV/DSB since the effects of hydration, energy transfer from proteins, chemical protection, etc., are mutually compensatory. The *apparent* efficiency of SSB formation remains around 50 eV/SSB, however, because the alkaline denaturation used to measure SSBs in mammalian DNA converts alkali-labile bonds (7, 14), which presumably are due to sugar damage, into SSBs; so the ratio of SSB : DSB is ~20 : 1. Light-sensitive reactions can also cause spurious increases in SSBs if certain indicators are present during cell lysis under ambient illunination (97).

Similar conclusions cannot be drawn with confidence, as yet, from results obtained under anoxic conditions, since for most cellular investigations the absence of crosslinking has not been demonstrated unequivocally, so those data will not be discussed further here. Definitive examination of such radiation chemistry is of basic importance, however, as oxygen ceases to be a cellular radiosensitizer at LET_∞s around 200–300 keV/μm (77). The crucial need for accurate information for anoxic cells is addressed elsewhere (17).

Induction of DSBs in proportion to dose by a radiation process of low efficiency presents a major difficulty for proponents of indirect action, especially since ˙OH radicals produced close to cellular DNA by hydrogen peroxide reactions at ambient temperature (7) cause many SSBs, but no DSBs, and do not kill cells (7). Two explanations have been offered. One requires that a *single* ˙OH radical causes two SSBs in close proximity on each strand of the DNA duplex (for discussion see 7, 17). The other proposes that DSBs result from proximal SSBs formed by clusters of ionizations in which several ˙OH radicals are generated close together near the DNA (7), in which case, of course, cellular radical scavengers that reduce DSBs *also must act near* the DNA (J. F. Ward, personal communication).

Although the notion of ionization clusters is a good one, it applies equally well to DNA, hydrated DNA, and nucleoproteins and, indeed, was first invoked to explain discrete DSB events in hydrated DNA (10, 17). The cluster calculations for water (7) cannot be applied *a priori* to DNA, and lack of detailed information about the oscillator strengths for the upper energy levels in DNA, etc., currently precludes such calculations for DNA (98), although some cluster tightening can be anticipated (98). Often, the G value of ~0.1 for DSB formation has been confused with the need for a 1000-eV event to induce a DSB. Not only is that untrue, because the same 1000 eV are responsible for 10 (20) SSBs, base damage, etc., and the upper limit for the energy of a covalent bond is only about 10 eV, but also the actual amount of energy involved is unknown and need not have a fixed value (17) above the prescribed threshold (99). Furthermore, when a localized energy event of that magnitude is produced in DNA, by a burst of Auger electrons, for example, the local molecular damage is both massive, see Section IV,C, and atypical of DNA damage produced by sparsely ionizing radiations. All that is really needed to explain the G value for DSB formation is the occurrence of relatively rare, discrete, events; hence, the proposal that a DSB sometimes can result from a radical ion pair ($G^{\cdot+}$ and $T^{\cdot-}$) produced by a single ionizing event (63, 67) deserves attention, as do its logical derivatives, the soliton hypothesis (99a) and use of condensed-matter physics to address the situation (15). The supposition that energy is transferred (along macromolecules) as solitary wave-forms (solitons) may be used to explain not only radiation effects in DNA but also aspects of the radiolysis of water (99b).

C. Effects of Linear Energy Transfer (LET$_\infty$): High Doses of Densely Ionizing Radiation

If the preceding considerations of ionization clustering, etc., are correct, then the effects of increasing LET$_\infty$ should be predictable. For sparsely ionizing radiations, the average energy loss per inelastic event in tissue-equivalent material (100), 60 eV, is close to the G value for SSB formation, and although the comparable value for DNA is not known (98), SSBs probably are formed with nearly maximum efficiency even by sparsely ionizing radiations. Increases in LET$_\infty$ should cause corresponding decreases in the efficiency of SSB formation, as they do in general for all "chemical" reactions. On the other hand, the probability of breaking adjacent DNA strands and forming DSBs should increase with LET$_\infty$ until the point of maximum efficiency is reached, and it should then decrease progressively, by analogy with SSB induction, as the additional energy is wasted. Just those effects of LET$_\infty$ are observed with DNA, (see Fig. 9), and *strand breakage is linear with dose* in every case.

A wide range in the severity of macromolecular damage occurs as the LET$_\infty$ increases from ~1 keV/μm for sparsely ionizing radiations (roughly 0.1–10 keV/μm), with rare densely ionizing events of >100

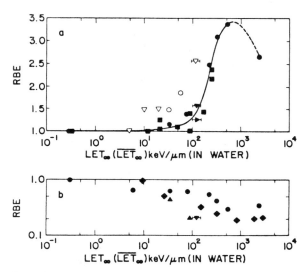

FIG. 9. Effect of linear energy transfer on induction of (a) DSBs and (b) TSBs in various systems. [Reproduced with permission from Lett (17); for details see (71).]

eV (100), to the massive energy deposition from the (fortunately) very rare ion of uranium-92 encountered in deep space. The dose can reach 1.6×10^6 MGy at an LET_∞ of 1.6×10^4 keV/μm (101) in the inner core of that HZE particle, which can also disintegrate upon nuclear collision to release a shower of primary particles (hadrons). Perhaps the most biologically dangerous HZE particle in deep space, in terms of flux and probable RBE, is the Fe-56 ion (5), the LET_∞ of which is some 200 keV/μm at relativistic energies (5, 77) but rises to many times that value as the ion deposits energy and comes to rest in an astronaut.

Illustration of the sheer molecular violence that can accompany very densely ionizing events is provided by the effects caused in DNA by the radioactive decay of I-125. Electron capture followed by decay of Te-125m evokes bursts of Auger electrons varying in number from 1 to 56 but with a mean number of 21 (102), deposition of 850 eV in a volume of 10-nm diameter (102), and destruction of the base that contained the radionuclide in plasmid pBR322 DNA to the point of extensive CO and CO_2 formation (103, 104). Local DSB formation with proximal multiple breaks, accompanied by extensive distal DSB induction (up to several hundred bp away) in thymine-rich regions (energy sinks), can be discerned, especially when the plasmid DNA is in the circular configuration (103, 104); but difficulties arise if use is made of the average dose per decay, which is $\sim 10^7$ Gy at the nano-meter level, to quantify the localized strand breaks (105).

Little wonder then that clusters of DSBs, etc. formed by very densely ionizing events stretching along particle tracks right through cellular DNA configurations are responsible for deletions of genomic material either directly or during the subsequent attempts by the cell to repair the damage (106). The rejoining of DNA strand-breaks observed as an aftermath of such violence (101) is mostly a residual metabolic response of rapidly dying cells (5), since the accuracy of repair systems will decrease as the LET_∞ of the incident radiation increases (17), even though strand rejoining and other processes may still appear to function, albeit to increasingly reduced extents (101, 107, 108).

From the biological standpoint, extensive wastage of energy occurs in the tracks of HZE particles at high LET_∞ (Fig. 10; the ions become very ineffective in reducing the reproductive integrity of cultured cells in terms of the *dose* delivered (109), and the RBEs for strand breakage fall far below those in Fig. 9 (101). Cores of intense damage, or "minile-sions," caused in organized tissues by radiations in deep space can be quite another matter. We concentrate, henceforth, on the ranges of LET_∞, up to a few hundred keV/μm, to be expected from densely ionizing radiations in the terrestrial environment—e.g., the α-particles from the short-lived radon progeny (Po-214, Po-218) that produce most of the background dose to the lung.

Neutrons, which for present purposes can be considered to interact

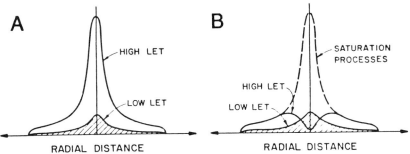

FIG. 10. Schematical representation of the dose distribution in a particle track. (A) Physical dose from a light and a heavy particle having the same specific energy but different LET_∞. (B) Biologically effective dose. In the inner part of the heavy particle track, saturation processes waste the majority of the energy deposited. [Reproduced with permission from Kraft (113).]

with matter to eject protons, usually are not useful analytical tools in radiation biology, because the response depends on the hydrogen content of the irradiated material, which is atypical of other ionizing radiations. Often the LET_∞ spectra of generated neutron beams are broad and the beams are contaminated with γ-rays, so data from neutron exposures should be considered separately from those for charged nuclei (71). Proper interpretation of the biological effects of neutrons will probably require information derived from experiments with charged particles. Nevertheless, analytical use of neutron beams can produce important information about DNA damage.

When oriented fibers of hydrated DNA (0.43 g/g DNA) are exposed to neutron beams (3% γ-photons) at 77 K, the chemical yields produced by the ejected protons depend upon the angle of incidence of the neutron beams (110). Neutron irradiation perpendicular to the fiber axis yields $G^{\cdot+}$ and $T^{\cdot-}$ in approximately equal amounts. Yet irradiation parallel to the fiber axis causes a threefold decrease in the yield of the radical ions, and $\cdot TH$ radicals are the major product, by reaction of $T^{\cdot-}$ with hydration water. A large asymmetrical migration of energy (over 50–500 nm), as a thermal spike, could explain this phenomenon (98, 111, 112); compare the formation of $\cdot TH$ from $T^{\cdot-}$ during annealing of γ-irradiated DNA (67). Other modes of energy transfer, including solitons, are also possible (98, 111, 112). In the present context, the implications are that DNA damage from densely ionizing radiations can depend, both qualitatively and quantitatively, upon the angle of incidence of the ionizing particle, and that the effects can be manifested at long range. A mechanistic model is being developed to explain such anisotropy. It involves electron migration through the DNA hydration shell (98).

Construction of Fig. 9 from information available before 1986 required substantial approximation, due primarily to uncertainties in LET_∞ values imposed on early studies with particles of short range (71); errors of $\pm 50\%$ for some LET_∞ ($\overline{LET_\infty}$) values are probable. Recent improvements in such high-energy machines as the BEVALAC at the Lawrence Berkeley Laboratory, University of California (77), and the UNILAC-plus-SIS at the Gesellschaft für Schwerionenforschung, Darmstadt, FDR (113), have facilitated the use of beam segment analysis with closely defined ranges of LET_∞ (5, 77). If Fig. 9 were extended with newer data obtained at higher LET_∞s, the changes would include a further reduction in the RBE_{SSB} and a decline in RBE_{DSB} below 1 (101). The latter curve then would have a shape similar to the RBE/ LET_∞ response for cell survival (77) compiled from data obtained under broadly comparable conditions.

Extension of Fig. 9 is not useful, however, because it is really composed of small segments from a spectrum of curves for different particles. Each ion (Z) has an individual overall track structure (see Glossary) and a shape of DSB/LET$_\infty$ response comparable to that for an "extended" Fig. 9(a) but with a unique range of LET$_\infty$ and height and position of the RBE peak (113–115). Nowadays, moreover, it is known that: (1) cellular RBE/LET$_\infty$ responses depend upon repair efficiency (2–5); (2) the LET$_\infty$ value for maximum cellular RBE varies with cell-cycle position; (3) for repair-deficient cells, the RBE need never exceed 1 at certain phases of the cell cycle (1, 2, 5, 17) when the cells behave "as though they were enzymes or viruses" (2, 5, 17). To attempt to absorb and retain all aspects of the different types of chemical, physical, and structural damage associated with strand breakage in DNA structures in situ generally is not constructive, although it can be useful to base a first level of recall on the Orwellian principle that all DSBs are equal but some DSBs are more equal than others.

As the LET$_\infty$ increases, ·OH radicals originating in particle tracks through bulk water will occur closer together and have increased opportunities to recombine rather than attack adjacent molecules, an effect observed, for example, with the Fricke dosimeter, which is based on the conversion of Fe^{2+} to Fe^{3+} in aqueous solution. Therefore, ·OH radical diffusion cannot explain the LET$_\infty$-mediated increases in DSB induction (Fig. 9) and water should play a reduced role in the process unless energy deposited close to DNA in hydration water is of paramount importance.

D. Strand Breakage from Low Doses of Ionizing Radiation

When strand breakage in one gram of a distribution of *linear* polymer molecules is proportional to dose (Gy), the efficiency of strand breakage, b, is given by Eq. (13), where M_{irr} and M_o are the irradiated and unirradiated number-

$$N(1/M_{irr} - 1/M_o) = bD \tag{13}$$

average relative molecular masses of the distribution, and the number average value, M_n, is given by Eq. (14), where n_i, M_i, and w_i are the number, number-average

$$M_n = \Sigma\, n_i M_i / \Sigma\, n_i = \Sigma\, w_i / \Sigma\, w_i\, M_i^{-1} \tag{14}$$

relative mass, and weight of the molecules in the ith fraction of the distribution (10, 34, 97, 116). From most experimental measurements, the weight-average value, M_w [Eq. (15)], or an even more complicated average value is obtained (10, 34, 97, 116). For a monodisperse

$$M_w = \Sigma\ w_i\ M_i / \Sigma\ w_i = \Sigma n_i M_i^2 / \Sigma\ n_i M_i \qquad (15)$$

distribution $M_w = M_n$, and for a random (116) distribution $M_w = 2M_n$. In other cases, the actual size distribution must be determined before M_n can be calculated, especially when only a limited number of an initially monodisperse distribution of molecules has been broken.

Moderate and relatively high doses of X-photons induce nearly random distributions (34) of strand breaks in the DNA of mammalian cells. If the analytical methods are not compromised by artifacts, and if the strand-breaking efficiency does not vary with dose below the experimental range, Eq. (13) can be used to determine M_o, *the size of the DNA molecules in unirradiated cells.* Alkaline denaturation yielded an M_o for single-stranded DNA of ~5×10^8, not the ~5×10^{10} anticipated from the chromosome-sized DNA molecules (32, 117, 117a) [Fig. 11(a)]; for duplex DNA [Fig. 11(b)], M_o was ~2×10^9 (114, 114a, 115). Since the results from alkaline sucrose sedimentation were independent of cell-cycle position (32, 117, 117a), subunit loops of mass ~10^9 Da in chromosomal DNA also were assumed to be associated with nuclear structures (118, 119). Analysis of the progression of alkaline hydrolysis of cellular DNA indicated that the ~10^9 Da subunits contained replicon-sized components and were themselves part of a chromosome-sized array (117, 120).

A maximum size of ~10^9 Da was obtained (114, 115) for the duplex molecules broken from protein-bound DNA by irradiation (and measured under neutral conditions), and on the assumption of random DSB induction, DNA loops of ~2×10^9 Da were presumed to be attached to the nuclear matrix (114, 115), in agreement with the result from Fig. 11(b) (115). Such loops originally were called "membrane associated superstructural units" (MASSUs); the designation was changed later to subunits, which is used here.

Supercoiling in cellular DNA (121, 122) and the attachment (anchoring) of loops (domains) of DNA to the chromosomal protein scaffold or nuclear matrix (skeleton) (123, 124), which can be revealed as an halo extending outside the periphery of the nucleus (125), now are beyond dispute. Relaxation of supercoiled domains in nucleoids by SSBs induced by X-photons can be used to estimate their sizes in mammalian cells (Table I), as can changes in the DNA species (molecules) released by alkaline hydrolysis (116–118). Destruction and reconstitution of the nuclear halo serve a similar, but less readily quantifiable, purpose (125).

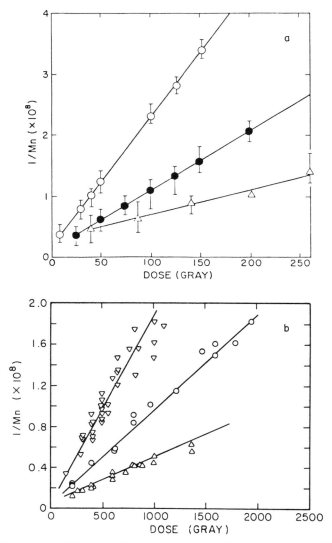

FIG. 11. Aerobic DNA strand breakage at high radiation doses. (a) TSBs in post-mitotic (G_0) cells of the retina: Co-60 γ-photons, $\bigcirc$; Ne-20 ions (LET$_\infty$: 35 keV/μm), $\bullet$; Ar-40 ions (LET$_\infty$: 90 keV/μm), $\triangle$. (b) DSBs in asynchronous V79 cells: X- or γ-photons, $\triangle$; α-particles (LET$_\infty$: 50 keV/μm), $\bigcirc$; α-particles (LET$_\infty$: 100 keV/μm), $\triangledown$. [Reproduced with permission from Lett *et al.* (*36*) and redrawn from Kampf (*114*).]

TABLE I

MASSES (IN DALTONS × 10^{-9}) OF SUPERCOILED DOMAINS RELAXED BY SINGLE-STRAND BREAKS INDUCED BY SPARSELY IONIZING RADIATIONS IN HUMAN AND MURINE CELLS[a]

Human HeLa cells (122)	Human B lymphocytes (159)	Human T_1 lymphocytes (159)	Mouse small thymocytes (160)	Mouse large thymocytes (160)
—	5.5	4.6	11	—
3.0	1.8	1.8	—	2.9
1.0	0.8	0.8	1.5	1.1
0.3	—	—	0.32	0.51

[a] The size groupings were made for convenience of presentation.

E. Possibilities for Specific Damage at Attachment Sites on the Nuclear Matrix

Attachment, or anchorage, sites maintained on the nuclear skeleton (matrix) by proteins and proteinaceous structural determinants in chromosomal architecture (123, 124) also raise the prospect of radiation effects different and separate from damage to bulk DNA in specific (radiosensitive) regions (117–119, 126). Chemical bonding of DNA with proteins (enzymes) and such changes in DNA structure as Z-DNA, single-stranded regions, enzyme related DSBs and SSBs, non-DNA linkers, etc., are possible in the attachment regions, which also could be sinks for energy transfer, sites accessible to diffusing radicals, or termini for chain reactions in lipids, etc. (1, 17, 51, 64, 119, 126). Difficulties posed by DSBs in (supercoiled) loops also could underlie cellular effects of LET_∞, deficiencies in the rejoining of DSBs, genomic deletions, etc.

Opinions are divided at present about localized DNA damage in attachment regions. Introduction of DSBs into the loops are believed to leave DNA residues attached to the matrix (114, 115); analysis of the DNA size distributions released by alkali favors random degradation superimposed upon localized damage (71, 116). Those interpretations are not mutually exclusive if localized damage is revealed only under alkaline conditions that denature proteins (enzymes) and also disclose features constrained within the attachment regions.

Interpretational difficulties have stemmed from sedimentation anomalies related to the very size of the DNA molecules under investigation. A phenomenon called "speed dependence" (127) is caused by size-dependent macromolecular orientation along the applied field. At high rotor speeds, the broad sedimentation profile expected from a distribution of randomly broken DNA molecules (*116*) can be sharpened at its leading edge and thus simulate profiles for distributions of partially broken molecules (*128, 129*), which can be reproduced readily by Monte Carlo procedures (*116*). Yet the converse change in shape can be caused by sucrose diffusion during the long sedimentation times at the low rotor speeds needed to obviate speed dependence (*97, 118*). For distributions of single-stranded DNA molecules obtained after appropriate doses of X-photons, fractionation and resedimentation of gradients with broad profiles obtained at low rotor speeds identified the spreading caused by diffusion (*97, 118*), and provided support for the value of M_o ~5×10^8 Da. Those fractionated studies showed also that, in accordance with theory, the smaller DNA sizes deduced from narrow sedimentation profiles obtained in certain rotors at high speeds (*130*) are speed-dependent artifacts. Some lytic conditions, moreover, cause the formation of gross, nonspecific gels (*97, 119*) and evoke the erroneous impression that DNA can be released from, or rejoined into, a "complex" (*130*).

Selected alkaline lysis followed by sedimentation through reoriented alkaline sucrose gradients in zonal rotors resolves a range of DNA species that are multiples of ~5×10^8 Da (*71, 97, 120, 131*), particularly in the ratios 2, 4, 8, etc., until sedimentation becomes overtly anomalous around 400 S (*97, 117, 120*). Decreasing sizes of such species appear in sedimentation profiles of mammalian DNA as the radiation dose increases, and the size sequence is reversed during post-irradiation incubation (*97, 126*), a pattern indicative of the reconstruction of chromosomal DNA domains (*97*) in surviving cells (*132*). After very low doses, the DNA-containing species sediment anomalously and although the exact nature of the damage is unknown, dose-dependent changes in, and the reconstruction of, *very large structures* can be determined. This attribute facilitates detection of damage from 0.05 Gy of X-photons in cells that cannot be labelled with radioactive markers—e.g., post-mitotic nervous cells of the CNS (*131*)—and from 0.02 Gy in cells that can be. A 20-fold increase in the limiting sensitivity of new monoclonal antibody assays (*133*) would be important in this regard because of the small numbers of cells required. Such high levels of sensitivity are crucial not only to determine whether break rejoining in *survivors* is complete but also because residual unrejoined breaks measured under *alkaline* conditions could actually be DSBs. Analogous sensitivities for overt DSB expression in large structures containing broken DNA molecules are not achievable at this time.

As yet, fractionation and re-sedimentation have not been performed

with the gradients obtained at low rotor speeds for duplex DNA derived from cells irradiated with moderate doses of X-photons (e.g.,
114–115), so the value of $M_0 = {\sim}2 \times 10^9$ Da could be too high (*71*), as
could be the estimated size of the loop if specific breakage occurs at
attachment sites (*71*). Furthermore, values of ${\sim}10^9$ Da have been obtained, after correction for speed-dependence, for DNA duplexes released from irradiated cells (*126, 134*). For DNA duplexes $>2 \times 10^9$ Da,
the rotor speeds needed for adequate size resolution are so low (*119,
126*) that extensive profile spreading occurs whatever the actual size
distribution. Such spreading precludes effective examination by extant sedimentation techniques of *unknown* size distributions resulting
from low radiation doses even if the DNA can be *liberated successfully*
from cellular structures. Attention has therefore turned to other techniques; unfortunately, neutral elution (*135*) became the method of
choice before even its underlying principles were properly understood, a situation that still persists (*136–138*).

F. Examination of Current Techniques for Measurement of Double-strand Breaks

One difficulty with the neutral elution method is that DNA from
S-phase cells appears to be larger than DNA from G_1 cells because it
elutes more slowly, an effect attributed to bifurcated or branched
molecules (*136*). Perhaps the real problem with DSB measurement for
bulk DNA is how to remove the structural proteins without introducing damage into, or revealing concealed features (damage) within the
attachment regions of, mammalian DNA. Use of pH 9.6 is thought to
resolve some of the difficulties with the elution technique (e.g., *136,
138*); yet it has long been known that extensive exposure to Pronase
even at pH 9.3 releases molecules of defined size (60-μm subunits)
from (G_1) CHO cells (*139*); see also *119*, where the history of attempts
to remove residual nonhistone proteins from DNA preparations, even
by repeated preparative cycles is reviewed in detail. Unless the
analytical method releases all folded and/or looped DNA structures
from sites maintained by proteins (*136*), variations in DSB induction
per se through the cell cycle should be viewed with caution, as also
should results obtained with asynchronous cell populations. Furthermore, radiation effects may also involve the accumulation of proteins
on, and the like removal of proteins from, the nuclear matrix (*125*).
Even though the DNA of (homologous) chromosomes may be separated on the nuclear matrix (*140*), consideration of the state, location,
and attachment of newly synthesized DNA is necessary for cells in
(late) S and G_2 (*71*). Passage of irradiated cells from G_1 through S, or

from S to G_1, could seem to be accompanied by (accelerated) DSB rejoining or degradation, respectively, *without* the occurrence of either process.

Putative nonlinearity of DSB induction at low doses of sparsely ionizing radiations could simply reflect the masking of DSBs in loops still anchored or maintained at their ends by proteins, or by DSB repair during post-irradiation manipulations prior to elution proper. Linear DSB induction by I-125 decay in marker cells does not circumvent these provisos. For any study of DNA damage in a system with repair mechanisms, the smaller the dose examined, the greater is the obfuscation likely to be caused by limited repair before the pertinent enzymes are inactivated; the true limiting case may not be achievable even with enzyme inhibitors. Use of alkali reduces these concerns (97), but then even the putative ability to quantify (frank) initial DSBs is lost. Further discussion of the problems with neutral elution, which may affect the conclusions of hundreds of published articles (see 7), is not presented here because the technique should be supplanted by pulsed field gel electrophoresis.

Gel electrophoresis suffers the same basic problem as centrifugation because increasing orientation of ever larger linear DNA molecules along the applied field eventually produces a migration rate that is independent of molecular size. For gel electrophoresis, the remedy for that problem may have been found through the pulsed application of asymmetric electric fields (*141*), a technique now being applied to measurement of DSB induction and rejoining in mammalian cells (*83, 84, 142*). Seemingly, with this technique DSB induction is linear with dose after low doses of X-photons (*83, 84, 142*). However, caveats again are necessary, as DNA from cells in S-phase migrates differently from G_1 DNA, and anchorage proteins must be removed effectively. As with neutral elution, the limiting sensitivity, currently 1–4 Gy (*83, 84*), is determined by the amount of DNA released from, and not direct measurement of changes in DNA-containing material retained within, the cell lysate (in the plug) (*83, 84*). Examination of such latter changes can be made, of course, by sedimentation through reoriented alkaline sucrose gradients in zonal rotors.

Two techniques capable of examining chromosome-sized DNA molecules, viscoelastometry (*143, 144*) and stereo electron microscopy (see *145*), are both subject to intrinsic limitations. Yet recent applications of each of them have prompted the conclusion that rodent chromosomal DNA is composed of several rings of relative mass $\sim 2-5 \times 10^{10}$ Da (*145*), in which DSBs can also be determined by viscoelastometric analysis (*146*). Use of such methods, the anticipated improvements in gel electrophoresis, the sensitivity of alkaline sucrose gradient sedimentation in zonal rotors, and the cytological methods to be examined next, should help to resolve those questions of cellular repair of DSBs concerned with the accuracy of the *restitution* of chromosomal (nucleoprotein) *architecture* and the retention of cellular reproductive integrity (radiosensitivity).

G. Breaks in Precondensed Chromosomes

Radiation-induced breakage of nuclear chromatin is linear with dose when expressed as fragmentation of "precondensed chromosomes" (PCCs) measured under conditions that permit correction for preanalysis repair or its elimination by the enzyme inhibitor 9-β-D-arabinofuranosyladenine (araA) (147–150). To date, that conclusion applies to G_1- and G_2-chromosomes, normally radioresistant and repair-deficient cells, and sparsely and densely ionizing radiations (150, 151). For a given dose, the number of PCC breaks is but a fraction of the DSBs induced, which reduction in efficiency presumably is a function of chromatin structure and can vary with cycle position and cell type (148–150). Furthermore, the α-particle RBEs for PCC breaks and DSBs are similar but not necessarily identical (151, 152).

At high radiation doses, induction of DSBs in asynchronous cells from patients homozygous for the disease ataxia telangiectasia (AT) and in normal human cells is similar (153). Yet induction of PCC breaks in those cell types at much lower doses also is similar in G_1 (149) but not in G_2 (150). Cycle variations in PCC breaks have also been reported for L5178Y cell lines (154). Such observations again should evoke caution about DSB measurements made at low radiation doses. If effects of structural proteins are not overcome, the DSB analyses could reflect damage both to chromatin structure and duplex DNA.

Since the discovery of cell-cycle-dependent repair deficiency was made with the L5178Y S/S cell (4), other analogous cell variants (mutants) have been isolated (5), and although only the S/S variant is known, as yet, to exhibit the important feature of temperature sensitivity, the defective cells show reduced efficiencies in DSB rejoining after supralethal doses of X-photons. Together with homozygous AT cells they also behave abnormally with respect to chromosomal aberrations. Chromosome-type aberrations appear at the next mitosis when normally radioresistant cells are X-irradiated in G_1, but for the variants (mutants), a significant percentage of the aberrations is of the chromatid-type, and >90% for the S/S variant. In due course, comprehension of the enzymatic processes underlying such important differences in the cytological expression of radiation damage will complete the sequence of correlations among: the patterns of energy deposition; damages to DNA and nucleoprotein; the genetic controls of repair systems; and cellular radiosensitivity. *Quantitative* analyses of the kinetics of mechanisms that process DNA damage also are essential, and have already begun.

Rejoining of PCC breaks induced by X-photons, for periods up to 24 hours, in normal human and AT cells held in G_0 (*148, 149, 155*), obeys kinetics approximated by

$$\text{Breaks unrejoined} = A + Be^{-\lambda t} \tag{16}$$

An equation such as Eq. (16) can represent a first-order reaction that does not reach completion, or two competing first-order reactions involved in fixation and repair or other combinations of processes. Initial numbers of PCC breaks are similar in both cell types, as are the rates of rejoining, but the numbers of residual (unrejoined) breaks, which in AT cells are six times those in normal cells after an X-photon dose of 6 Gy (*149*), are not a linear function of dose in normal human cells (*155*). The relationship was not determined for AT cells. Analysis of chromosomal aberrations at the subsequent mitoses indicates that some putatively unrejoined PCC breaks are the product of an inaccurate rejoining process. Such also may be true of the rejoining of G_2 PCC breaks in normal cells but not in AT cells where the formation of chromatid exchanges is unaffected by araA (*150*).

If chromosomal (chromosome-type) aberrations determine cell survival (*155*), the kinetics of their formation from original damage must be reflected in the shapes of survival curves. The survival curves for normal human fibroblasts exposed to X-photons in stationary phase are similar in shape to Curve D in Fig. 2, whereas those of AT fibroblasts are fair approximations to simple exponential functions (*155*). Derivation of definitive correlations among residual DSB damage (unrejoined or otherwise), the final products of PCC breakage, and cell survival must await quantitation of the formation and fate of DSBs from low radiation doses. Given the resolution of the technique, similarities of DSB induction frequencies and rates of DSB rejoining in normal human and AT cells after supralethal doses (*153*) *cannot* be used to postulate similarities in the final outcomes of the rejoining processes after radiobiologically significant doses, as the rejoining of PCC breaks attests (*149*). Strand-break analyses must be conducted after low doses, but to date this has only been achieved with the S/S variant, and then only with alkaline sucrose gradient sedimentation in zonal rotors (*19*).

The responses of the S/S variant reveal the types of information that may be obtained in due course with other repair-deficient variants (mutants). After 0.25 Gy of X-photons, G_1 S/S cells rejoin strand breaks within a few hours, but then, during a lengthy premitotic delay, DNA breakage seemingly equivalent to the original damage reappears. Subsequently, the DNA in dying cells is degraded but that in *survivors* returns to control size presumably via recombinational events, over several generations (*19, 132*) during which some cells in surviving colonies continue to die. Chromosomal (chromatid-type) aberrations revealed at the first post-irradiation mitosis cannot account for more than a third of the damage responsible for the deaths of S/S cells (*4*).

V. General Conclusions

Progress unimpaired by empiricism or entrenched dogma, from an inspirational breakthrough (*156*) to a current state of sophistication (*87*), is exemplified by the radiation biology of ultraviolet light.[4] Although comparable advances have not been made in the field of ionizing radiations, the end of the hiatus is being heralded in several ways. Systematic analysis of chemical change in irradiated DNA and nucleoprotein is elevating the challenge to the belief that ·OH radicals generated in bulk cellular water are the predominant causes of lethality. Resolution of that question will be assisted by theoretical approaches to radiation dosimetry (direct action) at the level of nucleoprotein structures (*157*), the simulation of ·OH radical attack (indirect action) at different sites within them (*158*), examination of possible reactions of $H_2O^{·+}$ radical ions with DNAs and the use of condensed-matter radiation physics to describe charge-transfer processes. Henceforth, theoretical treatments of radiation action in cells must consider charge-transfer processes. Quantification of DNA damage and its repair at radiobiologically significant doses will facilitate the development of rigorous biochemical theories of cellular radiosensitivity and their extension to permanently nondividing cells, especially those in the central nervous system (*2, 36, 71*). Marriage of the physical and biochemical theories then will result in a unifying general theory of cellular radiosensitivity (*5*); so, at long last, the scientific rigor employed originally by Lea (*20*) and Zimmer (*21*) will resume its rightful place in cellular radiation biology.

Future examinations of cellular radiation damage must differentiate between the biochemical responses of dying cells and survivors,

---

[4] See Polynucleotide–Protein Cross-Links Induced by Ultraviolet Light and Their Use for Structural Investigation of Nucleoproteins, by E. T. Budowsky and G. G. Abdurashidova, in Vol. 37 of this series. [Eds.]

and investigations of the underlying mechanisms should involve the utility of cell-cycle analysis. Complementation analysis with cell-cycle-dependent repair-deficient mutants and genomic incorporation of damage-carrying plasmids will exploit the strengths of molecular biology and genetics. The way has been opened for the development of specific repair inhibitors or promoters for possible improvements in radiation therapy.

Glossary

Relative biological effectiveness (RBE) and **G-value,** the radiation chemistry of dilute aqueous solutions of DNA and the effects on cell survival attributed to so-called **radical scavengers** have been described previously (7).

A **single-strand break (SSB)** occurs in one strand of the DNA duplex and a **double-strand break (DSB)** is formed by adjacent, or nearly adjacent, breaks in both strands (34). Alkaline treatment of irradiated DNA converts DSBs into SSBs and so expresses **total strand breaks (TSBs)**; other damage (alkali-labile bonds) also is converted into SSBs under alkaline conditions.

Crosslinks between adjacent DNA duplexes are **intermolecular,** as may be considered also links between spatially adjacent, but linearly distant, sections of a DNA duplex in the form of a (supercoiled) loop or ring. **Intramolecular** crosslinks occur between the complementary strands of the same duplex. Crosslinks involving protein that are broken by "proteolytic" enzymes are **DNA–protein crosslinks** (but see text).

Densities of **total** energy deposition per unit length of path, **usually in water,** as recorded in terms of **linear energy transfer (LET$_\infty$)** (keV/μm or MeV/g). Energy deposition from **sparsely ionizing radiations** (X-rays, γ-rays, etc.) is essentially uniform throughout a thin section of tissue, but ionizations occur locally in numbers 1, 2, 3 . . . with an average of 2 to 3; large clusters are **densely ionizing** events (see 7). Thus, the **macroscopic definition** of **dose,** 1 **Gray** $\equiv$ 1 J/kg, is inappropriate for events at the nanometer (nucleoprotein) level. **Densely ionizing radiations,** which mostly are positively charged nuclei (ions), deposit high local concentrations of energy, mainly by ejecting electrons in cylindrical distributions around their tracks (77). For descriptive purposes, these distributions may be divided into an inner cylinder, or **core,** of dense ionizations and a concentric outer cylinder, or **penumbra,** of sparse ionizations (77), although this distinction does not seem to be supported by measurements of radial electron distributions (113).

Diameters of track cores for charged particles of high atomic number (HZ) and energy (HZE particles) are comparable to those of cells (nuclei); penumbral diameters can extend for several cellular diameters (77). A very low macroscopic dose (e.g., 0.01 Gy) deposited by HZE particles is not homogeneous. Cells in the paths of the particles receive high *local* doses (dense ionization), perhaps equivalent to 1 Gy or more, while cells exposed to the energy penumbras receive correspondingly lower doses (sparse ionization), and cells beyond the penumbra receive no dose at all. Channels of localized energy deposition can occur in otherwise unaffected material.

The LET_∞ varies along the track of a particle as it deposits energy and slows down (the Bragg curve), and particles of different Z and E can yield the same LET_∞ even though the radial distributions of energy are different. Track structure, therefore, causes different distributions of macromolecular, cellular, or tissue damage at the same LET_∞, so use of LET_∞ and dose are retained here with the knowledge of their limitations. Furthermore, LET_∞ is a function of density, but dose in Gy (J/kg) is not, so the LET_∞ in DNA, protein, and hydration water will be different while the dose is not.

Cell lethality in the situations described here is assessed by reproductive integrity or clonogenic ability, unless otherwise qualified.

ACKNOWLEDGMENT

This article was written under the auspices of Grant NAG 9-10 from the National Aeronautics and Space Administration.

REFERENCES

1. J. T. Lett, *Br. J. Cancer* **55**, (Suppl. 8), 145 (1987).
2. J. T. Lett, A. B. Cox and D. S. Bergtold, *Radiat. Environ. Biophys.* **25**, 1 (1986).
3. K. Popper, "The Logic of Scientific Discovery." Hutchinson, London, 1972.
4. H. Nagasawa, A. B. Cox and J. T. Lett, *Proc. R. Soc. London, B* **211**, 25 (1980).
5. J. T. Lett, A. B. Cox, M. D. Story, U. K. Ehmann and E. A. Blakely, *Proc. R. Soc. London, B* **237**, 27 (1989).
6. International Commission on Radiation Units and Measurements, "Quantitative Concepts and Dosimetry in Radiobiology," Rep. 30. ICRU, Bethesda, MD, 1979.
7. J. F. Ward, *This Series* **35**, 95 (1988).
8. F. Hutchinson, *This Series* **32**, 115 (1985).
9. P. Alexander and J. T. Lett, *Nature* **187**, 933 (1960).
10. J. T. Lett, K. A. Stacey and P. Alexander, *Radiat. Res.* **14**, 349 (1961).
11. P. Alexander, J. T. Lett, P. Kopp and R. Itzhaki, *Radiat. Res.* **14**, 363 (1961).
12. J. T. Lett and P. Alexander, *Radiat. Res.* **15**, 159 (1961).
13. P. Alexander, J. T. Lett and M. G. Ormerod, *BBA* **51**, 507 (1961).
14. C. von Sonntag, "The Chemical Basis of Radiation Biology," p. 100. Taylor & Francis, London, 1987.

15. K. F. Baverstock and S. Will, *Int. J. Radiat. Biol.* **55**, 563 (1989).
16. D. Ewing and G. J. Kubala, *Radiat. Res.* **109**, 256 (1987).
17. J. T. Lett. in "Oxygen Radicals in Biology and Medicine" (M. G. Simic, K. A. Taylor, J. F. Ward and C. von Sonntag, eds.), p. 419. Plenum, New York, 1988.
18. P. Wardman and E. D. Clark, *Br. J. Cancer* **55**, (Suppl. 8), 129 (1987).
19. J. T. Lett, A. B. Cox, R. Okayasu and M. D. Story, *Radiat. Res.* **2**, 376 (1987).
20. D. E. Lea, "Actions of Radiations on Living Cells," 2nd ed. Cambridge Univ. Press, London, 1955.
21. K. G. Zimmer, *Adv. Radiat. Biol.* **9**, 411 (1981).
22. U. Hagen and J. T. Lett, *Radiat. Environ. Biophys.* **27**, 245 (1988).
23. R. Courant, "Differential and Integral Calculus," Vol. 1. Wiley (Interscience) New York, 1937.
24. T. Terasima and L. J. Tolmach, *Biophys. J.* **3**, 11 (1963).
25. A. Howard and S. R. Pelc, *Heredity* **6**, 261 (1953). [Reprinted in *Int. J. Radiat. Biol.* **49**, 207 (1986).]
26. J. S. Mitchell, "Studies in Radiotherapeutics." Blackwell Scientific, Oxford, 1960.
27. B. S. Jacobsen, *Radiat. Res.* **7**, 394 (1957).
28. M. M. Elkind and H. Sutton, *Nature* **184**, 1293 (1959).
29. W. Pohlit and L. Juling, *Br. J. Cancer* **49**, (Suppl. 6), 213 (1984).
30. G. Iliakis, *Int. J. Radiat. Biol.* **53**, 541 (1988).
31. N. M. S. Reddy and C. S. Lange, *Int. J. Radiat. Biol.* **56**, 239 (1989).
32. T. Alper, *Br. J. Radiol.* **50**, 459 (1977).
33. M. Frankenberg-Schwager, D. Frankenberg and R. Harbich, *Radiat. Res.* **114**, 54 (1988).
34. P. Alexander and J. T. Lett, *Compr. Biochem.* **27**, 267 (1967).
35. P. Alexander, J. T. Lett and C. J. Dean, *Prog. Biochem. Pharmacol.* **1**, 22 (1965).
36. J. T. Lett, D. S. Bergtold and P. C. Keng, in "Mechanisms of DNA Damage and Repair" (M. G. Simic, L. Grossman and A. C. Upton, eds.), p. 139. Plenum, New York, 1986.
37. D. T. Goodhead, *Radiat. Res.* **2**, 306 (1987).
38. S. Gregoli, M. Olast and A. Bertinchamps, *Radiat. Res.* **89**, 238 (1982).
39. M. Falk, K. A. Hartman, Jr., and R. C. Lord, *JACS* **84**, 3843 (1962).
40. M. L. Kopka, A. V. Fratins, H. R. Drew and R. E. Dickerson, *JMB* **163**, 129 (1983).
41. B. Wolf and S. Hanlon, *Bchem* **14**, 1661 (1975).
42. A. Szent-Györgyi, *Nature* **148**, 157 (1941).
43. R. Pethig, "Dielectric and Electronic Properties of Biological Molecules." Wiley, Chichester, England, 1979.
44. D. van Lith, M. P. de Haas, J. M. Warman and A. Hummel, *Biopolymers* **22**, 807 (1983).
45. D. van Lith, J. M. Warman, M. P. de Haas and A. Hummel, *JCS, Faraday Trans. 1* **82**, 2933 (1986).
46. S. Suhai, *J. Chem. Phys.* **57**, 5599 (1972).
47. D. Dee and M. E. Baur, *J. Chem. Phys.* **60**, 541 (1974).
48. D. van Lith, J. Eden, J. M. Warman and A. Hummel, *JCS, Faraday Trans. 1* **82**, 2945 (1986).
49. J. Eden, D. van Lith, J. M. Warman and A. Hummel, *JCS, Faraday Trans. 1* **85**, 991 (1989).
49a. J. H. Miller and C. E. Swenberg, *Can. J. Phys. (in press)* 1990.
50. J. Widom and A. Klug, *Cell* **43**, 207 (1985).
51. E. M. Fielden, S. C. Lillicrap and A. B. Robins, *Radiat. Res.* **48**, 421 (1971).

52. A. T. Al-Kazwini, P. O'Neill, E. M. Fielden and G. E. Adams, *Radiat. Phys. Chem.* **32**, 385 (1988).

53. P. O'Neill *et al.*, personal communication (1989).

54. F. Wilkinson, C. J. Willsher, P. Warwick, E. J. Land and F. A. P. Rushton, *Nature* **311**, 40 (1984).

55. P. O'Neill, A. T. Al-Kazwini, E. J. Land and E. M. Fielden, *Int. J. Radiat. Biol.* **55**, 531 (1989).

56. P. Alexander and A. Charlesby, *Nature* **173**, 578 (1954).

57. A. Norman and W. Ginoza, *Radiat. Res.* **9**, 77 (1958).

58. F. Patten and W. Gordy, *PNAS* **46**, 1137 (1960).

59. B. B. Singh, *Adv. Biol. Med. Phys.* **12**, 245 (1968).

60. S. C. Lillicrap and E. M. Fielden, *J. Chem. Phys.* **51**, 3503 (1970).

61. S. C. Lillicrap and E. M. Fielden, *Int. J. Radiat. Biol.* **21**, 137 (1972).

62. G. D. D. Jones, J. S. Lea, M. C. R. Symons and F. A. Taiwo, *Nature* **330**, 772 (1987).

63. M. C. R. Symons, *JCS, Faraday Trans. 1* **83**, 1 (1987).

64. P. M. Cullis, G. D. D. Jones, M. C. R. Symons and J. S. Lea, *Nature* **330**, 773 (1987).

65. P. M. Cullis, M. C. R. Symons, M. C. Sweeney, G. D. D. Jones and J. D. McClymont, *JCS, Perkin Trans. 2* p. 1671 (1986).

66. M. C. R. Symons, personal communication (1989).

67. P. J. Boon, P. M. Cullis, M. C. R. Symons and B. W. Wren, *JCS, Perkin Trans. 2* p. 1393 (1984).

68. P. J. Boon, P. M. Cullis, M. C. R. Symons and B. W. Wren, *JCS Perkin Trans. 2* p. 1056 (1985).

69. P. M. Cullis, M. C. R. Symons, B. W. Wren and S. Gregoli, *JCS Perkin Trans. 2* p. 1819 (1985).

70. P. M. Cullis, G. D. D. Jones, M. C. Sweeney, M. C. R. Symons and B. W. Wren, *Int. J. Radiat. Biol.* **53**, 901 (1988).

71. J. T. Lett. P. C. Keng, D. S. Bergtold and J. Howard, *Radiat. Environ. Biophys.* **26**, 23 (1987).

72. J. Cadet, A. Shaw, M. Berger, C. Decarroz, J. R. Wagner and J. van Lier. *Radiat. Res.* **2**, 181 (1987).

72a. U. Hagen, *Radiat. Environ. Biophys.* **25**, 261 (1986).

73. A. Chatterjee and J. L. Magee, *Radiat. Prot. Dosim.* **13**, 137 (1985).

74. M. D. Sevilla, *in* "Mechanisms of Radiation Interaction with DNA: Potential Implications to Radiation Protection," Conf. Rep. 870163 UC-48. Dep. Energy, Washington, D.C., 1988.

75. M. D. Sevilla and S. Swarts, *Radiat. Res.* **112**, 21 (1987).

76. U. Hagen and H. Wellstein, *Strahlentherapie* **24**, 275 (1964).

77. E. A. Blakely, F. Q. H. Ngo, S. B. Curtis and C. A. Tobias, *Adv. Radiat. Biol.* **11**, 295 (1984).

78. C. J. Koch, *Adv. Radiat. Biol.* **8**, 273 (1979).

79. D. Emmerson, G. Scholes, D. H. Thomson, J. F. Ward and J. J. Weiss, *Nature* **87**, 319 (1960).

80. P. H. Lloyd and A. R. Peacocke, *Proc. R. Soc. London, B* **164**, 40 (1966).

81. T. D. Tullius, *Nature* **332**, 663 (1988).

82. D. Murray, *CRC Crit. Rev. Thiol. Biochem.* in press (1990).

82a. Z. M. Bacq and P. Alexander, "Fundamentals of Radiobiology." Pergamon, Oxford, England, 1961.

83. D. D. Ager, W. C. Dewey, K. Gardiner, W. Harvey, R. T. Johnson and C. A. Walden, *Radiat. Res.* **122**, 181 (1990).

84. D. Blöcher, M. Einspenner and J. Zajackowski, *Int. J. Radiat. Biol.* **56**, 437 (1989).
85. M. Budd and R. K. Mortimer, *Mutat Res.* **103**, 19 (1982).
86. M. D. Story, Ph.D. thesis. Colorado State Univ., Fort Collins, 1989.
86a. J. E. Cleaver, G. H. Thomas, J. E. Trosko and J. T. Lett, *Exp. Cell Res.* **74**, 67 (1972).
87. A. K. Ganesan and G. Spivak, *in* "DNA Repair: A Laboratory Manual of Research Procedures" (E. C. Friedberg and P. C. Hanawalt, eds.), Vol. 3, Dekker, p. 295. 1988.
87a. V. A. Bohr, D. H. Phillips and P. C. Hanawalt, *Cancer Res.* **47**, 6426 (1987).
88. E. H. Kohfeldt, H. Bertram and U. Hagan, *Radiat. Environ. Biophys.* **27**, 123 (1988).
89. C. J. Dean, P. Feldschreiber and J. T. Lett, *Nature* **209**, 49 (1966).
90. P. M. Corry and A. Cole, *Nature NB* **245**, 100 (1973).
91. R. A. McGrath and R. W. Williams, *Nature* **212**, 534 (1966).
92. J. T. Lett, I. Caldwell, C. J. Dean and P. Alexander, *Nature* **214**, 790 (1967).
93. U. Hagen, *BBA* **134**, 45 (1967).
94. C. A. Thomas, *JACS* **78**, 1861 (1956).
95. J. E. Turner, J. L. Magee, H. A. Wright, A. Chatterjee, R. N. Hamm and R. H. Ritchie, *Radiat. Res.* **96**, 437 (1983).
96. R. Roots, G. Kraft and E. Gosschalk, *Int. J. Radiat. Oncol. Biol. Biophys.* **11**, 259 (1985).
97. J. T. Lett, *in* "Laboratory Procedures for DNA Repair Research" (E. C. Friedberg and P. C. Hanawalt, eds.), Vol. 1B, p. 363. Dekker, New York, 1981.
98. C. E. Swenberg, personal communication (1989).
99. D. T. Goodhead and D. Brenner, *Phys. Med. Biol.* **28**, 485 (1983).
99a. K. F. Baverstock and R. B. Crandall, *Nature* **332**, 312 (1988).
99b. W. G. Burns, *Nature* **339**, 519 (1989).
100. A. M. Rauth and J. A. Simpson, *Radiat. Res.* **22**, 643 (1964).
101. E. Aufderheide, H. Rink, L. Hieber and G. Kraft, *Int. J. Radiat. Biol.* **51**, 779 (1987).
102. D. E. Charlton and J. Booz, *Radiat. Res.* **87**, 10 (1981).
103. R. F. Martin and W. A. Haseltine, *Science* **213**, 896 (1981).
104. U. Linz and G. Stöcklin, *Radiat. Res.* **101**, 262 (1985).
105. D. E. Charlton, *Radiat. Res.* **114**, 192 (1988).
106. T. Ishihara and M. S. Sakai (eds.), *Prog. Top. Cytogenet.* **4**, (1983).
107. D. Blöcher, *Int. J. Radiat. Biol.* **54**, 761 (1988).
108. M. A. Ritter, J. E. Cleaver and C. A. Tobias, *Nature* **266**, 653 (1977).
109. H. Wulf, W. Kraft-Weyrather, H. G. Mittenburger, E. A. Blakely, C. A. Tobias and G. Kraft, *Radiat. Res.* **104**, 122 (1985).
110. C. M. Arroyo, A. J. Carmichael, C. E. Swenberg and L. S. Myers, Jr., *Int. J. Radiat. Biol.* **50**, 780 (1986).
111. J. H. Miller, W. E. Wilson, C. E. Swenberg, L. S. Myers and D. E. Charlton, *Int. J. Radiat. Biol.* **53**, 901 (1988).
112. C. E. Swenberg and J. H. Miller, *Int. J. Radiat. Biol.* **56**, 383 (1989).
113. G. Kraft, *in* "Terrestrial Space Radiation and Its Biological Effects" (P. D. McCormack, C. E. Swenberg and H. Bücker, eds.), p. 163. Plenum, New York, 1988.
114. G. Kampf, *Akad. Wiss. DDR* **ZfK504**, (1983).
114a. G. Kampf, *Radiobiol. Radiother.* **29**, 631 (1988).
115. K. Regel, K. Gunther and G. Kampf, *Radiat. Environ. Biophys.* **21**, 175 (1983).
116. U. K. Ehmann and J. T. Lett, *Radiat. Res.* **54**, 152 (1973).
117. J. T. Lett., E. S. Klucis and C. Sun, *Biophys. J.* **10**, 277 (1970).

117a. J. T. Lett and C. Sun, *Radiat. Res.* **44**, 771 (1970).
118. J. T. Lett, *in* "Molecular Mechanisms for Repair of DNA" (P. C. Hanawalt and R. B. Setlow, eds.), p. 655. Plenum, New York, 1975.
119. J. T. Lett, *in* "Aging, Carcinogenesis and Radiation Biology" (K. C. Smith, ed.), p. 11. Plenum, New York, 1976.
120. E. S. Klucis and J. T. Lett, *Anal. Biochem.* **35**, 480 (1970).
121. P. R. Cook and I. A. Brazell, *J. Cell Sci.* **19**, 261 (1976).
122. P. R. Cook and I. A. Brazell, *Nature* **263**, 679 (1976).
123. J. Mirkovitch, M.-E. Mirault and U. K. Laemmli, *Cell* **39**, 223 (1984).
124. T. Igo-Kemenes, T. Horz and H. G. Zachau, *ARB* **51**, 89 (1982).
125. A. Jaberaboansari, G. B. Nelson, J. L. Roti-Roti and K. T. Wheeler, *Radiat. Res.* **114**, 94 (1988).
126. A. Cole, F. Shonka, P. Corry and W. G. Cooper, *in* "Molecular Mechanisms for Repair of DNA" (P. C. Hanawalt and R. B. Setlow, eds.), p. 665. Plenum, New York, 1975.
127. B. H. Zimm, *Biophys. Chem.* **1**, 279 (1974).
128. J. Abelson and C. A. Thomas, *JMB* **18**, 262 (1966).
129. A. J. Rainbow, *Radiat. Res.* **60**, 155 (1974).
130. M. M. Elkind, *in* "Molecular Mechanisms for Repair of DNA" (P. C. Hanawalt and R. B. Setlow, eds), p. 689. Plenum, New York, 1975.
131. P. C. Keng, A. C. Lee, A. B. Cox, D. S. Bergtold and J. T. Lett, *Int. J. Radiat. Biol.* **41**, 127 (1982).
132. E. M. Goldin, A. B. Cox and J. T. Lett, *Radiat. Res.* **83**, 668 (1980).
133. G. P. van der Schans, A. A. W. M. van Loon, R. H. Groenendijk and R. A. Baan, *Int. J. Radiat, Biol.* **55**, 747 (1989).
134. C. S. Lange, *in* "Molecular Mechanisms for Repair of DNA" (P. C. Hanawalt and R. B. Setlow, eds.), p. 677. Plenum, New York, 1975.
135. M. O. Bradley and K. W. Kohn, *NARes* **7**, 793 (1979).
136. R. Okayasu and G. Iliakis, *Int. J. Radiat. Biol.* **55**, 569 (1989).
137. P. J. Meyer, C. S. Lange, M. O. Bradley and W. W. Nichols, *Radiat. Res.* in press (1990).
138. S. E. Sweigert, R. Rowley, R. L. Warters and L. A. Dethlefsen, *Radiat. Res.* **116**, 228 (1988).
139. J. C. Hozier and J. H. Taylor, *JMB* **93**, 181 (1975).
140. D. Pinkel, J. Landegent, C. Collins, J. Fuscoe, R. Segraves, J. Lucas and J. Gray, *PNAS* **85**, 9138 (1988).
141. D. C. Schwartz and C. R. Cantor, *Cell* **37**, 67 (1984).
142. T. Stamato, personal communication (1989).
143. L. C. Klotz and B. H. Zimm, *JMB* **72**, 779 (1972).
144. J. Y. Ostashevsky and C. S. Lange, *Biopolymers* **26**, 59 (1987).
145. C. S. Lange, *Genome* **31**, 448 (1989).
146. J. Y. Ostashevsky, *Radiat. Res.* **118**, 437 (1989).
147. J. S. Bedford and M. N. Cornforth, *Radiat. Res.* **111**, 406 (1987).
148. M. N. Cornforth and J. S. Bedford, *Science* **222**, 1141 (1983).
149. M. N. Cornforth and J. S. Bedford, *Science* **227**, 1589 (1985).
150. H. Mozdarani and P. E. Bryant, *Int. J. Radiat. Biol.* **55**, 71 (1989).
151. E. Goodwin, Ph.D. thesis. Univ. of California, Berkeley, 1988.
152. J. S. Bedford and D. T. Goodhead, *Int. J. Radiat. Biol.* **55**, 211 (1989).
153. A. R. Lehmann and S. Stevens, *BBA* **474**, 49 (1977).
154. D. Wlodek and W. N. Hittelman, *Radiat. Res.* **115**, 550 (1988).

155. M. N. Cornforth and J. S. Bedford, *Radiat. Res.* **111,** 385 (1987).
156. R. B. Setlow and W. L. Carrier, *PNAS* **51,** 226 (1964).
157. D. T. Goodhead and H. Nikjoo, *Int. J. Radiat. Biol.* **55,** 513 (1989).
158. A. Chatterjee and W. R. Holley, personal communication (1990).
159. E. J. van Rensburg, W. K. A. Louw, H. Izalt and J. J. van der Watt, *Int. J. Radiat. Biol.* **47,** 673 (1985).
160. I. V. Fillipovich, N. I. Sorokina, N. I. Soldatenkov and E. F. Romantzev, *Int. J. Radiat. Biol.* **42,** 31 (1982).

Index

R

S